Orban's

Oral histology and embryology

Edited by
HARRY SICHER, M.D., D.Sc.
Professor Emeritus, School of Dentistry,
Loyola University, Chicago, Illinois

With 288 text illustrations
and 4 color plates

Sixth edition

THE C. V. MOSBY COMPANY
Saint Louis   1966

Sixth edition

Copyright © 1966 by The C. V. Mosby Company

Third printing

Previous editions copyrighted 1944, 1949, 1953, 1957, 1962

Printed in the United States of America

Library of Congress Catalog Card Number 66-16960

Distributed in Great Britain by Henry Kimpton, London

Contributors

Myron S. Aisenberg, D.D.S.

Baltimore College of Dental Surgery, University of Maryland, Baltimore, Maryland

Gerrit Bevelander, Ph.D.

University of Texas Dental Branch, Houston, Texas

Leroy R. Boling, Ph.D.

School of Dentistry, Washington University, St. Louis, Missouri

Nicholas J. Brescia, D.D.S., M.S.

School of Dentistry, Loyola University, Chicago, Illinois

†Marvin S. Burstone, M.S., D.D.S.

National Institutes of Health, Bethesda, Maryland, and Emory School of Medicine, Emory University, Atlanta, Georgia

Samuel W. Chase, A.B., A.M., Ph.D.

School of Dentistry, Western Reserve University, Cleveland, Ohio

Harry E. Frisbie, D.D.S.

College of Dentistry, University of California, San Francisco, California

Donald A. Kerr, A.B., M.S., D.D.S.

School of Dentistry, University of Michigan, Ann Arbor, Michigan

George A. Krikos, D.D.S., Ph.D.

School of Dentistry, University of Pennsylvania, Philadelphia, Pennsylvania

†Edgar B. Manley, M.Sc., B.D.S., F.D.S.R.C.S.(Eng.)

Department of Dental Pathology, Medical School, University of Birmingham, Birmingham, England

Julia Meyer, Ph.D.

School of Dentistry, University of Illinois, Chicago, Illinois

Marie U. Nylen, D.D.S.

National Institute of Dental Research, Bethesda, Maryland

Alfred L. Ogilvie, M.S., D.D.S.

School of Dentistry, University of Washington, Seattle, Washington

John J. O'Malley, D.D.S., M.S.

School of Dentistry, Loyola University, Chicago, Illinois

---

†Deceased.

---

†Deceased.

†Balint J. Orban, D.D.S., M.D.

School of Dentistry, Loyola University, Chicago, Illinois

Dorothy Permar, B.S., M.S.

College of Dentistry, The Ohio State University, Columbus, Ohio

Hamilton B. G. Robinson, M.S., D.D.S.

College of Dentistry, University of Kansas City, Kansas City, Missouri

†Isaac Schour, M.S., D.D.S., Ph.D.

College of Dentistry, University of Illinois, Chicago, Illinois

David B. Scott, A.B., M.S., D.D.S.

National Institute of Dental Research, Bethesda, Maryland

†Deceased.

Harry Sicher, M.D., D.Sc.

School of Dentistry, Loyola University, Chicago, Illinois

Reidar F. Sognnaes, D.M.D., Ph.D.

School of Dentistry, University of California, Los Angeles, California

†Joseph P. Weinmann, M.D.

College of Dentistry, University of Illinois, Chicago, Illinois

Frank M. Wentz, D.D.S., M.S., Ph.D.

School of Dentistry, Loyola University, Chicago, Illinois

James A. Yaeger, D.D.S., M.S., Ph.D.

College of Dentistry, University of Illinois, Chicago, Illinois

†Deceased.

To **Balint J. Orban**

A clinician of consummate skill; a researcher of an incomparable power of observation and an unprejudiced intellect in interpretation; a teacher of unlimited patience and unstinting generosity

Preface

Teaching of histology today, be it in lectures, laboratory, or texts, is in a difficult period of transition. Students, of course, use the light microscope, but progress in histology rests strongly on the use of the electron microscope and the use of histochemical and cytochemical methods. It will, in my estimation, take quite some time until an integration of these methods is achieved. In the meantime, stress must be put on the use of the light microscope—even in research—because electron micrography and histochemistry must rest on a "total" exhaustion of the potentialities of the light microscope and the techniques for its best use.

In this, the sixth edition of Orban's text, the attempt was made to achieve a compromise between the "classic" and the ultramodern methods. I am fully aware not only of the difficulties of such a task but also of the impossibility of *not* making mistakes.

H. Sicher

Contents

I. Development of the face and oral cavity, 1

II. Development and growth of the teeth, 18

III. Enamel, 39

IV. Dentin, 96

V. Pulp, 127

VI. Cementum, 155

VII. Periodontal ligament, 176

VIII. Maxilla and mandible (alveolar process), 197

IX. Oral mucous membrane, 213

X. Salivary glands, 266

XI. Eruption of the teeth, 301

XII. Shedding of the deciduous teeth, 320

XIII. Temporomandibular joint, 335

XIV. Maxillary sinus, 344

XV. Histochemistry of the oral tissues, 352

Appendix Preparation of specimens for histologic study, 382

Color plates

Plate 1 Development of the human face, 2

2 Reconstruction of the skull of a human embryo 80 mm. in length, 198

3 Salivary glands of major secretion, 266

4 Photographs of several histochemical reactions, 360

Orban's Oral histology
and embryology

INTRODUCTION
DEVELOPMENT OF THE FACE
        Early development
        Formation of the primary palate
DEVELOPMENT OF THE SECONDARY PALATE
        Palatine processes
DEVELOPMENT OF THE TONGUE
        Branchial arches
        Cervical sinus
        Tongue
CLINICAL CONSIDERATIONS
        Facial malformations
        Cleft lip and jaw
        Cleft palate
        Labial pits
        Lingual anomalies
        Developmental cysts

Chapter I

Development of the face and oral cavity*

INTRODUCTION

The development of the face and oral cavity involves a dynamic series of events that begin during the second month of intrauterine life. The complex origin of this region from different growth centers, with the development of seven different processes which grow at varying rates and which unite to varying degrees, makes the relatively infrequent occurrence of malformations remarkable. Critical changes lead to formation of the embryonic face, the nasal duct, and the tongue and to the separation of the oral and nasal cavities by formation of the palate. This period can be divided into two phases.

In the first phase, during the fifth and sixth weeks, the building blocks of the face are prepared, communication between the oral cavity and foregut is established, and the nasal ducts are formed. At the end of this period the nasal cavity and the oral cavity communicate freely, and the tongue has developed. In the second phase, during the seventh and eighth weeks, the development of the palate takes place, leading to the separation of the oral and nasal cavities. The most common malformations of the face, cleft lip (harelip) and cleft palate, originate during the first and second phases, respectively.

DEVELOPMENT OF THE FACE

Early development. In the human embryo (Plate 1, *A*) that is 3 mm. long (3 weeks), the greater part of the face consists of the rounded prominence formed by the forebrain (prosencephalon). The forebrain is covered by a thin layer of mesoderm and by ectoderm. Below the rounded prominence (Fig. 1) there is a deep grove, the primary oral fossa (stomodeum, stomodeal pit). The stomodeum is bounded caudally by the mandibular arch (first branchial arch), lat-

---

*Rewritten by Hamilton B. G. Robinson.

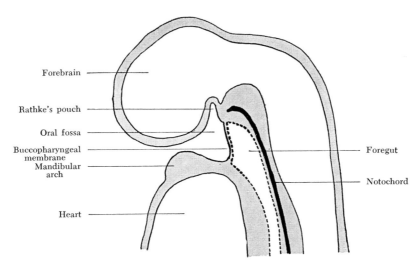

Forebrain

Rathke's pouch

Oral fossa

Buccopharyngeal
membrane
Mandibular
arch

Heart

Foregut

Notochord

Fig. 1. Diagram of a median section through the head of a human embryo 3 mm. in length. The oral fossa is separated from the foregut by a double layer of epithelium, the buccopharyngeal membrane.

erally by the maxillary processes, and cephalically by the frontonasal process (Plate 1, *B*). During early phases of development, two bulges may be observed laterally and anteriorly on the mandibular arch, united centrally by a copula (Plate 1, A to *E*). Later these bulges disappear (Plate 1, *F*).

The stomodeum (oral fossa) deepens to meet the blind end of the foregut (Fig. 1). The stomodeum and the foregut are separated by the buccopharyngeal membrane, which consists of two epithelial layers. There is an additional ectodermal pouch (Fig. 1), which is derived from the stomodeum, Rathke's pouch, that gives rise to the anterior lobe of the pituitary gland. The lining of the stomodeum is ectodermal. Therefore, the lining of the nasal and the oral cavities, the enamel of the teeth, and the salivary glands are of ectodermal origin. The pharyngeal lining is entodermal since it is formed from the foregut. Communication between the primary oral cavity and the foregut is established at about the third or fourth week when the buccopharyngeal membrane ruptures.

Essentially, the face is derived from seven primordia: the two mandibular processes, which unite very early, the two maxillary processes, the two lateral nasal processes, and the medial nasal process (Plate 1). The mandibular and maxillary processes originate from the first branchial arch, whereas the medial nasal and the two lateral nasal processes arise from the frontonasal process, which in turn arose in the prominence covering the forebrain.

The first significant change in the configuration of the face results from the rapid proliferation of the mesoderm covering the anterior portion of the brain (Plate 1, A and B). This prominence, the frontonasal process (Plate 1), will give rise to most of the structures of the upper and the middle portions of the face. Next, the formation and deepening of the stomodeum (Plate 1 and Fig. 1)

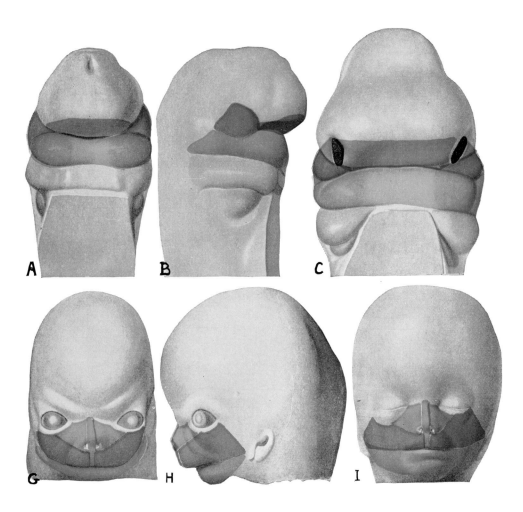

Plate 1. Development of the human face. **A** and **B**, Embryo 3 mm. in length, third week. The frontonasal process (blue) is undivided. It is caudal to the mandibular arch (yellow), the hyoid arch, and the third branchial arch. The depression on top of figure is the neuropore. **C**, Embryo 6.5 mm. in length, fourth week. Nasal pits divide the frontonasal process into the medial nasal process (blue) and lateral nasal processes (red). **D**, Embryo 9 mm. in length, fifth week. Fusion of the medial nasal and maxillary processes has narrowed entrance into the nasal pit. **E**, Embryo 9.2 mm. in length, sixth week. Fusion of the medial and lateral nasal processes has further narrowed the nostrils. The medial nasal process is reduced in relative width. The eyes are at the lateral edges of the face.

Medial nasal
process

Lateral
nasal
process

Maxillary
process

Mandibular
arch

F, Embryo 14.5 mm. in length, seventh week. The nasal area is slightly prominent. The nasal septum is further reduced in relative width. The eyes are on the anterior surface of the face. G and H, Embryo 18 mm. in length, eighth week. Lidless eyes are on the anterior surface of the face. Their distance is relatively reduced, and the mandible is short. I and J, Embryo 60 mm. in length, twelfth week. The lids are closed. The nostrils are closed by epithelial proliferation. Relation of the mandible to the maxilla is normal. K, Adult face: the derivatives of the medial nasal process (blue), lateral nasal processes (red), maxillary processes (green), and mandibular arch (yellow). (Modified after Sicher, H., and Tandler, J.: Anatomie für Zahnärzte [Anatomy for dentists], Vienna and Berlin, 1928, Julius Springer.)

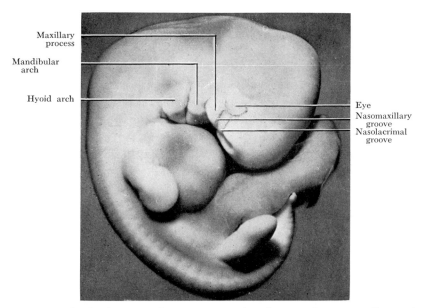

Maxillary
process

Mandibular
arch

Hyoid arch

Eye
Nasomaxillary
groove
Nasolacrimal
groove

Fig. 2. Photograph of a human embryo 10 mm. in length. Note the nasomaxillary and nasolacrimal grooves. (Courtesy Dr. P. Gruenwald.)

and olfactory (nasal) pits (Plate 1) and the division of the caudal portion of the
frontonasal process into the medial nasal and two lateral nasal processes (Plate
1, *C* to *F*) are most striking. The lateral nasal processes are adjacent to the
maxillary processes (Plate 1, *C*) and are separated from them by shallow furrows, the nasomaxillary grooves (Fig. 2). These grooves formerly were called
the nasolacrimal grooves, but it is now recognized that the nasolacrimal grooves,
which give origin to the nasolacrimal ducts, originate parallel and medial to the
nasomaxillary grooves[9] (Fig. 2).

The medial nasal process is at first larger than the lateral nasal processes
(Plate 1, *C* and *D*), but it later lags in growth (Plate 1, *E* to *G*). Its rounded
and prominent inferolateral corners are known as the globular processes (Plate
1, *D*). The globular processes are primarily united with the maxillary processes
on both sides. Here, a fusion does not occur (Plate 1, *E*). The lateral nasal
processes do not contribute to the upper boundary of the oral orifice.

The subsequent changes that occur are due only in part to union of primarily
separated processes. Careful examination of Plate 1 will show that the processes,
in most instances, were separated by shallow grooves (e.g., the maxillary and
mandibular processes) or by pits (e.g., the lateral and the medial nasal processes). For this reason most of the changes that are commonly considered as
"fusions" are the result of decreasing depth and disappearance of grooves or pits.

Formation of the primary palate. During the fifth and sixth weeks of intra-
uterine life, a structure known as the primary palate is formed. From it will
develop the upper lip and the anterior portion of the maxillary alveolar process.

The first step in its formation is the elevation of the borders of the olfactory (nasal) pits along the inferior (caudal) half (Fig. 3, *A* and *A'*). The borders of the olfactory pit are formed from the medial nasal process medially and from the lateral nasal and maxillary processes laterally. The inferior margins of the olfactory pit grow toward each other until they touch and unite (Fig. 3, *B* and *C*), reducing the size of the external opening of the pits, the primary nostrils, and transforming the pits into blind-ending sacs (Fig. 3, *B'* and *C'*).

At this stage of development the blind ends of the nasal sacs correspond to positions on the embryonic face just above the oral orifice. If the blind ends were to open at this period, the nasal ducts would open into the face instead of into the oral cavity. A change in the topographic relation of the nasal sac (Fig. 3, *B'* and *C'*) precedes the final stages, and the opening is into the oral cavity

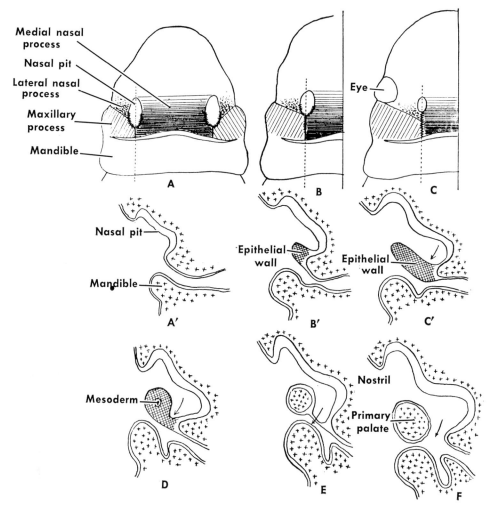

Fig. 3. For legend see opposite page.

(Fig. 3, *F*). These changes are effected through differential growth, with bulging of the mesoderm parallel to the oral orifice (Fig. 3, *D*) and continued forward growth of the mandibular arch (Fig. 3, *A'* to *F*). As the region immediately above the oral orifice enlarges (Fig. 3, *B'* and *C'*, epithelial wall, and Fig. 3, *D*, mesoderm), the base of the sac is brought into position adjacent to the primitive oral cavity.

The lateral and medial borders of the lower portion of the olfactory pit first are joined by epithelial union (Fig. 3, *B* and *C*), but the proliferating mesoderm (Fig. 3, *D*) invades the epithelial lamina and makes this union permanent. However, at the blind end of the sac that is formed from the olfactory pit, the epithelium is thinned out by growth of adjacent parts and is not replaced by mesoderm. The resulting nasobuccal membrane (Fig. 3, *E*) separates the primitive oral cavity from the olfactory sac. When this membrane ruptures (Fig. 3, *F*), the olfactory sac becomes the olfactory duct leading from the nostril to the opening into the oral cavity, the primary choana. The horizontal bar of tissue (seen in cross section in Fig. 3, *F*) formed by union of the medial nasal process with the lateral nasal processes and the maxillary processes is the primary palate (Figs. 3, *C*, and 4).

While the primary palate is being formed, the mandibular arch undergoes developmental changes that lead to the appearance of a median furrow and two small pits on either side of the midline. The furrow and median pits seem to disappear by union of the epithelium lining their walls.

The continued development of the future mature facial characteristics is the

---

Fig. 3. Diagrams showing six stages in the development of the primary palate. **A** and **A'**, Face of a human embryo 6.5 mm. in length (compare Plate 1, *C*). The zigzag line on the inferior border of the nasal pit marks the line of later fusion of the medial nasal process to the maxillary and lateral nasal processes. The broken line marks the plane of section **A'**. **B** and **B'**, Human embryo 9 mm. in length (compare Plate 1, *D*). The median nasal process has fused with the maxillary process. By this fusion an epithelial wall has been formed which is visible in section **B'**. The nasal pit is closed in its inferior part to form a short, blind olfactory sac. **C** and **C'**, Human embryo, 9.5 mm. in length (compare Plate 1, *E*). The medial nasal process is now fused to the maxillary and lateral nasal processes. The epithelial wall has lengthened, **C'**. The arrow in **C'** points to the area in which the epithelial wall separates the olfactory sac from oral cavity. **D**, Human embryo 12 mm. in length. The plane of section is as in **A'**, **B'**, and **C'**. The mesoderm has broken through the superior part of the epithelial wall, thus strengthening the primarily epithelial fusion of the medial nasal process to the maxillary and lateral nasal processes. The inferior part of the epithelial wall has thinned out (arrow). **E**, Human embryo 14 mm. in length. The destruction of the superior part of the epithelial wall by proliferating mesoderm (crosses) has advanced. The inferior part of the epithelial wall is thinned out to form the nasobuccal membrane (arrow). **F**, Human embryo 15 mm. in length. The nasobuccal membrane has disappeared. The nasal cavity communicates with the oral cavity through the primary choana (arrow). The superior part of the epithelial wall is entirely replaced by proliferating mesoderm forming the primary palate between the nasal and oral cavities. **A'**, **B'**, **C'**, **D**, **E**, and **F** represent sagittal sections corresponding to the broken lines in **A**, **B**, and **C** and comparable sections of three older embryos.

result of differential growth of the regions of the face (Plate 1). The most dramatic change is brought about by the slower growth in breadth of the derivatives of the medial nasal process in comparison with those from the lateral nasal and maxillary processes during later stages of embryonic life, while the middle third of the face increases in an anterior direction to bulge beyond the other surfaces areas (compare *F, G, H, I*, and *J* in Plate 1). The external nose is formed in this manner, and the eyes, which were situated on the lateral aspect of the head (Plate 1, *E*), come into their position close to, and on either side of, the nose (Plate 1, *I*).

The nose is not fully developed in the newborn infant, the nose of a young child being flat. Not until puberty does it develop its inherited size and shape.

The growth of the mandible follows a peculiar curve. During early development the mandible is small (Fig. 3, *B*) by comparison with the upper portions of the face, and then its growth in width and length spurts at some of the stages of palatal development (Fig. 3, *D* and *E*). Later, mandibular growth again lags (Plate 1, *G* and *H*). The fetus shows a physiologic micrognathia that disappears at, or soon after, birth. In early embryonic life the oral orifice is very wide, but as the maxillary and mandibular processes unite to form the cheeks, the width of the oral opening is reduced.

DEVELOPMENT OF THE SECONDARY PALATE

Palatine processes. At the time the primary palate is completed, the primary nasal cavity is a short duct leading from the nostril into the primitive oral cavity (Fig. 3, *F*). Its outer openings and inner openings (primary choanae) are separated from the face and oral cavity by the primary palate. As pointed out, the primary palate will develop into the upper lip, the anterior part of the alveolar process, and the anteriormost part of the palate.

As the primitive oral cavity increases in height, the tissue that separates the two primitive nostrils grows backward and downward to form the future nasal septum. The oral cavity has an incomplete, horseshoe-shaped roof (Fig. 4) formed anteriorly by the primary palate and laterally by the oral surface of the maxillary processes. On either side of the nasal septum the oral cavity communicates with the nasal cavities (Figs. 4 and 5).

Folds develop from the medial edge of the maxillary processes at the lateral portions of the oral roof. They grow downward almost vertically (Fig. 5) on either side of the tongue. The vertically disposed extension, which grows from the maxillary process, is the palatine process (Figs. 4 and 5). It extends posteriorly to the lateral walls of the pharynx. At this stage of development the tongue is narrow and high and reaches to the nasal septum (Fig. 5).

The secondary palate, which is destined to separate the oral and nasal cavities, is formed by union of the two palatine processes (Figs. 6 and 7), after the tongue assumes a more inferior position and the palatine processes have assumed horizontal positions. The anterior portion of the palatine processes also unites

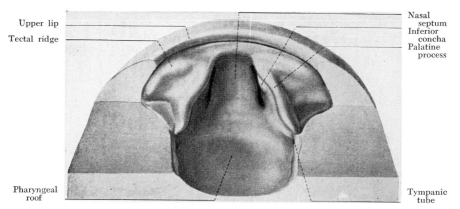

Upper lip
Tectal ridge
Nasal septum
Inferior concha
Palatine process
Pharyngeal roof
Tympanic tube

Fig. 4. Reconstruction of the roof of the primitive oral and pharyngeal cavities of a human embryo 23 mm. in length (eighth week). The primary palate and internal surface of the maxillary process form a horseshoe-shaped and incomplete roof of the oral cavity. In the center the oral cavity communicates with the nasal cavities. At the edges of the maxillary processes the palatine processes develop. (From Sicher, H., and Tandler, J.: Anatomie für Zahnärzte [Anatomy for dentists], Vienna and Berlin, 1928, Julius Springer.)

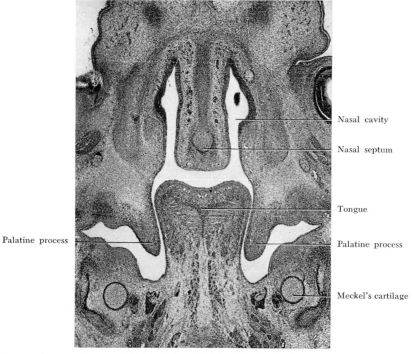

Nasal cavity
Nasal septum
Tongue
Palatine process
Palatine process
Meckel's cartilage

Fig. 5. Frontal section through the head of a human embryo 24 mm. in length (eighth week). The tongue is high and narrow between the vertical palatine processes. (Courtesy Dr. P. Gruenwald.)

Inferior concha

Nasal septum

Palatine process

Tectal ridge

Tongue

Meckel's cartilage

Fig. 6. Frontal section through the head of a human embryo 30 mm. in length (ninth week). The tongue has left the space between the palatine processes and lies flat and wide within the mandibular arch. The palatine processes have assumed a horizontal position. (Courtesy Dr. P. Gruenwald.)

with the nasal septum (Fig. 7). In this anterior region the hard palate develops. In the posterior region, in which the soft palate and uvula develop, there is no attachment to the nasal septum.

The transposition and union of the palatine processes can occur only when the tongue has moved downward, evacuating the space between the palatine processes. This takes place simultaneously with a marked growth spurt of the mandible in both length and width. This protrusion of the mandible is visible (Plate 1, *H* and *J*). The tongue moves into the wide space within the mandibular arch and assumes its natural shape with its width greater than its height (Figs. 5 to 7). The transposition of the palatine processes can occur because of accentuated growth of the mesoderm at the lateral aspect of these processes (Fig. 5). The dense arrangement of the cells and the presence of many mitotic figures identify this region as one of rapid growth.

The transposition of the near vertical palatine processes into a horizontal plane occurs also in organ cultures as soon as the tongue is removed from the space between the palatine shelves. Changes in the palatine processes and growth spurt of the mandible are precisely correlated in time so that the transposition of the palatine processes seems to be instantaneous.

Inferior concha

Nasal septum

Palatine process

Tectal ridge

Tongue

Meckel's cartilage

Fig. 7. Frontal section through the head of a human embryo slightly older than that shown in Fig. 6. The horizontal palatine processes have fused with each other and with the nasal septum. The secondary palate separates the nasal cavities from the oral cavity.

Upper lip
Tectal ridge

Tegmen oris

Soft palate
Pharyngeal roof

Tympanic tube
Uvula

Fig. 8. Reconstruction of the palate of a human embryo 28.5 mm. in length. The palatine processes are fused in the area of the hard palate. The fusion has not reached the soft palate and uvula. (From Sicher, H., and Tandler, J.: Anatomie für Zahnärzte [Anatomy for dentists], Vienna and Berlin, 1928, Julius Springer.)

When the palatine processes assume their horizontal position, they touch the lower border of the nasal septum but are still separated from each other by a median cleft (Fig. 6) which is wider posteriorly than it is toward the anterior aspect. The cleft gradually closes from the anterior to the posterior region. In earlier phases an epithelial suture is present between the two processes that formed the palate (Fig. 7). Later, most of this epithelium is invaded by the growing mesoderm, and, as it breaks up, epithelial rests are formed that may persist through later life. The epithelium persists at the anterior end where the palatine processes unite with, and partially overgrow, the primitive palate on its oral aspect. The persisting epithelium in this region forms two strands that begin in the nasal cavity and unite, below, with the oral epithelium. These are the primordia of the nasopalatine ducts, which are vestigial in man (see Chapter IX). It should be emphasized that not all of the palate arises from the palatine processes. Only the soft palate and the central portion of the hard palate (tegmen

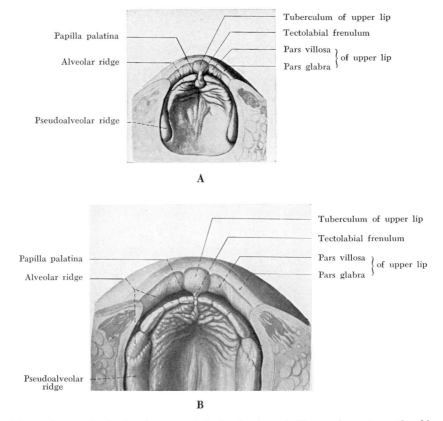

Papilla palatina

Alveolar ridge

Pseudoalveolar ridge

Tuberculum of upper lip

Tectolabial frenulum

Pars villosa } of upper lip
Pars glabra

A

Papilla palatina

Alveolar ridge

Pseudoalveolar ridge

Tuberculum of upper lip

Tectolabial frenulum

Pars villosa } of upper lip
Pars glabra

B

Fig. 9. Advanced stages in the development of the hard palate. **A,** Human fetus, 3 months old. **B,** Human fetus, 4 months old. **C,** Human newborn infant. Note the changes in the relationship of the palatine papilla and the frenulum and those between the alveolar ridge and the pseudoalveolar ridge. (From Sicher, H., and Tandler, J.: Anatomie für Zahnärzte [Anatomy for dentists], Vienna and Berlin, 1928, Julius Springer.)

oris, oral roof) are formed from the palatine processes. The horseshoe-shaped peripheral parts (tectal ridge) originate from the maxillary processes (Fig. 8).

The palate is separated from the lip by a shallow sulcus, in the depths of which two epithelial laminae arise (Fig. 15). The outer lamina is the vestibular lamina and the inner is the dental lamina (see Chapter II). Later, the alveolar process forms from the mesoderm between these laminae.

The palatine papilla develops quite early as a round prominence at the anterior part of the palate (Fig. 9). The palatine rugae cross the anterior aspect of the palate as transverse, irregular folds. At this stage the lip shows a definite division into an outer smooth zone, pars glabra, and an inner zone beset with fine villi, pars villosa (Fig. 9). In the upper lip the central portion of the pars villosa is prominent and forms the tubercle of the upper lip. A fold, tecto-labial frenum, connects the palatine papilla with the labial tubercle (Fig. 9, *A* and *B*).

When, in later stages, the growing alveolar process increases in size, the tectolabial frenum is separated from the palatine papilla and persists as the upper labial frenum, connecting the alveolar ridge with the upper lip (Fig. 9, *C*).

During these phases of development, a bulge appears in the molar region that may be mistaken for the alveolar ridge (Fig. 9). This structure, the pseudo-alveolar ridge, disappears as the true alveolar process grows posteriorly.

The development of the mandibular alveolar ridge is simple. There is no precedent pseudoalveolar ridge, the alveolar process gradually growing into the oral cavity within the limits of the labial sulcus. The labial sulcus deepens to

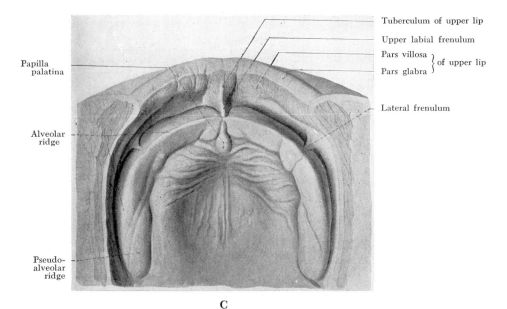

C

Fig. 9, cont'd. For legend see opposite page.

form the oral vestibule, which extends posteriorly into the regions bounded by the cheeks.

DEVELOPMENT OF THE TONGUE

Branchial arches. Because of the role of the branchial arches in formation of the tongue, the development of these structures should be understood. The branchial arches develop as four pairs of curved structures in the fetal neck. They are separated by shallow branchial grooves externally and by deeper

A

B

Fig. 10. Development of the tongue. The anterior wall of the pharynx and floor of the oral cavity are seen from within. **A,** Human embryo 3.5 mm. in length (third week). **B,** Human embryo 6.5 mm. in length (fourth week).

pharyngeal pouches internally (Fig. 10, *A*). Only the first and second arches extend to the midline, and each arch is successively smaller from the first to the fourth.

The entodermal epithelium of the pharyngeal pouches gives rise to a variety of organs: from the first pouch the auditory tube and the cavities of the midline ear are formed; in the second pouch the palatine tonsil originates; from the third pouch the inferior parathyroid gland and the thymus develop; and from the fourth pouch the superior parathyroid gland arises.

From the cartilaginous skeleton of the first arch, Meckel's cartilage, the malleus and the incus arise; from the second, the stapes, the styloid process, and the lesser horn of the hyoid; from the third, the remainder of the hyoid; and from the fourth, the thyroid cartilage.

Cervical sinus. Externally, the third and fourth arches are overgrown by a caudal outgrowth from the second arch (Plate 1, *C*) corresponding to the clos-

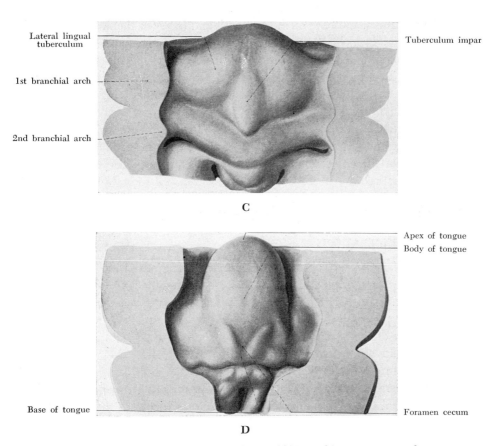

Fig. 10, cont'd. **C,** Human embryo 8 mm. in length (fifth week). **D,** Human embryo 11 mm. in length (sixth week). (From Sicher, H., and Tandler, J.: Anatomie für Zahnärzte [Anatomy for dentists], Vienna and Berlin, 1928, Julius Springer.)

ing of the caudal arches by the operculum in gill-bearing vertebrates. This places the last three arches in a deep recess, the cervical sinus. Later, this is closed when the operculum-like structure unites with the lateral wall of the neck. The cavity soon disappears, but its epithelium, if it persists, may give rise to branchial cysts.

Tongue. The tongue is derived from the first, second, and third branchial arches. The structures derived from the first branchial arches are divided, throughout life, from those from the more caudal arches by the terminal sulcus in the area of the vallate papillae (Fig. 212). The body and apex of the tongue originate in three prominences on the inner aspect of the mandibular or first branchial arch, as shown in Fig. 10. There are two lateral lingual prominences and one middle unpaired prominence, the tuberculum impar (Fig. 10, *A*). The base of the tongue develops from a prominence formed by the union of the bases of the second and third branchial arches, the copula (yoke). The tuberculum impar, which is at first prominent, is soon reduced in relative size (Fig. 10, *C*) and later almost disappears (Fig. 10, *D*).

In the midline at the base of the first arch and between the derivatives of the first and second branchial arches, the thyroid gland develops by progressive downward growth and differentiation. A transitory duct, the thyroglossal duct, originates in this region, growing downward through the developing tongue to the future site of the gland. Its oral end is marked on the adult tongue by the foramen cecum (Fig. 212). Thyroglossal duct cysts may develop in the region from the foramen cecum to the isthmus of the thyroid gland.

In later stages of development the tongue grows very rapidly, and various types of papillae are differentiated in the anterior part, whereas lymphatic tissue develops in the posterior part of the lingual mucosa (Chapter IX). The extrinsic muscles of the tongue grow into its primitive mesoderm, and the intrinsic muscles differentiate from the mesenchyme within the tongue.

CLINICAL CONSIDERATIONS

Facial malformations. The most frequent malformations of the face are clefts. Clefts of the lip, jaw, or palate, usually in some combination, occur once in about eight hundred births. Cleft lip (cheiloschisis, harelip) is a cleft, lateral to the midline, cutting through the lip. It may be bilateral or unilateral and is between the derivatives of the medial nasal and lateral processes. (Plate 1, *K*). Midline clefts of the lip are extremely rare. Gnathoschisis (cleft jaw) occurs in the maxilla between the derivatives of the same processes and likewise may be unilateral or bilateral. Uranoschisis (cleft palate) commonly involves both the hard and the soft palates. When only the soft palate is involved, the term staphyloschisis is used. Cleft palate is due to failure of union between the two palatine processes. The oblique facial cleft begins at some point in the upper lip and courses obliquely over the cheek to the eye along the line of junction of the maxillary and lateral nasal processes (Plate 1, *K*). Failure of complete union of the maxillary and mandibular processes produces macrostomia, an abnormally wide mouth.

Cleft lip and jaw. In most instances both lip and jaw are cleft (cheilognathoschisis). This cleft extends from the lower border of the nostril, lateral to the midline, through the upper lip and the maxillary alveolar process, to the region of the incisive foramen. This malformation was long considered simply as a lack of fusion of the medial nasal process with the lateral nasal process. It has been shown[13] that epithelial fusion does occur in cases of cleft lip and jaw, but the epithelial wall is not perforated by mesoderm, and the epithelial union opens. Cleft lip and jaw would be evident at 6 to 7 weeks in utero.

The relation of cleft jaw to the teeth and bone varies. In some instances the cleft is in the position between the premaxilla and the maxilla, usually lateral to the second incisor. Occasionally, it is medial to this site and medial to the second incisor. At other times the second incisor may be missing or a supernumerary tooth may develop. The skeletal parts and the teeth begin their development after the normal union of the facial processes has occurred. Hence, the teeth and skeletal parts develop in a uniform tissue without relation to the *exact* location of the former boundaries between the processes.

Cleft palate. In cleft palate there may be lack of union of both palatine processes with each other and with the nasal septum, or one palatine process may unite with the nasal septum but not with its counterpart. Palatal union, if it is to occur, usually is completed before the third month. Since union begins in the anterior region and progresses posteriorly, the degree of cleft may vary from complete nonunion to the relatively innocuous notched or bifid uvula.

Cleft palate is associated with cleft lip in 84 per cent of patients. In bilateral cleft lip and palate there may be a protruding mass of tissue formed from the medial nasal process. If there is atrophy of this tissue, a wide cleft results which may erroneously be diagnosed as a median cleft.

Heredity probably is a major factor in cleft formation, although nutritional deficiencies, infectious diseases, trauma in utero, and other factors may contribute. Other anomalies, such as cranioschisis, spina bifida, polydactylism, or clubfoot, are frequently found associated with facial clefts.

Labial pits. Small pits may persist on either side of the midline of the lower lip. They are due to the failure of the embryonic labial pits to disappear.

Lingual anomalies. Median rhomboid glossitis, an innocuous, red, rhomboid-shaped smooth zone of the tongue in the midline in front of the foramen cecum, is considered the result of persistence of the tuberculum impar. Lack of fusion between the two lateral lingual prominences may produce a bifid tongue. Thyroid tissue may be present in the base of the tongue. Part of the thyroglossal duct may persist and form cysts at the base of the tongue.

Developmental cysts. Epithelial rests in lines of union of facial or oral processes or from epithelial organs, i.e., vestigial nasopalatine ducts, may give rise to cysts lined with epithelium.

Branchial cleft (cervical) cysts or fistulas may arise from the rests of branchial pouches or the cervical sinus. They usually are laterally disposed on the neck. Thyroglossal duct cysts may occur at any place along the course of the duct, usually at or near the midline.

Cysts may arise from epithelial rests after the fusion of medial and lateral nasal processes. They are called globulomaxillary cysts and are lined with pseudostratified columnar epithelium and squamous epithelium. They may, however, develop as primordial cysts from a supernumerary tooth germ.

"Anterior palatine" cysts are situated in the midline of the maxillary alveolar process. Once believed to be from remnants of the fusion of two processes, they are now considered as primordial cysts of odontogenic origin. The term "anterior palatine cyst" is misleading and should be avoided.

Nasolabial cysts, originating in the base of the wing of the nose and bulging into the nasal and oral vestibule and the root of the upper lip, sometimes causing a flat depression on the anterior surface of the alveolar process, are also explained as originating from epithelial remnants in the harelip line. It is, however, more probable that they derive from excessive epithelial proliferations that normally, for some time in embryonic life, plug the nostrils. It is also possible that they are retention cysts of vestibular nasal glands or that they develop from the epithelium of the nasolacrimal duct.

REFERENCES

1. Arey, L. B.: Developmental anatomy, ed. 6, Philadelphia, 1957, W. B. Saunders Co.
2. Burket, L. W.: Nasopalatine duct structures and peculiar bony patterns in the anterior maxillary region, Arch. Path. **23**:793, 1937.
3. Grace, L. G.: Frequency of occurrence of cleft palate and hare lips, J. D. Res. **22**:495, 1943.
4. Hochstetter, F.: Beiträge zur Entwicklungsgeschichte des menschlichen Gaumens (Contributions to the development of the human palate), Morphol. Jahrb. **77**:179, 1936.
5. Keibel, F., and Mall, F. P.: Manual of human embryology, Philadelphia and London, 1910, J. B. Lippincott Co.
6. Kraus, Bertram S.: Prenatal growth and morphology of the human bony palate, J. D. Res. **39**:1177, 1960.
7. Moriarty, T. M., Weinstein, S., and Gibson, R. D.: The development in vitro and in vivo of fusion of the palatal processes of rat embryos, J. Embryol. Exp. Morph. **11**:605, 1963.
8. Peter, K.: Die Entwicklung des Saugetiergaumens (Development of the mammalian palate), Ergebn. d. Anat. Entwcklngsgesch. **25**:448, 1924.
9. Politzer, G.: Die Grenzfurche des Oberkieferfortsatzes und die Tränennasenrinne beim Menschen (The limiting sulcus of the maxillary process and the nasolacrimal groove in man), Ztschr. f. Anat. u. Entwcklngsgesch. **105**:329, 1936.
10. Robinson, H. B. G.: Classification of cysts of the jaws, Am. J. Orthodont. & Oral Surg. **31**:370, 1945.
11. Sicher, H., and Pohl, L.: Zur Entwicklung des menschlichen Unterkiefers (Development of the human mandible—a contribution to the origin of the fistulae of the lower lip), Ztschr. f. Stomatol. **32**:552, 1934.
12. Sicher, H., and Tandler, J.: Anatomie für Zahnärzte (Anatomy for dentists), Vienna and Berlin, 1928, Julius Springer.
13. Veau, V., and Politzer, G.: Embryologie du bec-de-lièvre; le palais primaire (Embryology

of the harelip: the primary palate. Formation and anomalies), Ann. d' anat. path. **13:** 275, 1936.

14. Walker, B. E., and Fraser, F. C.: Closure of the secondary palate in three strains of mice, J. Embryol. Exp. Morph. **4** (part 2):176, 1956.

15. Zeiler, K. B., Weinstein, S., and Gibson, R. D.: A study of the morphology and the time of closure of the palate in the albino rats, Arch. Oral Biol. **9:**545, 1964.

INTRODUCTION
DEVELOPMENTAL STAGES
   Dental lamina and bud stage
      Dental lamina
      Tooth buds (primordia of teeth)
   Cap stage
      Outer and inner dental epithelium
      Stellate reticulum (enamel pulp)
      Dental papilla
      Dental sac
   Bell stage
      Inner dental epithelium
      Stratum intermedium
      Stellate reticulum
      Outer dental epithelium
      Dental lamina
      Dental papilla
      Dental sac
      Advanced bell stage
      Function of the dental lamina
      Fate of the dental lamina
      Vestibular lamina
   Hertwig's epithelial root sheath and root formation
HISTOPHYSIOLOGY AND CLINICAL
   CONSIDERATIONS
      Initiation
      Proliferation
      Histodifferentiation
      Morphodifferentiation
      Apposition

Chapter II

Development and growth of the teeth*

INTRODUCTION

By the time the human embryo is 3 weeks old, the stomodeum has formed at its cephalic end (see Chapter I). The ectoderm that lines the stomodeum comes in contact with the endoderm of the foregut, and the union of these two layers forms the buccopharyngeal membrane. This membrane soon ruptures, and then the primitive oral cavity communicates with the foregut.

The ectoderm of the primitive oral cavity consists of a basal layer of high cells and a surface layer of flattened cells. These cells appear empty in routine preparations of slides because of the loss of glycogen in their cytoplasm by the usual methods of microtechnique.

The oral ectoderm rests upon the underlying mesenchyme. The two tissues are separated by a basement membrane.

Each tooth develops from a tooth bud that forms deep beneath the surface in the area of the primitive mouth that will become the jaws. A tooth bud consists of three parts: (1) a *dental organ*, which is derived from the oral ectoderm, (2) a *dental papilla*, which is derived from the mesenchyme, and (3) a *dental sac*, which is also derived from the mesenchyme (Fig. 18). The dental organ produces the tooth enamel, the dental papilla produces the tooth pulp and the

---

*First draft submitted by Isaac Schour in collaboration with Maury Massler; revised by Nicholas J. Brescia.

dentin, and the dental sac produces not only the cementum but also the perio-dontal ligament.

Two or three weeks after the rupture of the buccopharyngeal membrane, when the embryo is 5 or 6 weeks old, the first sign of tooth development is seen. In the oral ectoderm, which will, of course, give rise to the oral epithelium, certain areas of basal cells begin to proliferate at a more rapid rate than do cells in adjacent areas. The result is the formation of a band, an ectodermal thickening in the region of the future dental arches extending along a line that represents the margin of the jaws (Fig. 13). This band of thickened ectoderm is the *dental lamina.*

At certain points on the dental lamina, each representing the location of one of the ten mandibular and ten maxillary deciduous teeth, the ectodermal cells of the dental lamina multiply still more rapidly and form a little knob that presses slightly into the underlying mesenchyme (Figs. 12 and 14). Each of these little downgrowths on the dental lamina represents the beginning of the dental organ of the tooth bud of a deciduous tooth. Not all of these dental organs start to develop at the same time. The first to appear are in the anterior mandibular region.

As cell proliferation continues, each dental organ increases in size and changes in shape. As it develops, it takes on a shape that somewhat resembles a cap, with the outside of the cap directed toward the oral surface (Figs. 15 to 17).

Inside of the cap (i.e., inside the depression of the dental organ), the mesen-chymal cells increase in number, and the tissue here appears more dense than the surrounding mesenchyme. With this proliferation, the area of mesenchyme becomes the dental papilla.

Now, surrounding the deeper side of this structure (i.e., the combined dental organ and dental papilla), the third part of the tooth bud forms. The mesen-chyme in this area becomes somewhat fibrous in appearance, the fibers encircling the deep side of the papilla and the dental organ. These encircling fibers are the dental sac (Fig. 18).

During and after these developments, the shape of the dental organ continues to change. The depression occupied by the dental papilla deepens until the dental organ assumes a shape which has been described as resembling that of a bell. And as these developments take place, the dental lamina, which has thus far connected the dental organ to the oral epithelium, breaks up, and the tooth bud loses its connection with the epithelium of the primitive oral cavity.

DEVELOPMENTAL STAGES

Despite the obvious fact that tooth development (as the development of any other organ) is a continual process, it is not only traditional but also didactically necessary to divide the developmental history of a tooth into several "stages." They are named from the shape of the epithelial part of the tooth germ. Since the odontogenic epithelium not only produces enamel but also is indispensable for the initiation of dentin formation, the terms enamel organ and outer and

Fig. 11. Diagrammatic illustration of the life cycle of the tooth. (Modified from Schour, I., and Massler, M.: J.A.D.A. **27**:1785, 1940.)

GROWTH   CALCIFICATION   ERUPTION   ATTRITION

A   B   C   D   E   F   G   H
Initiation Proliferation   Morphodifferentiation Apposition and (Before   (After
(Bud stage) (Cap stage)   Histodifferentiation   emergence) emergence)
                            (Bell stage)

A

Tooth buds and
dental lamina

Dental organs

B

Dental organs
of deciduous
teeth
Primordium of
permanent
tooth

C

Primordium of first
permanent
molar

Fig. 12. Diagrammatic reconstruction of the dental lamina and dental organs of the mandible.
A, 22 mm. embryo, bud stage (eighth week). **B,** 43 mm. embryo, cap stage (tenth week).
C, 163 mm. embryo, bell stage (about 4 months). The primordia of permanent teeth are
seen as thickenings of the dental lamina on the lingual side of each tooth germ. Distal exten-
sion of the dental lamina with the primordium of the first molar. (Modified from Norberg, O.:
Untersuchungen über das dento-gingivale Epithelleistensystem im intrauterinen Leben des
Menschen [Investigations of the dentino-gingival epithelium in human intra-uterine life],
Stockholm, 1929, A. B. Fahlcrantz' Boktrycheri.)

A

Upper jaw

Dental lamina

Dental lamina

Lower jaw

Oral cavity

Tongue

Mitosis in epithelium

Basement membrane

Mitosis

Mitosis in mesoderm

B

Fig. 13. Initiation of tooth development. Human embryo 13.5 mm. in length, fifth week. **A,** Sagittal section through the upper and lower jaws. **B,** High magnification of thickened oral epithelium. (From Orban, B.: Dental histology and embryology, Philadelphia, 1929, P. Blakiston's Son & Co.)

inner enamel epithelium are best replaced by the terms *dental* organ and *dental* epithelium.

Dental lamina and bud stage

Dental lamina. The first sign of human tooth development is seen during the sixth week of embryonic life (11 mm. embryo). At this stage the oral epithelium consists of a basal layer of high cells and a surface layer of flattened cells. The glycogen droplets in their cytoplasm are lost in routine preparations, giving them an empty appearance. The epithelium is separated from the connective tissue by a basement membrane. Certain cells in the basal layer of the oral epithelium begin to proliferate at a more rapid rate than do the adjacent cells. An epithelial thickening arises in the region of the future dental arch and extends along the entire free margin of the jaws (Figs. 12 and 13). It is the primordium of the

Central
incisor

Lateral
incisor

Tooth
bud in
upper
jaw

Tooth
bud in
lower
jaw (in-
cisor)

A   B

Lip-furrow
band

Tooth bud

Mesoderm

C

Fig. 14. Bud stage of tooth development, proliferation stage. Human embryo 16 mm. in length, sixth week. **A,** Wax reconstruction of the germs of the lower central and lateral incisors. **B,** Sagittal section through the upper and lower jaws. **C,** High magnification of the tooth germ of a lower incisor in bud stage. (From Orban, B.: Dental histology and embryology, Philadelphia, 1929, P. Blakiston's Son & Co.)

ectodermal portion of the teeth known as the dental lamina. Mitotic figures are seen not only in the epithelium but also in the subjacent mesoderm (Fig. 13).

Tooth buds (primordia of teeth). Simultaneous with the differentiation of the dental lamina there arise from it in each jaw round or ovoid swellings at ten different points, corresponding to the future position of the deciduous teeth, the primordia of the dental organs, the tooth buds (Fig. 14). Thus the development of the tooth germs is initiated, and the cells continue to proliferate faster than

A

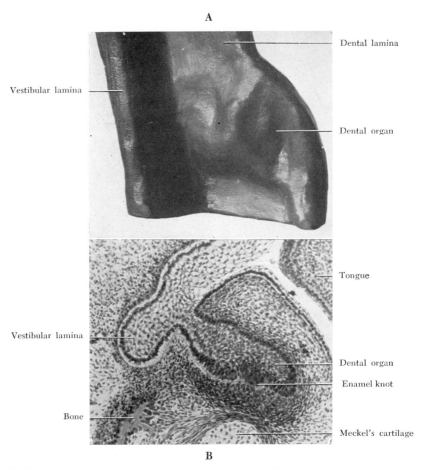

Dental lamina

Vestibular lamina

Dental organ

Tongue

Vestibular lamina

Dental organ

Enamel knot

Bone

Meckel's cartilage

B

Fig. 15. Cap stage of tooth development. Human embryo 31.5 mm. in length, ninth week. **A,** Wax reconstruction of the dental organ of a lower lateral incisor. **B,** Labiolingual section through the same tooth. (From Orban, B.: Dental histology and embryology, Philadelphia, 1929, P. Blakiston's Son & Co.)

the adjacent cells. The dental lamina is shallow, and microscopic sections often show the tooth buds close to the oral epithelium.

Cap stage

As the tooth bud continues to proliferate, it does not expand uniformly into a larger sphere. Unequal growth in the different parts of the bud leads to formation of the cap stage, which is characterized by a shallow invagination on the deep surface of the bud (Figs. 12, *B*, and 15).

Outer and inner dental epithelium. The peripheral cells of the cap stage form the outer dental epithelium at the convexity, consisting of a single row of cuboidal cells, and the inner dental epithelium at the concavity, consisting of a layer of tall cells (Figs. 15 and 16).

Stellate reticulum (enamel pulp). The cells in the center of the epithelial

Vestibular lamina

Dental organ

A

Tongue

Vestibular
lamina

Dental organ

Dental papilla

Bone

Meckel's
cartilage

B

Fig. 16. Cap stage of tooth development. Human embryo 41.5 mm. in length, tenth week. **A,** Wax reconstruction of the dental organ of a lower central incisor. **B,** Labiolingual section through the same tooth. (From Orban, B.: Dental histology and embryology, Philadelphia, 1929, P. Blakiston's Son & Co.)

dental organ, situated between the outer and inner epithelia, begin to separate by an increase of the intercellular fluid and arrange themselves in a network called the stellate reticulum (Figs. 18 and 19). The cells assume a branched reticular form. The spaces in this reticular network are filled with a mucoid fluid rich in albumin, giving the stellate reticulum a cushionlike consistency that later supports and protects the delicate enamel-forming cells.

The cells in the center of the dental organ are densely packed and form the

Lip-furrow band

Dental organ

A

Dental lamina

Lip-furrow band

Dental organ

Dental papilla

Bone

B

Fig. 17. Cap stage of tooth development. Human embryo 60 mm. in length, eleventh week. **A,** Wax reconstruction of the dental organ of a lower lateral incisor. **B,** Labiolingual section through the same tooth. (From Orban, B.: Dental histology and embryology, Philadelphia, 1929, P. Blakiston's Son & Co.)

enamel knot (Fig. 15). This knot projects in part toward the underlying dental papilla, so that the center of the epithelial invagination shows a slightly knoblike enlargement that is bordered by the labial and lingual enamel grooves (Fig. 15). At the same time there arises in the increasingly high dental organ a vertical extension of the enamel knot, called the enamel cord (Fig. 18). Both are temporary structures that disappear before enamel formation begins.

Dental papilla. Under the organizing influence of the proliferating epithelium of the dental organ, the mesenchyme, partially enclosed by the invaginated portion of the inner dental epithelium, proliferates. It condenses to form the dental papilla, which is the formative organ of the dentin and the primordium of the pulp (Figs. 15 and 16). The changes in the dental papilla occur concomitantly with the development of the epithelial dental organ. While the epithelium exerts a dominating influence over the adjacent connective tissue, the condensation of the latter should not be considered as a passive crowding by the proliferating epithelium. The dental papilla shows active budding of capillaries and mitotic figures, and its peripheral cells adjacent to the inner dental epithelium enlarge and later differentiate into the odontoblasts.

Fig. 18. Bell stage of tooth development. Human embryo 105 mm. in length, fourteenth week. A, Wax reconstruction of a lower central incisor. B, Labiolingual section of the same tooth. X, See Fig. 19. (From Orban, B.: Dental histology and embryology, Philadelphia, 1929, P. Blakiston's Son & Co.)

Mitosis

Inner dental epithelium

Stratum intermedium

Basement membrane

Dental papilla

Stellate reticulum

Outer dental epithelium

Fig. 19. The layers of the epithelial dental organ in high magnification. Area X of Fig. 18.

Dental sac. Concomitant with the development of the dental organ and the dental papilla, there is a marginal condensation in the mesenchyme surrounding the dental organ and dental papilla. In this zone, gradually a denser and more fibrous layer develops, which is the primitive dental sac.

The epithelial dental organ, the dental papilla, and the dental sac are the formative tissues for an entire tooth and its periodontal ligament.

Bell stage

As the invagination of the epithelium deepens and its margins continue to grow, the enamel organ assumes a bell shape (Figs. 12, C, 17, and 18).

Inner dental epithelium. The inner dental epithelium consists of a single layer of cells that differentiate prior to amelogenesis into tall columnar cells, the ameloblasts (Figs. 18 and 19). They are 4 to 5 microns in diameter and about 40 microns high. In cross section they assume a hexagonal shape, similar to that seen later in transverse sections of the enamel rods.

The cells of the inner dental epithelium exert an organizing influence upon the underlying mesenchymal cells, which differentiate into odontoblasts.

Stratum intermedium. Several layers of squamous cells, called stratum intermedium, appear between the inner dental epithelium and stellate reticulum (Fig. 19). This layer seems to be essential to enamel formation. It is absent in the part of the tooth germ that outlines the root portions of the tooth but does not form enamel.

Stellate reticulum. The stellate reticulum expands further, mainly by increase of the intercellular fluid. The cells are star shaped, with long processes that anastomose with those of adjacent cells (Fig. 19). Before enamel formation begins, the stellate reticulum shrinks by loss of the intercellular fluid. Its cells then are hardly distinguishable from those of the stratum intermedium. This change begins at the height of the cusp or the incisal edge and progresses cervically (Figs. 60 and 97).

Outer dental epithelium. The cells of the outer dental epithelium flatten to a low cuboidal form. At the end of the bell stage, preparatory to and during the formation of enamel, the formerly smooth surface of the outer dental epithelium is laid in folds. Between the folds the adjacent mesenchyme of the dental sac forms papillae that contain capillary loops and thus provide a rich nutritional supply for the intense metabolic activity of the avascular enamel organ.

Dental lamina. In all teeth except the permanent molars, the dental lamina proliferates at its deep end to give rise to the dental organ of the permanent tooth, while it disintegrates in the region between the dental organ and the oral epithelium. The dental organ is gradually separated from the dental lamina at about the time when the first dentin is formed.

Dental papilla. The dental papilla is enclosed in the invaginated portion of the dental organ. Before the inner dental epithelium begins to produce enamel, the peripheral cells of the mesenchymal dental papilla differentiate into odontoblasts under the organizing influence of the epithelium. They assume a cuboidal and later a columnar form and acquire the specific potentiality to produce dentin.

The basement membrane separating the epithelial dental organ and dental papilla at the time just preceding dentin formation is called membrana preformativa.

Dental sac. Before formation of dental tissues begins, the dental sac shows a circular arrangement of its fibers and resembles a capsular structure. With the development of the root, the fibers of the dental sac differentiate into the periodontal fibers that become embedded in the cementum and alveolar bone.

Advanced bell stage. During the advanced bell stage, the boundary between inner dental epithelium and odontoblasts outlines the future dentinoenamel junction (Figs. 18 and 20). In addition, the junction of the inner and outer dental epithelia at the basal margin of the epithelial organ, in the region of the cervical line, will give rise to the epithelial root sheath of Hertwig.

Function of the dental lamina. The functional activity of the dental lamina and its chronology may be considered in three phases. The first phase is concerned with the initiation of the entire deciduous dentition that occurs during the second month in utero (Fig. 12, *A* and *B*). The second phase deals with the initiation of the successors of the deciduous teeth. It is preceded by the growth of the free end of the dental lamina (successional lamina), lingual to the dental organ of each deciduous tooth, and occurs from about the fifth month in utero for the permanent central incisors to 10 months of age for the second premolar (Fig. 12, *C*). The third phase is preceded by the extension of the dental lamina distal to the dental organ of the second deciduous molar, which

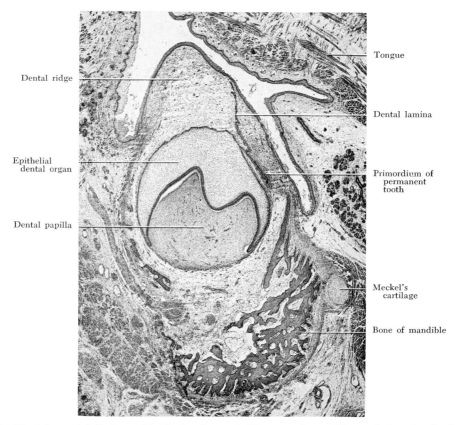

Fig. 20. Advanced bell stage of tooth development. Human embryo 200 mm. in length, about 18 weeks. Labiolingual section through the deciduous lower first molar.

begins in the 140 mm. embryo (Fig. 12, *C*). The permanent molars arise directly from the distal extension of the dental lamina. The time of initiation is about 4 months of fetal life (in the 160 mm. embryo) for the first permanent molar, the first year for the second permanent molar, and the fourth to fifth year for the third permanent molar.

It is thus evident that the total activity of the dental lamina extends over a period of about five years. Any particular portion of it functions for a much briefer period, since only a relatively short time elapses after initiation before the dental lamina begins to disintegrate at that particular location. However, the dental lamina may still be active in the third molar region after it has disappeared elsewhere except for occasional epithelial remnants. The distal proliferation of the dental lamina is responsible for the peculiar location of the germs of the permanent molars. They develop in the ramus of the mandible and in the tuberosity of the maxilla.

Fate of the dental lamina. During the cap stage the dental lamina maintains a broad connection with the dental organ, but in the bell stage it begins to

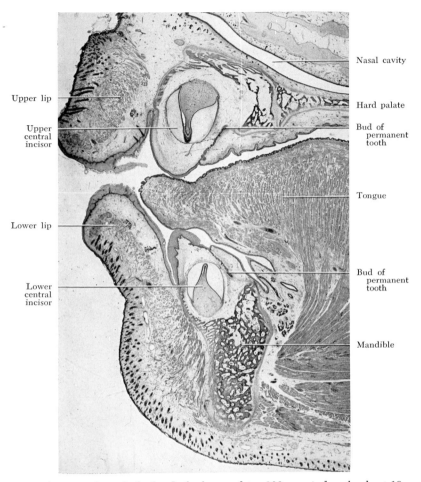

Fig. 21. Sagittal section through the head of a human fetus 200 mm. in length, about 18 weeks, in the region of the central incisors.

break up by mesenchymal invasion, which first penetrates its central portion and divides it into the lateral lamina and the dental lamina proper. The mesenchymal invasion is at first incomplete and does not perforate the dental lamina (Fig. 18). The dental lamina proper proliferates only at its deeper margin, which becomes a free end situated lingually to the dental organ and forms the primordium of the permanent tooth (Fig. 18). The epithelial connection of the dental organ with the oral epithelium is severed by the proliferating mesoderm. Remnants of the dental lamina may persist as epithelial pearls.

Vestibular lamina. Labial and buccal to the dental lamina, another epithelial thickening develops independently and somewhat later. It is the vestibular lamina, also termed lip-furrow band. (See Figs. 16 and 17.) It subsequently hollows out and forms the oral vestibule between the alveolar portion of the jaws and the lips and cheeks (Figs. 20 and 21).

Hertwig's epithelial root sheath and root formation

The development of the roots begins after enamel and dentin formation has reached the future cementoenamel junction. The epithelial dental organ plays an important part in root development by forming Hertwig's epithelial root sheath, which molds the shape of the roots and initiates dentin formation. Hertwig's root sheath consists only of the outer and inner dental epithelia, without a stratum intermedium and stellate reticulum.[2] The cells of the inner layer remain short and normally do not produce enamel. When these cells have induced the differentiation of connective tissue cells into odontoblasts and the first layer of dentin has been laid down, the epithelial root sheath loses its continuity and its close relation to the surface of the tooth. Its remnants persist as epithelial rests of Malassez in the periodontal ligament.

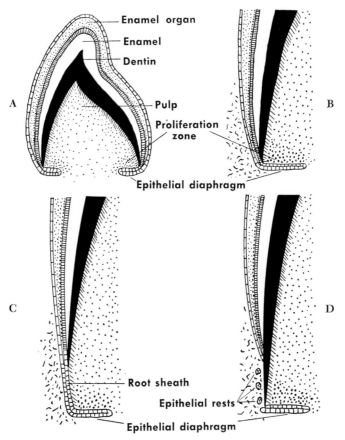

Fig. 22. Diagrams showing three stages in root development. **A,** Section through a tooth germ. Note the epithelial diaphragm and proliferation zone of pulp. **B,** Higher magnification of the cervical region of **A. C,** "Imaginary" stage showing the elongation of Hertwig's epithelial sheath coronal to the diaphragm. Differentiation of odontoblasts in the elongated pulp. **D,** In the area of proliferation, dentin has been formed. The root sheath is broken up into epithelial rests and is separated from the dentinal surface by connective tissue. Differentiation of cementoblasts.

There is a marked difference in the development of Hertwig's epithelial root sheath in teeth with one root and in those with two or more roots. Prior to the beginning of root formation, the root sheath forms the epithelial diaphragm (Fig. 22). The outer and inner dental epithelia bend at the future cemento-enamel junction into a horizontal plane, narrowing the wide cervical opening of the tooth germ.[13] The plane of the diaphragm remains relatively fixed during the development and growth of the root[8] (see Chapter XI). The proliferation of the cells of the epithelial diaphragm is accompanied by proliferation of the cells of the connective tissue of the pulp, which occurs in the area adjacent to the diaphragm. The free end of the diaphragm does not grow into the connective tissue, but the epithelium proliferates coronally to the epithelial diaphragm (Fig. 22, B). The differentiation of odontoblasts and the formation of dentin succeed the lengthening of the root sheath. At the same time the connective tissue of the dental sac surrounding the sheath proliferates and divides the continuous double epithelial layer (Fig. 22, C) into a network of epithelial strands (Fig. 22, D). The epithelium is moved away from the surface of the dentin so that connective tissue cells come into contact with the outer surface of the dentin and differen-

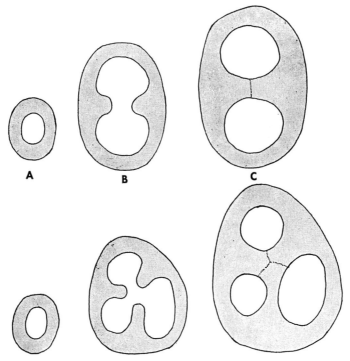

Fig. 23. Three stages in the development of a tooth with two roots and one with three roots. Surface view of the epithelial diaphragm. During growth of the tooth germ, the simple diaphragm, **A,** expands eccentrically so that horizontal epithelial flaps are formed, **B.** Later these flaps proliferate and unite (dotted lines in **C**) and divide the single cervical opening into two or three openings.

tiate into cementoblasts, which deposit a layer of cementum onto the surface of the dentin. The rapid sequence of proliferation and destruction of Hertwig's root sheath explains the fact that it cannot be seen as a continuous layer on the surface of the developing root (Fig. 22, *D*). In the last stages of root development the proliferation of the epithelium in the diaphragm lags behind that of the pulpal connective tissue. The wide apical foramen is reduced first to the width of the diaphragmatic opening itself and later further narrowed by apposition of dentin and cementum at the apex of the root.

Differential growth of the epithelial diaphragm in multirooted teeth causes the division of the root trunk into two or three roots.[16] During the general growth of the coronal epithelial dental organ, the expansion of its cervical opening occurs in such a way that long tonguelike extensions of the horizontal diaphragm develop (Fig. 23). Two such extensions are found in the germs of lower molars and three in the germs of upper molars. Before division of the root trunk occurs, the free ends of these horizontal epithelial flaps grow toward each other and fuse. The single cervical opening of the coronal enamel organ is then divided into two or three openings. On the pulpal surface of the dividing epithelial bridges, dentin formation starts (Fig. 24, *A*), and on the periphery of each opening, root development follows in the same way as described for single-rooted teeth (Fig. 24, *B*).

If cells of the epithelial root sheath remain adherent to the dentin surface, they may differentiate into fully functioning ameloblasts and produce enamel.

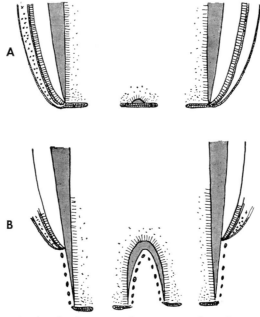

Fig. 24. Two stages in the development of a two-rooted tooth. Diagrammatic mesiodistal sections of a lower molar. **A,** Beginning of dentin formation at the bifurcation. **B,** Formation of the two roots in progress. (Details as shown in Fig. 22.)

Such droplets of enamel, called enamel pearls, are sometimes found in the area of furcation of the roots of permanent molars. If the continuity of Hertwig's root sheath is broken or is not established prior to dentin formation, a defect in the dentinal wall of the pulp ensues. Such defects are found in the pulpal floor corresponding to the furcation if the fusion of the horizontal extensions of the diaphragm remains incomplete, or on any point of the root itself. This accounts for the development of accessory root canals opening on the periodontal surface of the root (see Chapter V).

HISTOPHYSIOLOGY AND CLINICAL CONSIDERATIONS

A number of physiologic growth processes participate in the progressive development of the teeth (Table 1). Except for initiation, which is a momentary event, these processes overlap considerably, and many are continuous over several histologic stages. Nevertheless, each tends to predominate in one stage more than in another.

For example, the process of histodifferentiation characterizes the bell stage in which the cells of the inner dental epithelium differentiate into functional ameloblasts. However, proliferation still progresses at the deeper portion of the dental organ.

Initiation. The dental lamina and tooth buds represent that part of the oral epithelium which has potencies for tooth formation. Specific cells contain the entire growth potential of certain teeth and respond to those factors which initiate tooth development. Different teeth are initiated at definite times. Initiation is set off by unknown factors just as the growth potential of the ovum is set off by the fertilizing spermatozoon.

Teeth may develop in abnormal locations, e.g., in the ovary (dermoid tumors or cysts) or in the hypophysis. In such instances the tooth undergoes stages of development similar to those in the jaws.

A lack of initiation results in the absence of teeth, which may involve single teeth, most frequently the permanent upper lateral incisors, third molars, and

Table 1. Stages in tooth growth

Morphologic stages	Physiologic processes
Dental lamina ←————————→	Initiation
Bud stage	
Cap stage (early)	Proliferation
Cap stage (advanced)	
Bell stage (early)	Histodifferentiation
Bell stage (advanced)	Morphodifferentiation
Formation of enamel and dentin matrix	Apposition

lower second premolars, or there may be a complete lack of teeth, anodontia. On the other hand, abnormal initiation may result in the development of single or multiple supernumerary teeth.

Proliferation. Marked proliferative activity ensues at the points of initiation and results successively in the bud, cap, and bell stages of the odontogenic organ. Proliferative growth causes regular changes in the size and proportions of the growing tooth germ (Figs. 13 and 17).

During the stage of proliferation, the tooth germ has the potentiality to progress to more advanced development. This is illustrated by the fact that explants of these early stages continue to develop in tissue culture through the subsequent stages of histodifferentiation and appositional growth. A disturbance or experimental interference has entirely different effects, according to the time of occurrence and the stage of development that it affects.

Histodifferentiation. Histodifferentiation succeeds the proliferative stage. The formative cells of the tooth germs developing during the proliferative stage undergo definite morphologic as well as functional changes and acquire their functional assignment (the appositional growth potential). The cells become restricted in their potencies. They give up their capacity to multiply as they assume their new function (a law that governs all differentiating cells). This phase reaches its highest development in the bell stage of the dental organ, just preceding the beginning of formation and apposition of dentin and enamel (Fig. 18).

The organizing influence of the inner dental epithelium on the mesenchyme is evident in the bell stage and causes the differentiation of the adjacent cells of the dental papilla into odontoblasts. With the formation of dentin, the cells of the inner dental epithelium differentiate into ameloblasts, and enamel matrix is formed opposite the dentin. Enamel does not form in the absence of dentin as demonstrated by the failure of transplanted ameloblasts to form enamel when no dentin is present.[3] Dentin formation therefore precedes and is essential to enamel formation. The differentiation of the epithelial cells precedes and is essential to the differentiation of the odontoblasts and the initiation of dentin formation.

In vitamin A deficiency the ameloblasts fail to differentiate properly. In consequence, their organizing influence upon the adjacent mesenchymal cells is disturbed, and atypical dentin, known as osteodentin, is formed.

Morphodifferentiation. The morphologic pattern or basic form and relative size of the future tooth is established by morphodifferentiation, i.e., by differential growth. Morphodifferentiation, therefore, is impossible without proliferation. The advanced bell stage marks not only active histodifferentiation but also an important stage of morphodifferentiation of the crown by outlining the future dentinoenamel junction (Figs. 18 and 20).

The dentinoenamel and dentinocemental junctions, which are different and characteristic for each type of tooth, act as a blueprint pattern. In conformity with this pattern, the ameloblasts, odontoblasts, and cementoblasts deposit

enamel, dentin, and cementum and thus give the completed tooth its characteristic form and size. For example, the size and form of the cuspal portion of the
crown of the first permanent molar are established at birth, prior to formation
of hard tissues.

The frequent statement in the literature that endocrine disturbances affect
the size or form of the crown of teeth is not tenable unless such effects occur
during morphodifferentiation, i.e., in utero or in the first year of life. Size and
shape of the root, however, may be altered by disturbances in later periods.
Clinical examination shows that the retarded eruption that occurs in persons
with hypopituitarism and hypothyroidism results in a small clinical crown that
is often mistaken for a small anatomic crown.

Disturbances in morphodifferentiation may affect the form and size of the
tooth without impairing the function of the ameloblasts or odontoblasts. New
parts may be differentiated (supernumerary cusps or roots), twinning may result, a suppression of parts may occur (loss of cusps or roots), or the result may
be a peg or malformed tooth (e.g., Hutchinson's incisor) with enamel and dentin
that may be normal in structure.[11]

Apposition is the deposition of the matrix of the hard dental structures. It
will be described in separate chapters on enamel, dentin, and cementum. This
chapter deals with certain aspects of apposition in order to complete the discussion of the physiologic processes concerned in the growth of teeth.

Apposition. Appositional growth of enamel and dentin is a layerlike deposition of an extracellular matrix. This type of growth is, therefore, additive. It is
the fulfillment of the plans outlined at the stages of histodifferentiation and
morphodifferentiation. Appositional growth is characterized by regular and
rhythmic deposition of the extracellular material, which is of itself incapable of
further growth. Periods of activity and rest alternate at definite intervals.

The matrix is deposited by the cells along the site outlined by the formative
cells at the end of morphodifferentiation, determining the future dentinoenamel
and dentinocemental junctions, and according to a definite pattern of cellular
activity that is common to all types and forms of teeth.

REFERENCES

1. Brunn, A. v.: Uber die Audehnung des Schmelzorganes und seine Bedeutung für die
   Zahnbildung (Concerning the extent of the enamel organ and its significance in tooth
   development), Arch. f. mikr. Anat. **29**:367, 1887.
2. Diamond, M., and Applebaum, E.: The epithelial sheath, J. D. Res. **21**:403, 1942.
3. Hahn, W. E.: The capacity of developing tooth germ elements for self-differentiation
   when transplanted, J. D. Res. **20**:5, 1941.
4. Johnson, P. L., and Bevelander, G.: The role of the stratum intermedium in tooth development, Oral Surg., Oral Med., & Oral Path. **10**:437, 1957.
5. Manley, E. B.: Adamantinoma in relation to tooth development, Australian J. Dent. **58**:
   137, 1954.
6. Marsland, E. A.: Histological investigation of amelogenesis in rats, Brit. D. J. **91**:251,
   1951; **92**:109, 1952.
7. Norberg, O.: Untersuchungen über das dento-gingivale Epithelleistensystem im intra-

uterinen Leben des Menschen (Investigations of the dentino-gingival epithelium in human intra-uterine life), Stockholm, 1929, A. B. Fahlcrantz' Boktryckeri.

8. Orban, B.: Growth and movement of the tooth germs and teeth, J.A.D.A. **15**:1004, 1928.
9. Orban, B.: Dental histology and embryology, Philadelphia, 1929, P. Blakiston's Son & Co.
10. Orban, B., and Mueller, E.: The development of the bifurcation of multirooted teeth, J.A.D.A. **16**:297, 1929.
11. Sarnat, B. C., Schour, I., and Heupel, R.: Roentgenographic diagnosis of congenital syphilis in unerupted permanent teeth, J.A.M.A. **116**:2745, 1941.
12. Schour, I., and Massler, M.: Studies in tooth development: the growth pattern of human teeth, J.A.D.A. **27**:1785, 1918, 1940.
13. Sicher, H.: Tooth eruption: axial movement of teeth with limited growth, J. D. Res. **21**:395. 1942.

Chapter III

Enamel*

HISTOLOGY
  Physical characteristics
  Chemical properties
  Structure
      Rods
      Submicroscopic structure
      Rod sheaths
      Striations
      Interprismatic substance
      Direction of rods
      Hunter-Schreger bands
      Incremental lines of Retzius
      Surface structures
      Enamel cuticle
      Enamel lamellae
      Enamel tufts
      Dentinoenamel junction
      Odontoblastic processes and enamel
          spindles
  Age changes
  Clinical considerations

DEVELOPMENT
  Epithelial dental organ
      Outer dental epithelium
      Stellate reticulum
      Stratum intermedium
      Inner dental epithelium
      Cervical loop
  Life cycle of the ameloblasts
      Morphogenic stage
      Organizing stage
      Formative stage
      Maturative stage
      Protective stage
      Desmolytic stage
  Amelogenesis
      Formation of the enamel matrix
          Dentinoenamel membrane
          Development of Tomes' processes
          Distal terminal bars
          Transformation of Tomes' processes
      Mineralization and maturation of the enamel
          matrix
  Clinical considerations

HISTOLOGY
Physical characteristics

Enamel forms a protective covering of variable thickness over the entire surface of the crown. On the cusps of human molars and premolars, the enamel attains a maximum thickness of about 2 to 2.5 mm., thinning down to almost a knife edge at the neck of the tooth. The shape and contour of the cusps receive their final modeling in the enamel.

Due to its high content of mineral salts and their crystalline arrangement, enamel is the hardest calcified tissue in the human body. The specific function of the enamel is to form a resistant covering of the teeth, rendering them suitable for mastication.

The enamel varies in hardness from apatite, which is fifth in the scale of

---

*First draft submitted by Charles F. Bodecker; revised by Reidar F. Sognnaes, David B. Scott, Marie U. Nylen, and James A. Yaeger.

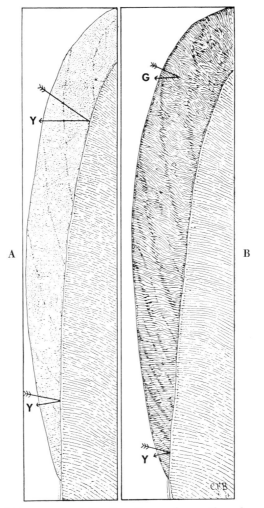

Fig. 25. Influence of thickness and calcification of enamel upon the color of the tooth. **A,** Thin, well-calcified translucent enamel giving the tooth a yellowish appearance, Y. **B,** Thick, less calcified opaque enamel giving the tooth a grayish appearance, G. In the cervical area the enamel is thin, giving the tooth a yellowish color, Y. (From Bodecker, C. F.: Internat. J. Orthodontia **19:**386, 1933.)

Mohs,* to topaz, which is eighth. The specific structure and hardness of the enamel render it brittle, which is particularly apparent when the enamel loses its foundation of sound dentin. The specific gravity of enamel is 2.8.

Another physical property of enamel is its permeability. It has been found with radioactive tracers that the enamel can act in a sense like a semipermeable

---

*In this scale hardness is compared to that of ten different minerals: (1) talc, (2) gypsum, (3) calcite, (4) fluorite, (5) apatite, (6) orthoclase (feldspar), (7) quartz, (8) topaz, (9) sapphire (corundum), and (10) diamond.

membrane, permitting complete or partial passage of certain molecules: C^{14}— urea, I^{131}, etc.[2,76,84] The same phenomenon has also been demonstrated by means of dyestuffs.[36,40]

The color of the enamel-covered crown ranges from yellowish white to grayish white. It has been suggested that the color is determined by differences in the translucency of enamel, yellowish teeth having a thin, translucent enamel through which the yellow color of the dentin is visible and grayish teeth having a more opaque enamel (Fig. 25).[11] The translucency may be due to variations in the degree of calcification and homogeneity of the enamel. Grayish teeth frequently show a slightly yellowish color at the cervical areas, presumably because the thinness of the enamel permits the light to strike the underlying yellow dentin and be reflected. Incisal areas may have a bluish tinge where the thin edge consists only of a double layer of enamel.

Chemical properties

The enamel consists mainly of inorganic material (96 per cent) and only a small amount of organic substance and water (4 per cent). The inorganic material of the enamel is similar to apatite.[53,79,80] The bar graph in Fig. 26 indicates the composition by volume of mineralized tissues in which odontoblast processes have been replaced with peritubular dentin (sclerotic dentin) and the equivalent situation in bone in which osteocyte lacunae are filled with mineral.

The origins shown at the left of Fig. 26 reflect the facts that enamel matrix mineralization begins immediately after it is secreted and that the lag in mineralization after matrix formation is greater in dentin than in bone. Enamel primary mineralization and secondary mineralization (maturation) increase mineral content in a relatively smooth curve. In both bone and dentin, well over one-half of the mineral accumulates rapidly (primary mineralization). The curves then flatten as secondary mineralization occurs. The curves continue to rise slowly as cell-occupied space is filled with mineralized matrix (secondary matrix formation) in bone and dentin.

The relative *space occupied* by the organic framework and the entire enamel are almost equal. Fig. 27 illustrates this by comparing a stone and a sponge of approximately *equal size*. The stone represents the mineral content, and the sponge represents the organic framework of the enamel. Although their sizes are almost equal, their weights are vastly different. The stone is more than one hundred times heavier than the sponge, or, expressed in percentage, the weight of the sponge is less than 1 per cent of that of the stone.

The nature of the organic elements of enamel is incompletely understood. In development and histologic staining reactions, the enamel matrix resembles keratinizing epidermis. More specific methods have revealed sulfhydryl groups and other reactions suggestive of keratin. Similarly, hydrolysates of mature enamel matrix have shown a ratio of amino acids (histidine 1 : lysine 3 : arginine 10) suggestive of a keratin.[9,78] X-ray diffraction studies reveal that the molecular

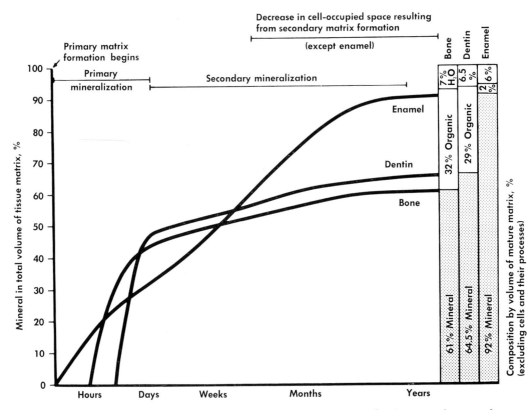

Fig. 26. Formation, mineralization, and maturation of some mineralized tissues. (Figures for bone from Robinson, R. A.: Chemical analysis and electron microscopy of bone. In Rodahl, K., Nicholson, J. T., and Brown, E. M. [editors]: Bone as a tissue, New York, 1960, The Blakiston Division, McGraw-Hill Book Co., Inc., pp. 186-250. Figures for dentin and enamel from Brudevold, F.: Chemical composition of the teeth in relation to caries. In Sognnaes, R. F. [editor]: Chemistry and prevention of dental caries, Springfield, Ill., 1962, Charles C Thomas, Publisher, pp. 32-88). (Courtesy Dr. J. A. Yaeger.)

Fig. 27. A sponge, **A**, and a stone, **B**, are comparable to the organic and mineral elements of enamel. Their sizes are approximately equal, but their weights differ greatly. (From Bodecker, C. F.: D. Rev. **20**:317, 1906.)

structure is typical of the group of keratins called cross-β keratins.[24,49] In addition, histochemical reactions have suggested that the enamel-forming cells of developing teeth also contain a polysaccharide-protein complex[18] and that an acid mucopolysaccharide enters the enamel itself at the time when calcification becomes a prominent feature.[86] Tracer studies have indicated that the enamel of erupted teeth of rhesus monkeys can transmit and exchange radioactive isotopes originating from the saliva and the pulp.[76] Considerable investigation is still required to determine the normal physiologic characteristics and the age changes that occur in the enamel.

Structure

Rods. The enamel is composed of enamel rods or prisms, rod sheaths, and a cementing interprismatic substance. The number of enamel rods has been estimated[15] as ranging from 5 million in the lower lateral incisors to 12 million in the upper first molars. From the dentinoenamel junction the rods run outward to the surface of the tooth. The length of most rods is greater than the thickness of the enamel because of the oblique direction and the wavy course of the rods.

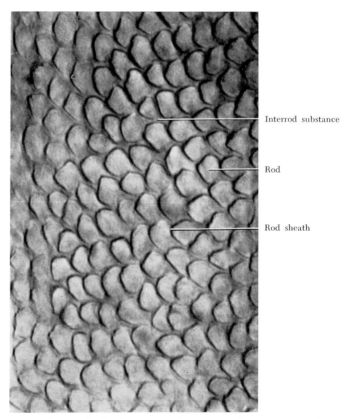

Interrod substance

Rod

Rod sheath

Fig. 28. Decalcified section of enamel of a human tooth germ. Rods cut transversely appear like fish scales.

The rods located in the cusps, the thickest part of the enamel, are longer than those at the cervical areas of the teeth. It is stated generally that the diameter of the rods averages 4 microns, but this measurement necessarily varies, since the outer surface of the enamel is greater than the dentinal surface where the rods originate. It is claimed[15,50] that the diameter of the rods increases from the dentinoenamel junction toward the surface of the enamel at a ratio of about 1:2.

The enamel rods were first described by Retzius[54] in 1837. Normally they have a clear crystalline appearance, permitting the light to pass through them. In cross section they occasionally appear hexagonal. Sometimes they appear round or oval. Many rods resemble fish scales in cross sections of human enamel (Fig. 28).

Fig. 29. Oval, **A**, and scale-shaped, **B**, rod contours seen under the electron microscope in cross sections of demineralized mature human enamel. (×5,000.) (From Scott, D. B.: Internat. D. J. **4**: 1953.)

Submicroscopic structure. The structural elements which make up the enamel rods are so small that they cannot be observed directly under the light microscope. With the advent of the electron microscope, which has now been applied to tooth structure for more than fifteen years, new information about both the organic matrix and the crystalline component of the enamel has been gained. The examination of sections of decalcified mature enamel has revealed the presence of a network of fine organic fibrils throughout the rods.[20,66] (See Fig. 29.) There is some evidence that the apatite crystals may not only be laid down within the openings in this fibrillar mesh but that they may also form around the fibrils themselves.[21]

Under the electron microscope the apatite crystals appear somewhat flat and ribbonlike, and they are arranged with their long axes in the main roughly paralleling the long axis of the rod (Fig. 30).[22,69] This direct observation of parallelism among the crystals corroborates similar conclusions drawn earlier from birefringence studies made with polarized light[14] and from orientation studies made by means of roentgen ray diffraction.[79] The parallel arrangement within rods is far from perfect, and groups of crystals may diverge as much as 40 degrees from the axial plane of the rod.[31,42,56] (See Fig. 31.) The dimensions of the basic enamel crystals are not yet well defined, and reported lengths have

Fig. 30. Hydroxyapatite crystals within a single longitudinally sectioned enamel rod. In this type of electron microscopic preparation, which is a replica, or reproduction, of the surface of a ground section, small groups of individual crystals are removed from the enamel for observation. (×57,000.) (From Scott, D. B.: The crystalline component of dental enamel, Fourth International Conference on Electron Microscopy, Berlin, 1960, Springer-Verlag.)

Fig. 31. An electron photomicrograph illustrating the orientation of crystals at an angle to the long axes of the enamel rods. Note also the minimal interprismatic substance in this particular region. (×8,000.)

Fig. 32. The fibrillar character of the rod sheath, as seen electron microscopically in the sectioned matrix of demineralized human enamel. (×15,000.) (From Scott, D. B., Ussing, M. J., Sognnaes, R. F., and Wyckoff, R. W. G.: J. D. Res. **31**:74, 1952.)

varied between 0.05 and 1 micron.[22,23] Their diameters are most often reported as measuring from 0.02 to 0.04 micron.[56]

Rod sheaths. A thin peripheral layer of each rod shows a different refractive index, stains darker than the rod, and is relatively acid resistant. It may be concluded that it is less calcified and contains more organic substance than the rod itself. This layer is interpreted by some as a rod sheath (Figs. 28 and 32).[10,75] Recent investigations with the electron microscope have shown that this structure is often incomplete.[67]

Striations. Each enamel rod is built up of segments separated by dark lines that give it a striated appearance (Fig. 33). These transverse striations demar-

Fig. 33. Ground section through enamel. Rods cut longitudinally. Cross striation of rods.

cate rod segments and become more visible by the action of mild acids. The striations are more marked in enamel that is insufficiently calcified. The rods are segmented because the enamel matrix is formed in a rhythmic manner. In man these segments seem to be of uniform length of about 4 microns.[62]

Interprismatic substance. Enamel rods are not in direct contact with each other but are cemented together by the interprismatic substance, which has a slightly higher refractive index than the rods.[72] Discussion is still active concerning the structure of the interprismatic substance. (See Fig. 34.) It appears to be at a minimum or absent in the enamel of human teeth.[56] In some animals, such as the dog or pig, however, the enamel contains a considerable amount of interprismatic substance.

Under the electron microscope the structures observed in this region have appeared identical to those within the rods in every respect except their spatial orientation.[66,68] Between adjacent rods both the organic matrix fibrils and the apatite crystals are arranged at sharply oblique angles to the long axes of the rods (Fig. 35). Whether or not there is a lower proportion of mineral in the interprismatic region, as usually stated, still remains to be settled.

Direction of rods. Generally the rods are oriented at right angles to the dentin surface. In the cervical and central parts of the crown of a deciduous tooth they are approximately horizontal (Fig. 36, *A*). Near the incisal edge or tip of the cusps they change gradually to an increasingly oblique direction until they are almost vertical in the region of the edge or tip of the cusps. The arrangement

Fig. 34. Decalcified section of enamel. Rods, rod sheaths, and interprismatic substance are well differentiated. Photographed with ultraviolet light. (From Bodecker, C. F.: D. Rev. **20:**317, 1906.)

Rod

Interprismatic
substance

A

Rod

B

Interprismatic
substance

Fig. 35. Orientation of matrix fibrils (**A**, demineralized section, ×7,000) and inorganic crystals (**B**, undemineralized ground section, ×20,000) of the interprismatic substance at a sharp angle to the longitudinal rod axis. (Courtesy Dr. D. B. Scott.)

of the rods in permanent teeth is similar in the occlusal two-thirds of the crown. In the cervical region, however, the rods deviate from the horizontal in an apical direction. (See Fig. 36, *B*.)

The rods are rarely, if ever, straight throughout. They follow a wavy course from the dentin to the enamel surface. The most significant deviations from a straight radial course can be described as follows. If the middle part of the crown is divided into thin horizontal discs, the rods in the adjacent discs bend in opposite directions. For instance, in one disc the rods start from the dentin in an oblique direction and bend more or less sharply to the left side (Fig. 37, *A*). In the outer third of the enamel they change often to an almost straight radial course. In the adjacent disc the rods bend toward the right (Fig. 37, *B*).

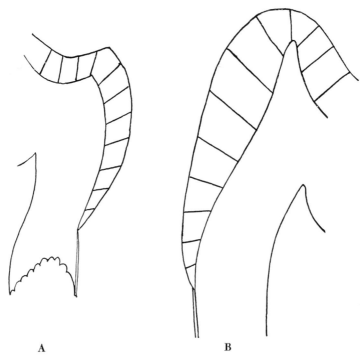

Fig. 36. Diagrams indicating the general direction of enamel rods. **A,** Deciduous tooth. **B,** Permanent tooth.

Fig. 37. Horizontal ground section through enamel near the dentinoenamel junction. **A** and **B** show change in the direction of rods in two adjacent layers of enamel, made visible by a change in the focus of the microscope.

This alternating clockwise and counterclockwise deviation of the rods from the radial direction can be observed at all levels of the crown if the discs are cut in the planes of the general rod direction (Fig. 36).

If the discs are cut in an oblique plane, especially near the dentin in the region of the cusps or incisal edges, the rod arrangement appears to be further complicated—the bundles of rods seem to intertwine more irregularly. This optical appearance of enamel is called gnarled enamel.

The enamel rods forming the developmental fissures and pits, as on the occlusal surface of molars and premolars, converge in their outward course.

Hunter-Schreger bands. The more or less regular change in the direction of rods may be regarded as a functional adaptation, minimizing the risk of cleavage in the axial direction under the influence of occlusal masticatory forces. The change in the direction of rods is responsible for the appearance of the Hunter-Schreger bands. These are alternating dark and light strips of varying widths (Figs. 38 and 39) that can best be seen in a longitudinal ground section under

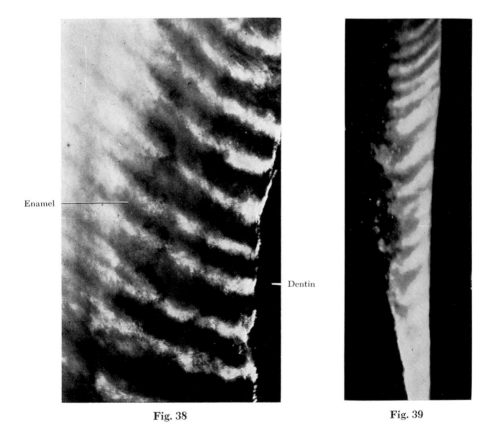

Enamel

Dentin

Fig. 38

Fig. 39

Fig. 38. Longitudinal ground section through enamel photographed by reflected light. Hunter-Schreger bands.

Fig. 39. Decalcified enamel, photographed by reflected light, showing Hunter-Schreger bands.

oblique reflected light. They originate at the dentinoenamel border and pass outward, ending at some distance from the outer enamel surface. Some investigators claim that there are variations in calcification of the enamel which coincide with the distribution of the bands of Hunter-Schreger. Careful decalcification and staining of the enamel have provided further evidence that these structures may not be the result solely of an optical phenomenon but that they are composed of alternate zones having a slightly different permeability and a different content of organic material.[35,75,86]

Incremental lines of Retzius. The incremental lines of Retzius appear as brownish bands in ground sections of the enamel. They illustrate the incremental pattern of the enamel, i.e., the successive apposition of layers of enamel matrix during formation of the crown. In longitudinal sections they surround the tip of the dentin. (See Fig. 40, *A*.) In the cervical parts of the crown they run obliquely. From the dentinoenamel junction to the surface they deviate occlusally. (See Fig. 40, *B*.) In transverse sections of a tooth the incremental

Fig. 40. Incremental lines of Retzius in longitudinal ground sections. **A,** Cuspal region. **B,** Cervical region, *X*.

lines of Retzius appear as concentric circles. (See Fig. 41.) They may be compared to the growth rings in the cross section of a tree. The term "incremental lines" designates these structures appropriately, for they do, in fact, reflect variations in structure and mineralization, either hypomineralized or hypermineralized,[16,30] that occur during growth of the enamel. The exact nature of these developmental changes is not known. The incremental lines have been attributed to periodic bending of the enamel rods,[28,29,54,60] to variations in the basic organic structure (Fig. 42),[4,36,73] or to a physiologic calcification rhythm.[62]

The incremental lines of Retzius, if present in moderate intensity, are con-

Fig. 41. Incremental lines of Retzius in transverse ground section, arranged concentrically.

Fig. 42. Carefully decalcified section through enamel. Thickening of the interrod substance (*SR*) in Retzius lines. (From Bodecker, C. F.: D. Rev. **20**:317, 1906.)

sidered normal. However, the rhythmic alternation of periods of enamel matrix formation and of rest can be upset by metabolic disturbances, causing the rest periods to be unduly prolonged and close together. Such an abnormal condition is responsible for the broadening of the incremental lines of Retzius, rendering them more prominent.

Surface structures. The principal microscopic details that have been observed on outer enamel surfaces of newly erupted teeth are perikymata, rod ends, and cracks (lamellae).[63-65,88]

Perikymata are transverse, wavelike grooves, thought to be the external manifestations of the striae of Retzius. They are continuous around a tooth and usually lie parallel to each other and to the cementoenamel junction. (See Figs. 43 to 45.) Ordinarily there are about 30 perikymata per millimeter in the region of the cementoenamel junction, and their concentration gradually decreases to about 10 per millimeter near the occlusal or incisal edge of a surface. Their course usually is fairly regular, but in the cervical region it may be quite irregular.

The enamel rod ends are concave and vary in depth and shape. They are shallowest in the cervical regions of surfaces and deepest near the incisal or occlusal edges (Fig. 44).

Fig. 43   Fig. 44

Fig. 43. Perikymata on a lateral incisor.

Fig. 44. Shadowed replica of the surface of intact enamel (buccal surface of an upper left second molar showing the perikymata). (×1,500.) (From Scott, D. B., and Wyckoff, R. W. G.: Pub. Health Rep. **61**:1397, 1946.)

Fig. 45. Progressive loss of surface structure with advancing age. **A,** Surface of a recently erupted tooth, showing pronounced enamel prism ends and perikymata. Patient 12 years of age. **B,** Early stage of structural loss which occurs during the first few years (wear is more rapid on anterior teeth than on posterior teeth and more rapid on facial or lingual surfaces than on proximal surfaces). Note small regions where prism ends are worn away. Patient 25 years of age. **C,** Later stage. Here the elevated parts between perikymata are worn smooth, while the structural detail in the depths of the grooves is still more or less intact. Eventually wearing proceeds to the point where all prism ends and perikymata disappear. Patient 52 years of age. [N. B. Since these are negative replicas, surface details appear inverted. Raised structures represent depressions in the actual surface.] **D,** Surface worn completely smooth, showing only "cracks," which actually represent the outer edges of lamellae. Patient 50 years of age. (All magnifications ×105.) (From Scott, D. B., and Wyckoff, R. W. G.: J.A.D.A. **39:** 275, 1949.)

The term "cracks" originally was used to describe the narrow, fissurelike structures that are seen on almost all surfaces (Fig. 45). It has since been demonstrated that they are actually the outer edges of lamellae (see discussion of enamel lamellae).[65] They extend for varying distances along the surface, at right angles to the cementoenamel junction, from which they originate. Most of them are less than a millimeter in length, but some are longer, and a few reach the occlusal or incisal edge of a surface. They are fairly evenly spaced, but long lamellae appear wider than short ones.

The enamel of the deciduous teeth develops partly before and partly after birth. The boundary between the two portions of enamel in the deciduous teeth

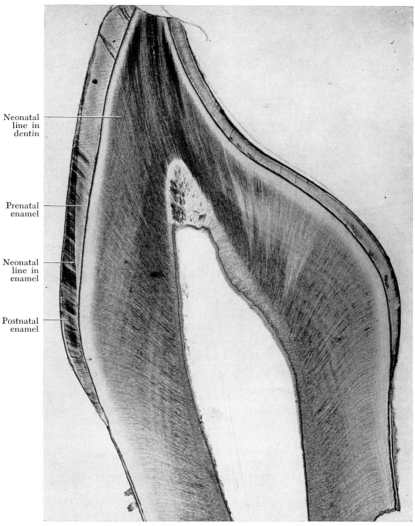

Neonatal line in dentin

Prenatal enamel

Neonatal line in enamel

Postnatal enamel

Fig. 46. Neonatal line in the enamel. Longitudinal ground section of a deciduous canine. (From Schour, I.: J.A.D.A. **23**:1946, 1936.)

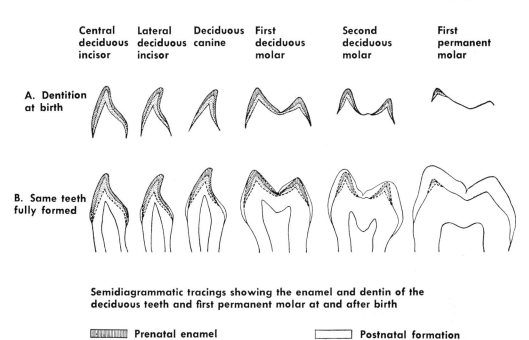

| | Central deciduous incisor | Lateral deciduous incisor | Deciduous canine | First deciduous molar | Second deciduous molar | First permanent molar |

A. Dentition at birth

B. Same teeth fully formed

Semidiagrammatic tracings showing the enamel and dentin of the deciduous teeth and first permanent molar at and after birth

▨ Prenatal enamel   ▭ Postnatal formation

▨ Prenatal dentin   ---- Neonatal line in enamel and dentin

Fig. 47. Enamel and dentin of deciduous teeth and a first permanent molar at and after birth. (From Schour, I.: J.A.D.A. **23**:1946, 1936.)

is marked by an accentuated incremental line of Retzius, the neonatal line or neonatal ring.[61] It appears to be the result of the abrupt change in the environment and nutrition of the newborn infant. The prenatal enamel usually is better developed than the postnatal. (See Fig. 46.) This is explained by the fact that the fetus develops in a well-protected environment with an adequate supply of all the essential materials, even at the expense of the mother. Because of the undisturbed and even development of the enamel prior to birth, perikymata are absent in the occlusal parts of the deciduous teeth, whereas they are present in the postnatal cervical parts. The amount of enamel matrix formed during the prenatal and postnatal periods is shown diagrammatically in Fig. 47.

In microradiographs of ground sections a hypermineralized zone about 30 microns wide can usually be distinguished at the enamel surface. A similar zone can sometimes be distinguished at the dentinoenamel junction, especially before mineralization is complete.[4,16,28,41,60]

Enamel cuticle. A delicate membrane, called Nasmyth's membrane[39] after its first investigator,[47] covers the entire crown of the newly erupted tooth. When the ameloblasts have produced the enamel rods, they produce a thin, continuous layer, sometimes termed the primary enamel cuticle, which covers the entire surface of the enamel. Because this cuticle is more resistant to acid than the enamel itself, it can be floated off. It is worn off early from all exposed surfaces. Ex-

Fig. 48. Section from an unerupted mouse molar, showing enamel matrix, *E,* enamel cuticle, *EC,* and ameloblasts, *A.* The enamel cuticle is intimately connected with both the enamel matrix and the ameloblasts. (×9,400.) (From Ussing, Marie J.: Acta odont. scandinav. **13:**123, 1955; reprinted J. West. Soc. Periodont. 3:71, 1955.)

amination of the primary enamel cuticle of unerupted teeth under the electron microscope reveals it as a continuous membrane of about 0.2 micron in thickness, being organically connected to both the enamel matrix and the ameloblasts (Figs. 48 and 49).[82]

Mastication wears away the enamel cuticles on the incisal edges, occlusal surfaces, and contact areas of the teeth. On other exposed surfaces they may be worn off by other mechanical influences, e.g., brushing of teeth. In protected areas (proximal surfaces and gingival sulcus) they may remain intact throughout life.

Enamel lamellae. Enamel lamellae are thin, leaflike structures that extend from the enamel surface toward the dentinoenamel junction (Figs. 50*A* and 50*B*). They may extend to, and sometimes penetrate into, the dentin. They consist of organic material, with but little mineral content. In ground sections these structures may be confused with cracks caused by grinding of the specimen (Fig. 41). Careful decalcification of ground sections of enamel makes possible the distinction between cracks and enamel lamellae. The former disappear, while the latter persist (Figs. 50 and 51).

Lamellae may develop in planes of tension. Where rods cross such a plane, a short segment of the rod may not fully calcify. If the disturbance is more severe, a crack may develop that is filled either by surrounding cells, if the crack occurred in the unerupted tooth, or by organic substances from the oral cavity, if the crack developed after eruption. Three types of lamellae can thus be differentiated[12]: Type A, lamellae composed of poorly calcified rod segments[19]

Ameloblasts

Cuticle

Enamel space

Ameloblasts

Cuticle

Enamel space

Fig. 49. A, Paraffin section through the enamel epithelium isolated by acid flotation from the surface of an unerupted human tooth. The enamel cuticle appears as a thin membrane at the ends of the ameloblasts. (Hematoxylin and eosin stain; ×1,300.) **B,** An electron photomicrograph from a thin section through a similar cuticular isolate. The enamel cuticle has become separated from the ameloblasts and appears as a continuous membrane across the ends of the cells. (×12,000.) (From Ussing, Marie J.: Acta odont. scandinav. **13:**123, 1955; reprinted J. West. Soc. Periodont. **3:**71, 1955.)

(Fig. 51, *B*); Type B, lamellae consisting of degenerated cells; Type C, lamellae arising in erupted teeth where the cracks are filled with organic matter, presumably originating from saliva.[25,34,75] The latter type (Fig. 51, *A*) may be more common than formerly believed. While lamellae of Type A are restricted to the enamel, those of Types B and C may reach into the dentin. If cells from the enamel organ fill a crack in the enamel, those in the depth degenerate, whereas those close to the surface may remain vital for a time and produce a hornified cuticle in the cleft.[25] In such cases the greater inner parts of the lamella consist

Fig. 50A   Fig. 50B

Fig. 50A. Decalcified incisor with moderately severe mottled enamel (from material obtained in Texas). Numerous lamellae can be observed. (×8.)

Fig. 50B. Maxillary first permanent molar of caries-free 2-year-old rhesus monkey. Numerous bands of organic matter, lamellae, can be seen after decalcification. (×8.) (From Sognnaes, R. F.: J. D. Res. **29:**260, 1950.)

of an organic cell detritus, the outer parts of a double layer of the cuticle. If connective tissue invades a crack in the enamel, cementum may be formed. In such cases lamellae consist entirely or partly of cementum.[48]

Lamellae extend in the longitudinal and radial direction of the tooth, from the tip of the crown toward the cervical region (Figs. 50A and 50B). This arrangement explains why they can be observed better in horizontal sections. It has been suggested that enamel lamellae may be a site of weakness in a tooth and may form a road of entry for bacteria that initiate caries.[10,25]

Enamel tufts. Enamel tufts (Fig. 53) arise at the dentinoenamel junction and reach into the enamel to about one-fifth to one-third of its thickness. They were so termed because they resemble tufts of grass when viewed in ground sections. This picture is erroneous.[6,48] An enamel tuft does not spring from a single small area but is a narrow, ribbonlike structure, the inner end of which arises at the dentin. The impression of a tuft of grass is created by examining such structures in thick sections under low magnification. Under these circumstances the imperfections, lying in different planes and curving in different directions (Fig. 37), are projected into one plane (Fig. 53).

Tufts consist of hypocalcified enamel rods and interprismatic substance. Like the lamellae they extend in the direction of the long axis of the crown. Therefore, they are abundantly seen in horizontal, and rarely in longitudinal, sections. Their presence and their development are a consequence of, or an adaptation to, the spatial conditions in the enamel.

Dentinoenamel junction. The surface of the dentin at the dentinoenamel

Fig. 51. **A,** Paraffin section through reduced enamel epithelium, enamel cuticle, and a lamella, isolated together by acid flotation from the surface of an unerupted human tooth. Note the intimate relationship between the three elements. (Hematoxylin and eosin stain; ×1,300.) **B,** Paraffin section of decalcified enamel of a human molar showing the relation between a lamella and surrounding organic interprismatic substance. (Hematoxylin and eosin stain; ×1,000.) (**A** from Ussing, Marie J.: Acta odont. scandinav. 13:23, 1955; reprinted J. West. Soc. Periodont. 3:71, 1955; **B** courtesy Dr. R. F. Sognnaes.)

junction is pitted. Into the shallow depressions of the dentin fit rounded projections of the enamel. This relation assures the firm hold of the enamel cap on the dentin. In sections, therefore, the dentinoenamel junction appears not as a straight but as a scalloped line (Figs. 53 and 54). The convexities of the scallops are directed toward the dentin. The pitted dentinoenamel junction is already

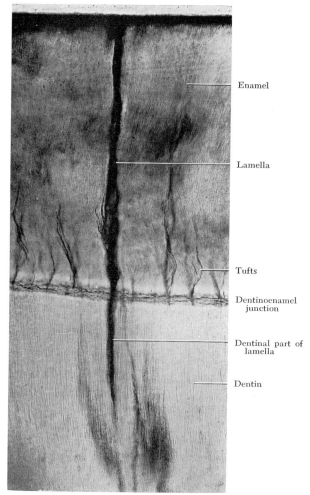

Enamel

Lamella

Tufts

Dentinoenamel
  junction

Dentinal part of
  lamella

Dentin

Fig. 52. Transverse ground section through a lamella reaching from the surface into the dentin.

preformed in the arrangement of the ameloblasts and the basement membrane of the dental papilla, prior to the development of hard substances (Fig. 61).

In microradiographs of ground sections, a hypermineralized zone about 30 microns thick can sometimes be demonstrated at the dentinoenamel junction. It is most prominent before mineralization is complete. This zone is similar to the hypermineralized surface enamel.[4,16,28,41,60]

Odontoblastic processes and enamel spindles. Occasionally, odontoblastic processes pass across the dentinoenamel junction into the enamel. Since many are thickened at their end (Fig. 55), they have been termed enamel spindles. They seem to originate from processes of odontoblasts that extended into the enamel epithelium before hard substances were formed. The direction of the odontoblastic processes and spindles in the enamel corresponds to the original

Enamel

Tufts

Dentinoenamel
junction

Dentin

Fig. 53. Transverse ground section through a tooth under low magnification. Numerous tufts extending from the dentinoenamel junction into the enamel.

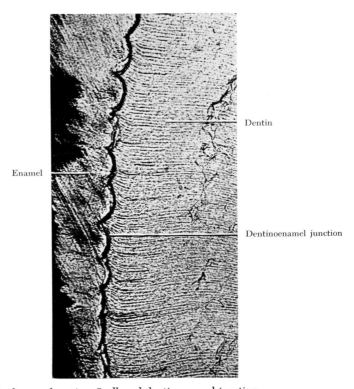

Dentin

Enamel

Dentinoenamel junction

Fig. 54. Longitudinal ground section. Scalloped dentinoenamel junction.

Enamel spindle

Enamel

Odontoblastic
process in
enamel

Dentinoenamel
junction

Dentinal tubule

Dentin

Fig. 55. Ground section. The odontoblastic process extends into the enamel as enamel spindles.

direction of the ameloblasts, at right angles to the surface of the dentin. Since the enamel rods are formed at an angle to the axis of the ameloblasts, the direction of spindles and rods is divergent. In ground sections of dried teeth the organic contents of the spindles disintegrate and are replaced by air. Then the spaces appear dark in transmitted light.

Age changes

The most apparent age change in enamel is attrition or wear of the occlusal surfaces and proximal contact points as a result of mastication. This is evidenced by a loss of vertical dimension of the crown and by a flattening of the proximal contour. In addition to these gross changes, the outer enamel surfaces themselves undergo posteruptive alterations in structure at the microscopic level. These result from environmental influences and occur with a regularity that can be related to age.[64] (See Fig. 45.)

The surfaces of unerupted and recently erupted teeth are covered completely with pronounced rod ends and perikymata. At the points of highest contour of the surfaces, these surface structures soon begin to disappear. This is followed by a generalized loss of the rod ends and a much slower flattening of the perikymata. Finally, the perikymata disappear completely. The rate at which structure is lost depends on the location of the surface on the tooth and on the location of the tooth in the mouth. Facial and lingual surfaces lose their structure much more rapidly than do proximal surfaces, and anterior teeth lose their structure more rapidly than do posterior teeth.

Age changes within the enamel proper have been difficult to discern microscopically. The fact that alterations do occur has been brought out by chemical analysis, but the changes are not well understood. For example, the total amount of organic matrix is said by some to increase, by others to remain unchanged, and by still others to decrease.[20,59] Localized increases of certain elements, such as nitrogen and fluorine, however, have been found in the superficial enamel layers of older teeth.[59,77,89] This suggests a continuous uptake, probably from the oral environment, during aging. As a result of age changes in the organic portion of enamel, presumably near the surface, the teeth may become darker, and their resistance to decay may be increased.[7,8] Suggestive of an aging change is the greatly reduced permeability of older teeth to fluids.[71] There is insufficient evidence to show that enamel becomes harder with age.[55]

Clinical considerations

The course of the enamel rods is of importance in cavity preparations. The choice of instruments depends upon the location of the cavity in the tooth. Generally, the rods run at a right angle to the underlying dentin or tooth surface. Close to the cementoenamel junction the rods run in a more horizontal direction (Fig. 36, *B*). In preparing cavities, it is important that unsupported enamel rods are not left at the cavity margins because they would soon break and produce a leakage. Bacteria would lodge in these spaces, inducing secondary dental caries. Enamel is brittle and does not withstand forces in thin layers or in areas where it is not supported by the underlying dentin. (Fig. 56A.)

Deep enamel fissures are predisposing to caries. Although these deep clefts between adjoining cusps cannot be regarded as pathologic, they afford areas for retention of caries-producing agents. Caries penetrates the floor of fissures rapidly because the enamel in these areas is very thin.[39] (See Fig. 56B.) As the destructive process reaches the dentin, it spreads along the dentinoenamel junction, undermining the enamel. An extensive area of dentin becomes carious without giving any warning to the patient because the entrance to the cavity is minute. Careful examination is necessary to discover such cavities because most enamel fissures are more minute than a single toothbrush bristle and cannot be detected with the dental probe.

Enamel lamellae may also be predisposing locations for caries because they contain much organic material. Primarily from the standpoint of protection against caries, the structure and reactions of the outer enamel surface are subject to much current research. In vitro tests have shown that the acid solubility of enamel can be markedly reduced by treatment with various chemical agents, particularly fluoride compounds.[27,70] Clinical trials based on these leads have demonstrated reductions of 40 per cent or more in the incidence of caries in children following topical applications of sodium or stannous fluoride.[46,70] Incorporation of fluorides in dentifrices has also proved promising and is now being pursued further.[33,45,70]

The most effective means for mass control of dental caries to date has been adjustment of the fluoride level in communal water supplies to 1 part per million. Epidemiologic studies in areas in which the drinking water contained natural

Fig. 56A. Diagrammatic illustration of the course of enamel rods in a molar in relation to cavity preparation. *1* and *2* indicate wrong preparation of cavity margins. *3* and *4* indicate correct preparation.

Fig. 56B. Diagrammatic illustration of the development of a deep enamel fissure. Note the thin enamel layer forming the floor of the fissure. (From Kronfeld, R.: J.A.D.A. **22**:1131, 1935.)

fluoride revealed that the caries prevalence in both children and adults was about 65 per cent lower than in nonfluoride areas.[44,70] and long-term studies have demonstrated that the same order of protection is afforded through water fluoridation programs.[1,70] The mechanisms of action are thought to be primarily a combination of changes in enamel resistance, brought about by incorporation of fluoride during calcification, and alterations in the environment of the teeth, particularly with respect to the oral bacterial flora.[44,70]

The surface of the enamel in the cervical region should be kept smooth and well polished by proper home care and by regular cleansing by the dentist. If the surface of the cervical enamel becomes decalcified, or otherwise roughened, food debris, bacterial plaques, etc., accumulate on this surface. The gingiva in contact with this roughened, debris-covered enamel surface undergoes inflammatory changes. The ensuing gingivitis, unless promptly treated, may lead to more serious periodontal disease.

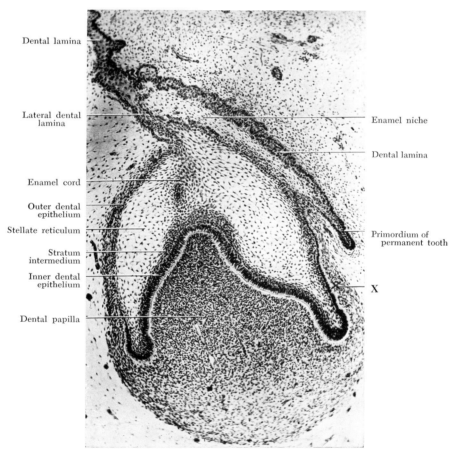

Fig. 57. Tooth germ (deciduous lower incisor) of a human embryo (105 mm., fourth month). Four layers of the enamel organ. X, See Fig. 59.

DEVELOPMENT
Epithelial dental organ

The early development of the dental organ and its differentiation have been discussed in Chapter II. At the stage preceding the formation of hard structures, dentin and enamel, the dental organ, originating from the stratified epithelium of the primitive oral cavity, consists of four distinct layers: outer dental epithelium, stellate reticulum, stratum intermedium, and inner dental epithelium (ameloblastic layer) (Fig. 57). The border line between the inner dental epithelium and the connective tissue of the dental papilla is the subsequent dentino-enamel junction. Thus, its outline determines the pattern of the occlusal or incisal part of the crown. At the border of the wide basal opening of the dental organ, the inner dental epithelium reflects onto the outer dental epithelium. This is the cervical loop.[98] The inner and outer dental epithelia are separated from each other by a large mass of cells differentiated into two distinct layers. The layer that is close to the inner dental epithelium consists of two to three rows of flat polyhedral cells—the stratum intermedium. The other layer, which is more loosely arranged, constitutes the stellate reticulum.

The different layers of epithelial cells of the dental organ are named accord-

Fig. 58. Capillaries in contact with the outer dental epithelium. The basement membrane separates the outer dental epithelium from connective tissue.

ing to their morphology, function, or location. The stellate reticulum derives its name from the morphology of its cells. The outer dental epithelium and the stratum intermedium are so named because of their location. The inner dental epithelium is so named on the basis of its anatomic relation. On the basis of function it is called the ameloblastic layer.

Outer dental epithelium. In the early stages of development of the dental organ, the outer dental epithelium consists of a single layer of cuboidal cells, separated from the surrounding connective tissue of the dental sac by a delicate basement membrane (Fig. 58). Prior to the formation of hard structures, this regular arrangement of the outer dental epithelium is maintained only in the cervical parts of the dental organ. At the highest convexity of the organ (Fig. 57), the cells of the outer dental epithelium become irregular in shape and cannot be distinguished easily from the outer portion of the stellate reticulum. The capillaries in the connective tissue surrounding the epithelial dental organ proliferate and protrude toward the dental organ (Fig. 58). Immediately before

Fig. 59. Region of the cervical loop (higher magnification of area X in Fig. 57). Transition of the outer into the inner dental epithelium.

enamel formation commences, capillaries may even invade the stellate reticulum.[112] This increased vascularity ensures a rich metabolism when a plentiful supply of substances from the bloodstream to the inner enamel epithelium is required.

Stellate reticulum. In the stellate reticulum, which forms the middle part of the dental organ, the neighboring cells are separated by wide intercellular spaces filled by a large amount of intercellular substance. The cells are star shaped, with long processes reaching in all directions from a central body (Figs. 58 and 59). They are connected with each other and with the cells of the outer dental epithelium and the stratum intermedium by intercellular bridges (desmosomes).[126]

The structure of the stellate reticulum renders it resistant and elastic. There-

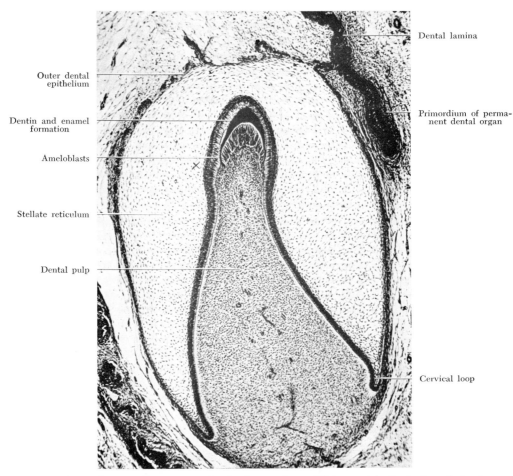

Fig. 60A. Tooth germ (lower incisor) of a human fetus (fifth month). Beginning of dentin and enamel formation. The stellate reticulum at the tip of the crown reduced in thickness. *X,* See Fig. 61.

fore, it seems probable that it acts as a buffer against physical forces that might distort the conformation of the developing dentinoenamel junction, giving rise to gross morphologic changes. It seems to permit only a limited flow of nutritional elements from the outlying blood vessels to the formative cells. Indicative of this is the fact that the stellate reticulum is noticeably reduced in thickness when the first layers of dentin are laid down, and the inner dental epithelium is thereby cut off from the dental papilla, its original source of supply (Figs. 60A and 60B).

Stratum intermedium. The cells of the stratum intermedium are situated between the stellate reticulum and the inner dental epithelium. They are flat to cuboid in shape and are arranged in one to three layers. They are connected with each other and with the neighboring cells of the stellate reticulum and the inner dental epithelium by desmosomes.[126,140] Tonofibrils, with an orientation parallel to the surface of the developing enamel, are found in the cytoplasm. The function of the stratum intermedium is not understood, but it is thought to play a

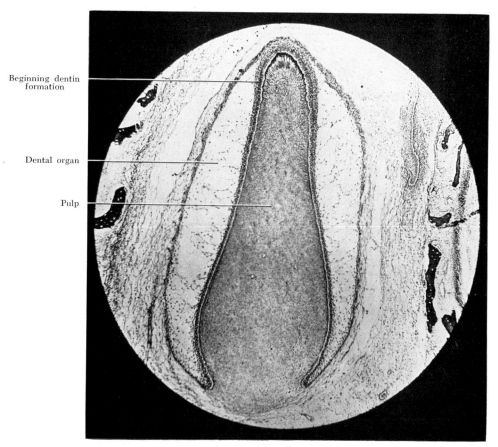

Beginning dentin formation

Dental organ

Pulp

Fig. 60B. Tooth germ with beginning dentin formation. Silver impregnation. (Courtesy Dr. Gerrit Bevelander.)

role in production of the enamel itself, either through control of fluid diffusion into and out of the ameloblasts or by the actual contribution of necessary formative elements or enzymes.[99,143,147] The cells of the stratum intermedium show mitotic division even after the cells of the inner dental epithelium cease to divide.

Inner dental epithelium. The cells of the inner dental epithelium are derived from the basal cell layer of the oral epithelium. Before enamel formation begins, these cells assume a columnar form and differentiate into ameloblasts that produce the enamel matrix. The changes in shape and structure that the cells of the inner enamel epithelium undergo will be described in detail in the discussion of the life cycle of the ameloblasts. It should be mentioned, however, that cell differentiation occurs earlier in the region of the incisal edge or cusps than in the area of the cervical loop.

Cervical loop. At the free border of the dental organ, the outer and inner dental epithelial layers are continuous and reflected into one another as the cervical loop (Figs. 57 and 58).[98] In this zone of transition between the outer dental epithelium and the inner dental epithelium, the cuboidal cells gradually gain in length. When the dental organ of the crown has been formed, the cells of this portion give rise to Hertwig's epithelial root sheath (see Chapter II).

Life cycle of the ameloblasts

According to their function, the life span of the cells of the inner dental epithelium can be divided into six stages: (1) morphogenic, (2) organizing, (3) formative, (4) maturative, (5) protective, and (6) desmolytic. Since the differentiation of ameloblasts is most advanced in the region of the incisal edge or tips of the cusps and least advanced in the region of the cervical loop, all or some stages of the developing ameloblast can be observed in one tooth germ.

Morphogenic stage. Before the ameloblasts are fully differentiated and produce the enamel, they play an important part in determining the shape of the crown, the later dentinoenamel junction (Figs. 60A and 60B). During this morphogenic stage, the cells are short and columnar, with large oval nuclei that almost fill the cell body.

The Golgi apparatus and the centrioles are located in the proximal end of the cell,* whereas the mitochondria are evenly dispersed throughout the cytoplasm.[123] During ameloblast differentiation, terminal bars appear concomitantly with the migration of the mitochondria to the basal region of the cell (Fig. 62, A). Both structures retain their basal position throughout the formative stage. (Figs. 65B and 66A.) The terminal bars represent points of close contact between cells. They were previously thought to consist of dense intercellular

---

*In modern usage, to conform with the terminology applied to other secretory cells, the dentinal end of the ameloblast, at which enamel is formed, is called *distal,* and the end facing the stratum intermedium is called *basal* or *proximal.*

Ameloblasts

Dentin

Odontoblasts

Cells of inner
dental epithelium

Pulp cells and inner
dental epithelium
in contact

Stellate reticulum

Cell-free zone

Stratum intermedium

Pulp

Cell-free zone

Cells of inner
dental epithelium

Fig. 61. High magnification of the inner dental epithelium from area X in Fig. 60A. In the cervical region the cells are short, and the outermost layer of the pulp is cell free. Occlusally the cells are long, and the cell-free zone of the pulp has disappeared. The ameloblasts are again shorter where dentin formation has set in and enamel formation is imminent. (From Diamond, M., and Weinmann, J. P.: J. D. Res. **21**:403, 1942.)

Stratum intermedium

Terminal bars

Mitochondria

Ameloblast nuclei

Ameloblast nuclei

Endoplasmic reticulum

Golgi complex

Secretory granules

Fig. 62. Portions of longitudinally sectioned fully differentiated ameloblasts as seen under the electron microscope. The basal ends of the cells are shown in **A** (×5,000), and the cell bodies distal to the nuclei are shown in **B** (×5,500). For the extreme distal ends of the ameloblasts, see Fig. 64. (From Nylen, M. U., and Scott, D. B.: J. Indiana State D. A. **39**:406, 1960; and Scott, D. B., and Nylen, M. U.: Ann. New York Acad. Sc. **85**:133, 1960.)

substance, but under the electron microscope it has been found that they comprise thickenings of the opposing cell membranes, associated with condensations of the underlying cytoplasm.[118,133]

The inner dental epithelium is separated from the connective tissue of the dental papilla by a delicate basement membrane.[116,122,133] The adjacent pulpal layer is a cell-free, narrow, light zone containing fine argyrophil fibers and the cytoplasmic processes of the superficial cells of the pulp (Fig. 61).

Organizing stage. In the organizing stage of development, the inner dental epithelium exerts an influence upon the adjacent connective tissue cells that causes them to differentiate into odontoblasts. This stage is characterized by a change in the appearance of the cells of the inner dental epithelium. They become longer, and the nucleus-free zones at the distal ends of the cells become almost as long as the proximal parts containing the nuclei (Fig. 61). In preparation for this development, a reversal of the functional polarity of these cells takes place by the migration of the centrioles and Golgi regions from the proximal ends of the cells into their distal ends (Fig. 62).[120,123,132]

Special staining methods reveal the presence of fine acidophil granules in the proximal part of the cell.[124] Electron microscope studies[123,128,129,148] have shown that these granules are actually the mitochondria, which have become concentrated in this part of the cell (Fig. 62, *A*). At the same time, the clear cell-free zone between the inner dental epithelium and the dental papilla disappears (Fig. 61), probably due to elongation of the epithelial cells toward the papilla. Thus, the epithelial cells come into close contact with the connective tissue cells of the pulp, which are induced to differentiate into odontoblasts. During the terminal phase of the organizing stage, the formation of the dentin by the odontoblasts begins (Fig. 61).

The first appearance of dentin seems to be a critical phase in the life cycle of the inner dental epithelium. As long as it is in contact with the connective tissue of the dental papilla, it receives nutrient material from the blood vessels of this tissue. When dentin forms, however, it cuts off the ameloblasts from their original source of nourishment, and from then on they are supplied by the capillaries which surround and may even penetrate the outer dental epithelium. This reversal of nutritional source is characterized by proliferation of capillaries of the dental sac and by reduction and gradual disappearance of the stellate reticulum (Figs. 60*A* and 60*B*). Thus, the distance between the capillaries and the stratum intermedium and the ameloblast layer is shortened. Experiments with vital stains demonstrate this reversal of the nutritional stream.[146]

Formative stage. The ameloblasts enter their formative stage after the first layer of dentin has been formed. The presence of dentin seems to be necessary to induce the beginning of enamel matrix formation just as it was necessary for the epithelial cells to come into close contact with the connective tissue of the pulp to induce differentiation of the odontoblasts and the beginning of dentin formation. This mutual interaction between one group of cells and another is one of the fundamental laws of organogenesis and histodifferentiation.[104,107]

During formation of the enamel matrix, the ameloblasts retain approximately the same length and arrangement. Changes in the organization and number of cytoplasmic organelles and inclusions are related to the initiation of secretion of enamel matrix.[123,129]

Maturative stage. Enamel maturation (full mineralization) occurs after most of the thickness of the enamel matrix has been formed in the occlusal or incisal area. In the cervical parts of the crown, enamel matrix formation is still progressing at this time. During enamel maturation, the ameloblasts are slightly reduced in length and are closely attached to the enamel matrix. The cells of the stratum intermedium lose their cuboidal shape and regular arrangement and assume a spindle shape. It is certain that the ameloblasts also play a part in the maturation of the enamel. Ultimately they produce the enamel cuticle. During maturation, ameloblasts display microvilli at their distal extremities, and cyto-

Dentin

Basement membrane (dentinoenamel membrane)

Pulp

Basement membrane

Ameloblasts

Fig. 63. Basement membrane of the dental papilla can be followed on the outer surface of the dentin, forming the dentinoenamel membrane. (From Orban, B., Sicher, H., and Weinmann, J. P.: J. Am. Coll. Dentists **10:**13, 1943.)

plasmic vacuoles containing material resembling enamel matrix are present. These structures perhaps indicate an absorptive function of these cells.[130,131]

Protective stage. When the enamel has completely developed and has fully calcified, the ameloblasts cease to be arranged in a well-defined layer and can no longer be differentiated from the cells of the stratum intermedium and outer dental epithelium. These cell layers then form a stratified epithelial covering of the enamel, the so-called reduced enamel epithelium. The function of the reduced enamel epithelium is that of protecting the mature enamel by separating it from the connective tissue until the tooth erupts. If connective tissue comes in contact with the enamel, anomalies may develop. Under such conditions the enamel may be either resorbed or covered by a layer of cementum.[114, 152]

Desmolytic stage. The reduced enamel epithelium proliferates and seems to induce atrophy of the connective tissue separating it from the oral epithelium, so that fusion of the two epithelia can occur (see Chapter IX). It is probable that the epithelial cells elaborate enzymes that are able to destroy connective tissue fibers by desmolysis. Premature degeneration of the reduced enamel epithelium may prevent the eruption of a tooth.[152]

Amelogenesis

On the basis of ultimate structure and composition, two processes are involved in the development of enamel: organic matrix formation and mineraliza-

Distal ends of
ameloblasts

Dentinoenamel membrane
Dentinoenamel junction

Dentin

Fig. 64. The dentinoenamel membrane as seen in the electron microscope. (×5,500.)

tion. Although the inception of mineralization does not await the completion of matrix formation, the two processes will be treated separately.

Formation of the enamel matrix

Dentinoenamel membrane. The ameloblasts (Fig. 62) begin their secretory activity when a small amount of dentin has been laid down. The first enamel matrix is deposited extracellularly by the ameloblasts in a thin layer along the dentin.[101,111,123,149] (See Fig. 63.) This has been termed the dentinoenamel mem-

Fig. 65B

Fig. 65A

Fig. 65A. Formation of Tomes' processes and terminal bars as the first step in enamel rod formation. Rat incisor. (From Orban, B., Sicher, H., and Weinmann, J. P.: J. Am. Coll. Dentists **10:**13, 1943.)

Fig. 65B. Electron photomicrograph showing an early stage in the formation of enamel in the lower incisor of the rat. At this stage, dentin (at the bottom of the photomicrograph) is well developed. Enamel, *e*, appears as a less dense layer on the surface of the dentin and consists of thin, ribbon-shaped elements running more or less perpendicular to the dentinoenamel junction and masses of a less dense stippled material, *s*. Separating the enamel from the cytoplasm of the ameloblasts which occupies most of the upper part of the photomicrograph is the ameloblast plasma membrane. Parts of three ameloblasts are shown. In the middle of the photomicrograph in a region bounded by the membranes of the three ameloblasts lies another mass of stippled material, s_1, while a second mass, s_2, lies at the right surrounded by membrane, but within the bounds of the ameloblast. Numerous small, membrane-bound granules lie within the cytoplasm. The contents of these have the same general consistency as the stippled material, but rather higher density. It is possible that these represent unsecreted granules of stippled material which in turn is a precursor of enamel matrix. (×24,000.) (From Watson, M. L.: J. Biophys. & Biochem. Cytol. **7:**489, 1960.)

brane,[125, 137] and it is continuous with the interprismatic substance that forms subsequently. Its presence accounts for the fact that the distal ends of the enamel rods are not in direct contact with the dentin. (See Fig. 64.)

Development of Tomes' processes. After formation of the dentinoenamel membrane, matrix is deposited between the distal ends of the ameloblasts. It completely surrounds the ends of the cells, delineating what have become known as Tomes' processes (Fig. 65A). In sections this matrix appears as a row of projections about 4 microns long, extending intercellularly from the last-formed

Fig. 65C

Basal terminal bars

Ameloblasts

Distal terminal bars

Enamel matrix

Fig. 65D

Intercellular matrix

Tomes' process

Enamel matrix

Dentinoenamel junction

Fig. 65C. A phase-contrast photomicrograph showing the formation of Tomes' processes and terminal bars, the first step in enamel rod formation. Rodent incisor. (×1,000.)

Fig. 65D. An electron photomicrograph showing the Tomes' process region in more detail. (×8,000.) (From Nylen, M. U., and Scott, D. B.: J. Indiana State D. A. **39:**406, 1960.)

Fig. 66A

Fig. 66B

Basal terminal bars
Mitochondria

Ameloblasts

Distal terminal bars

Enamel matrix

Tomes' process

Fig. 66C

Partially filled in
Tomes' process

Completely filled in
Tomes' process

Fig. 66A. Terminal bar apparatus of the ameloblasts in surface view. (From Orban, B., Sicher, H., and Weinmann, J. P.: J. Am. Coll. Dentists **10**:13, 1943.)

Fig. 66B. A phase-contrast photomicrograph showing the Tomes' processes and their transformation into enamel matrix. Rodent incisor. (×700.)

Fig. 66C. An electron photomicrograph showing the steps in conversion of the newly formed Tomes' processes (top) into matrix segments (bottom). (×7,000.) (From Nylen, M. U., and Scott, D. B.: J. Indiana State D. A. **39**:406, 1960.)

matrix (Figs. 65*B*, 65*C*, and 66). During the formation of prenatal enamel in deciduous teeth, this phase of intercellular matrix formation is absent. It is probably minimized in other human teeth in which interprismatic substance is at a minimum.[133,134] The cytoplasm of Tomes' processes contains numerous granules but no organelles.[128,149]

Distal terminal bars. At the time Tomes' processes begin to form, terminal bars appear at the distal ends of the ameloblasts, separating the Tomes' processes from the cell proper (Figs. 65*A*, 65*C*, 66*A*, and 66*B*). Structurally, they are localized condensations of cytoplasmic substance closely associated with the cell membranes.[129] They are observed only during the enamel-producing stage of the ameloblast,[117,127] but their exact function is not known.

Transformation of Tomes' processes. The next step in enamel matrix formation is the "filling in" of the distal ends of Tomes' processes with matrix material to form segments of enamel rods.[123,140] Recent investigations on the development of rodent enamel show that Tomes' processes may actually become cut off from the parent cells by infolding of the lateral cell membranes prior to their change into rod substance.[123] Similar double sheaths have been observed between individual rod segments in developing human enamel,[106] although electron photomicrographs of developing human deciduous enamel indicate that these may be filamentous septa rather than cell membranes.[133] The transformation of the Tomes' processes into matrix substance secreted by the ameloblasts takes place from the periphery inward. As one row of processes is transformed, new

Fig. 67A. Homogenization of the dentinal ends of Tomes' processes and their transformation into preenamel matrix in a picket fence arrangement. The rods are at an angle to the ameloblasts and Tomes' processes. (From Orban, B., Sicher, H., and Weinmann, J. P.: J. Am. Coll. Dentists **10:**13, 1943.)

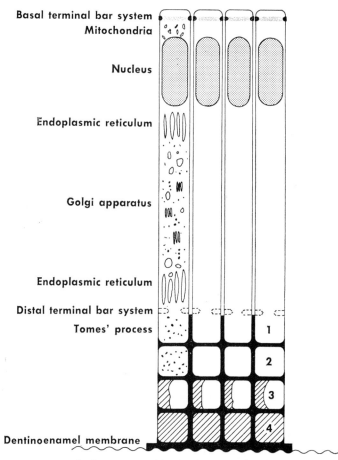

Basal terminal bar system
Mitochondria

Nucleus

Endoplasmic reticulum

Golgi apparatus

Endoplasmic reticulum

Distal terminal bar system
Tomes' process

Dentinoenamel membrane

1. **Formation of Tomes' process by deposition of intercellular matrix**

2. **Isolation of Tomes' process from the cell**

3. **Deposition of matrix in isolated Tomes' process**

4. **Fully formed segment of enamel rod**

Fig. 67B. Diagrammatic illustration of enamel matrix formation. The ameloblast and enamel rod are shown in linear arrangement, although they are always at an angle to each other. (Courtesy Dr. D. B. Scott.)

processes are outlined basal to the preceding ones as a result of continued inter-cellular matrix deposition and re-formation of the terminal bars. (Figs. 65D, 66C, and 67A.)

These two steps, e.g., formation of Tomes' processes and their change into matrix, are repeated again and again until the entire thickness of enamel is formed (Fig. 67B). The primary segmentation of the rods that results from this rhythmic deposition is considered the basis for the cross striations seen in mature rods as the length of the developmental segments (4 microns) corresponds to the distance between the striations. The ameloblasts generally are at an angle to the developing rod segments (Fig. 67A). They may bend first to one side, then to the other, which would explain the wavy course of the finished rods in certain regions. Although the bulk of each enamel rod is derived from a single ameloblast,[92] smaller portions are derived from one or two adjacent cells in human deciduous enamel.[133] This fact may explain the regular deviations from the long axis of the rod of groups of apatite crystals.[134]

The end product of the ameloblasts is the enamel cuticle, a thin organic membrane that covers the entire enamel surface (Fig. 68).

Mineralization and maturation of the enamel matrix

Mineralization of the enamel matrix takes place in two stages, although the time interval between the two appears to be very small.[93,94] In the first stage an

Fig. 68. A demineralized section showing the outer enamel layer of a recently completed human tooth. The enamel cuticle is interposed between the matrix and the shortened amelo-blasts. (Hematoxylin and eosin stain; ×1,300.) (From Ussing, M. J.: Acta odont. scandinav. **13**:123, 1955; reprinted J. West. Soc. Periodont. 3:71, 1955.)

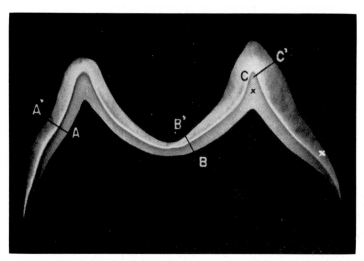

Fig. 69. Microradiograph of a ground section through a developing deciduous molar. From the gradation in radiopacity, maturation can be seen to progress from the dentinoenamel junction toward the enamel surface. Mineralization is more advanced occlusally than in the cervical region. The lines *A*, *B*, and *C* indicate planes in which actual microdensitometric tracings were made. (×15.) (From Hammarlund-Essler, E.: Tr. Royal Schools Dent., Stockholm and Umea 4:15, 1958.)

Fig. 70. Diagram showing the pattern of mineralization of an incisor tooth. The stippled zones represent consecutive layers of partly mineralized enamel matrix. The black areas indicate the advance of final mineralization during maturation. (From Crabb, H. S. M.: Proc. Royal Soc. Med. **52:**118, 1959; and Crabb, H. S. M., and Darling, A. I.: Arch. Oral Biol. **2:**308, 1960.)

immediate partial mineralization occurs in the matrix segments and the inter-prismatic substance as they are laid down. Chemical analyses indicate that the initial influx may amount to 25 to 30 per cent of the eventual total mineral content.[150] It has been shown recently by electron microscopy and diffraction that this first mineral actually is in the form of crystalline apatite (Fig. 71A).[102,103,123,149]

The second stage, or *maturation,* is characterized by the gradual completion of mineralization. The process of maturation starts from the height of the crown and progresses cervically. (See Fig. 69.) However, at each level, maturation seems to begin at the dentinal end of the rods.[90,93,108-110] Thus, there is an integration of two processes: each rod matures from the depth to the surface, and

Tomes' process

Intercellular
   matrix process

Crystals

A

B

Fig. 71. Electron photomicrographs illustrating the difference between the short, needlelike crystals laid down in newly deposited enamel matrix, **A,** and the long, ribbonlike crystals seen in mature enamel, **B.** (×70,000.)

the sequence of maturing rods is from cusp or incisal edge toward the cervical line.[150]

Maturation begins before the matrix has reached its full thickness. Thus, it is going on in the inner, first-formed matrix at the same time as initial mineralization is taking place in the outer, recently formed matrix. The advancing front is at first parallel to the dentinoenamel junction and later to the outer enamel surface. Following this basic pattern, the incisal and occlusal regions reach maturity ahead of the cervical regions. (Fig. 70.)

A   B   C

Fig. 72. Electron photomicrographs of transverse sections through enamel rods, showing three stages in the growth of apatite crystals during enamel maturation in the rat incisor. From **A** (recently formed enamel) through **C** (more mature enamel) the crystals increase in thickness more rapidly than in width. The spaces between the crystals will become even smaller as maturation is completed. (×240,000.) (Modified by permission of the Rockefeller Institute Press, from Nylen, M. U., Eanes, E. D., and Omnell, K.-Å.: J. Cell Biol. **18:**109, 1963.)

At the ultrastructural level, maturation is characterized by growth and eventual fusion of the crystals seen in the primary phase (Fig. 71).[102,103,134,138,140] The original ribbon-shaped crystals increase in thickness more rapidly than in width, until they are slightly elongated hexagons in cross section (Fig. 72).[121,134,144] Concomitantly the fibrils of the organic matrix gradually become thinned and more widely spaced to make room for the growing crystals.[142] It is likely, however, that some of the organic fibrils actually become embedded in the crystals.[102,135,139] Chemical analysis shows that the loss in volume of the organic matrix is due to withdrawal of a substantial amount of protein, but mostly water, from the matrix.[95,96,105] When demineralized longitudinal sections through the

Fig. 73. An electron photomicrograph of a demineralized longitudinal section through the rods of developing mouse molar enamel. Cross-linked ribbons of organic matter are visible. When sectioned transversely, these ribbons are seen to form sheaths surrounding individual enamel crystals. (×120,000.) (Courtesy Dr. J. A. Yaeger.)

rods of nearly mature enamel are examined in the electron microscope, filaments or ribbons of organic matrix can be seen (Fig. 73). When cut transversely to the long axes of the rods, the organic matter appears to form sheaths around individual apatite crystals.[135,141,144]

Clinical considerations

Clinical interest in amelogenesis is centered primarily on the perfection of enamel formation. While there is relatively little the dentist can do directly to alter the course of events in amelogenesis, it may be possible to minimize certain of the factors thought to be associated with the etiology of defective enamel structure. The principal expressions of pathologic amelogenesis are hypoplasia, which is manifested by pitting, furrowing, or even total absence of the enamel, and hypocalcification, in the form of opaque or chalky areas on normally contoured enamel surfaces. The causes of such defective enamel formation can be generally classified as systemic,[115,136] local,[119] or genetic.[151,153] The most common systemic influences are nutritional deficiencies, endocrinopathies, febrile diseases, and certain chemical intoxications. It thus stands to reason that the dentist should exert his influence to ensure sound nutritional practices and recommended immunization procedures during periods of gestation and postnatal amelogenesis. Chemical intoxication of the ameloblasts is not prevalent and is limited essentially to the ingestion of excessive amounts of water-borne fluoride. Where the drinking water contains fluorides in excess of 1.5 parts per million, chronic endemic fluorosis may occur as a result of continuous use throughout the period of amelogenesis.[97] In such areas it is important to urge substitution of a water with levels of fluoride (about 1 part per million) well below the threshold for fluorosis, yet optimal with regard to protection against dental caries (see discussion of clinical considerations in section on histology).

Since it has been realized that enamel development occurs in two phases, i.e., matrix formation and maturation, developmental disturbances of the enamel can be understood more fully. If matrix formation is affected, enamel hypoplasia will ensue. If maturation is lacking or incomplete, hypocalcification of the enamel results. In the case of hypoplasia a defect of the enamel is found. In the case of hypocalcification a deficiency in the mineral content of the enamel is found. In the latter the enamel persists as enamel matrix and is, therefore, soft and acid insoluble in routine preparation after formalin fixation.

Hypoplasia, as well as hypocalcification, may be caused by systemic, local, or hereditary factors. Hypoplasia of systemic origin is termed chronologic hypoplasia because the lesion is found in the areas of those teeth where the enamel was formed during the systemic (metabolic) disturbance. Since the formation of enamel extends over a longer period and the systemic disturbance is, in most cases, of short duration, the defect is limited to a circumscribed area of the affected teeth. A single narrow zone of hypoplasia (smooth or pitted) may be indicative of a disturbance of enamel formation during a short period in which only those ameloblasts were affected which at that time had just started enamel formation. Multiple hypoplasia develops if enamel formation is interrupted on more than one occasion.[136]

No specific etiology of chronologic hypoplasia has been established as yet. Recent investigations have demonstrated that exanthematous diseases are not so frequently a cause of enamel hypoplasia as was heretofore commonly believed.[136] The most frequent etiologic factors are said to be rickets and hypoparathyroidism, but hypoplasia cannot be predicted with any reliability even in the most severe forms of those diseases.[136]

The systemic influences causing enamel hypoplasia are, in the majority of cases, active during the first year of life. Therefore, the teeth most frequently affected are the incisors, canines, and first molars. The upper lateral incisor is sometimes found unaffected because its development starts later than that of the other teeth mentioned.

Local factors affect single teeth, in most cases only one tooth. If more than one tooth is affected by local hypoplasia, the location of the defects shows no relation to chronology of development. The cause of local hypoplasia may be an infection of the pulp with subsequent infection of the periapical tissues of a deciduous tooth if the irritation occurred during the period of enamel formation of its permanent successor.

The hereditary type of enamel hypoplasia is probably a generalized disturbance of the ameloblasts. Therefore, the entire enamel of all the teeth, deciduous as well as permanent, is affected rather than merely a beltlike zone of the enamel of a group of teeth, as in systemic cases. The anomaly is transmitted as a mendelian dominant character. The enamel of such teeth is so thin that it cannot be noticed clinically or in radiographs. The crowns of the teeth of affected family members are yellow-brown, smooth, glossy, and hard, and their shape resembles teeth prepared for jacket crowns.[151, 152]

An example of systemic hypocalcification of the enamel is the so-called mottled enamel. A high fluoride content in the water is the cause of the deficiency in calcification. Fluoride hypocalcification is endemic, i.e., it is limited in its distribution to definite areas in which the drinking water contains more than 1 part of fluoride per 1 million parts of water. It has been demonstrated that a small amount of fluoride (about 1 to 1.2 parts per million) reduces susceptibility to dental caries without causing mottling. For this reason, many communities are adding small quantities of fluoride to the community water supplies.

The same local causes that might affect the formation of the enamel can disturb maturation. If the injury occurs in the formative stage of enamel development, hypoplasia of the enamel will result. An injury during the maturation stage will cause a deficiency in calcification.

The hereditary type of hypocalcification is characterized by the formation of a normal amount of enamel matrix that, however, does not fully mature.[151,152]

Such teeth, if investigated before or shortly after eruption, show a normal shape. Their surfaces do not have the luster of normal enamel but appear dull. The enamel is opaque. The hypocalcified soft enamel matrix is soon discolored, abraded by mastication, or peeled off in layers. When parts of the soft enamel are lost, the teeth show an irregular, rough surface. When the enamel is altogether lost, the teeth are small and brown, and the exposed dentin is extremely sensitive.

REFERENCES

Histology

1. Arnold, F. A., Jr.: Grand Rapids fluoridation study—results pertaining to the eleventh year of fluoridation, Am. J. Pub. Health 47:539, 1957.
2. Bartelstone, H. J., Mandel, I. D., Oshry, E., and Seidlin, S. M.: Use of radioactive iodine as a tracer in the study of the physiology of the teeth, Science 106:132, 1947.
3. Battistone, G. D., and Burnett, G. W.: The amino acid composition of human enamel protein, J. D. Res. 35:260, 1956.
4. Baud, C. A., and Held, A. J.: Silberfärbung, Röntgenmikrographie und Mineralgehalt der Zahnhartgewebe (Silver impregnation, microradiography and mineral content of calcified tooth structure), Deutsche zahnärztl. Z. 11:309, 1956.
5. Bergman, G., Hammerlund-Essler, E., and Lysell, L.: Studies on mineralized dental tissues. XII. Microradiographic study of caries in deciduous teeth, Acta odont. scandinav. 16:113, 1958.
6. Beust, T.: Morphology and biology of the enamel tufts with remarks on their relation to caries, J.A.D.A. 19:488, 1932.
7. Bhussry, B. R., and Bibby, B. G.: Surface changes in enamel, J. D. Res. 36:409, 1957.
8. Bibby, B. G., and Van Huysen, G.: Changes in the enamel surfaces; a possible defense against caries, J.A.D.A. 20:828, 1933.
9. Block, R. J., Horwitt, M. K., and Bolling, D.: Comparative protein chemistry; the composition of the proteins of human enamel and fish scales, J. D. Res. 28:518, 1949.
10. Bodecker, C. F.: Enamel of the teeth decalcified by the celloidin decalcifying method and examined by ultraviolet light, D. Rev. 20:317, 1906.
11. Bodecker, C. F.: The color of the teeth as an index of their resistance to decay, Internat. J. Orthodontia 19:386, 1933.
12. Brabant, H., and Klees, L.: Histological contribution to the study of lamellae in human dental enamel, Internat. D. J. 8:539, 1958.
13. Burgess, R. C., Nikiforuk, G., and Maclaren, C.: Chromatographic studies of carbohydrate components in enamel, Arch. Oral Biol. 1:8, 1960.
14. Cape, A. T., and Kitchin, P. C.: Histologic phenomena of tooth tissue as observed under polarized light; with a note on the roentgen ray spectra of enamel and dentin, J.A.D.A. 17:193, 1930.
15. Chase, S. W.: The number of enamel prisms in human teeth, J.A.D.A. 14:1921, 1927.
16. Crabb, H. S., and Darling, A. I.: The pattern of progressive mineralisation in human dental enamel, Internat. Ser. Monogr. Oral Biol. 2:1, 1962.
17. Eastoe, J. E.: Organic matrix of tooth enamel, Nature 187:411, 1960.
18. Engel, M. B.: Glycogen and carbohydrate-protein complex in developing teeth of the rat, J. D. Res. 27:681, 1948.
19. Fish, E. W.: An experimental investigation of enamel, dentin and the dental pulp, London, 1932, John Bale Sons & Danielsson, Ltd.
20. Frank, R.: Études sur l'infrastructure microscopique de l'émail et sur la surface libre coronale de la dent (Studies on the submicroscopic structure of the enamel and the free coronal surface of the tooth), Schweiz. Monatschr. Zahnhk. 60:1109, 1950.
21. Frank, R. M., and Sognnaes, R. F.: Electron microscopy of matrix formation and calcification in rat enamel, Arch. Oral Biol. 1:339, 1960.

22. Frank, R. M., Sognnaes, R. F., and Kern, R.: In Sognnaes, R. F. (editor): Calcification in biological systems, Washington, D. C., 1960, American Association for the Advancement of Science.

23. Glas, J. E., and Omnell, K. A.: Studies on the ultrastructure of dental enamel, J. Ultrastructure Res. 3:334, 1960.

24. Glimcher, M. J., Bonar, L. C., and Daniel, E. J.: The molecular structure of the protein matrix of bovine dental enamel, J. Molecular Biol. 3:541, 1961.

25. Gottlieb, B.: Aetiologie und Prophylaxe der Zahnkaries (Etiology and prophylaxis of dental caries), Ztschr. f. Stomatol. 19:129, 1921.

26. Gottlieb, B.: Dental caries, Philadelphia, 1947, Lea & Febiger.

27. Gray, J. A., Schweizer, H. C., Rosevear, F. B., and Broge, R. W.: Electron microscopic observations of the differences in the effects of stannous fluoride and sodium fluoride on dental enamel, J. D. Res. 37:638, 1958.

28. Gustafson, A.-G.: A morphologic investigation of certain variations in the structure and mineralization of human dental enamel, Odont. Tskr. 67:361, 1959.

29. Gustafson, G.: The structure of human dental enamel, Odont. Tskr. 53(supp.): 1945.

30. Gustafson, G., and Gustafson, A.-G.: Human dental enamel in polarized light and contact micro-radiography, Acta odont. scandinav. 19:259, 1961.

31. Helmcke, Von J.-G.: Elektronenmikroskopische Strukturuntersuchungen an gesunden und kranken Zähnen (Investigations of electron microscopic structure in sound and pathological teeth), Deutsche zahnärztl. Z. 10:1461, 1955.

32. Hess, W. C., Lee, C. Y., and Neidig, B. A.: The amino acid composition of enamel protein, J. D. Res. 32:585, 1953.

33. Hill, T. J.: Fluoride dentifrices, J.A.D.A. 59:1121, 1959.

34. Hodson, J. J.: An investigation into the microscopic structure of the common forms of enamel lamellae with special reference to their origin and contents, Oral Surg., Oral Med. & Oral Path. 6:305, 383, 495, 1953.

35. Hollander, F., Bodecker, C. F., Applebaum, E., and Saper, E.: A study of the bands of Schreger by histological and grenz-ray methods, D. Cosmos 77:12, 1935.

36. Jansen, M. T., and Visser, J. B.: Permeable structures in normal enamel, J. D. Res. 29:622, 1950.

37. Klees, L.: Les lamelles, les buissons, et le développement de la carie dans l'émail dentaire humain (Lamellae, tufts and the development of caries in human dental enamel), Bull. du Group Int. pour la Recher. Scient. en Stomatol. 1:1, 1961.

38. Klees, L., and Klees, K.: Ueber die Regenerationsfähigkeit des Schmelzoberhäutchens (The regenerative capacity of the enamel cuticle), Stroma 2:58, 1958.

39. Kronfeld, R.: First permanent molar; its condition at birth and its postnatal development, J.A.D.A. 22:1131, 1935.

40. Lefkowitz, W., and Bodecker, C. F.: Concerning the "vitality" of the calcified dental tissue. II. Permeability of the enamel, J. D. Res. 17:453, 1938.

41. Losee, F. L., Jennings, W. H., Lawson, M. E., and Forziati, A. F.: Microstructure of the human tooth, J. D. Res. 36:911, 1957.

42. Lyon, D. G., and Darling, A. I.: Orientation of the crystallites in human dental enamel, Brit. D. J. 102:483, 1957.

43. Manly, R. S.: A structureless recurrent deposit on teeth, J. D. Res. 22:479, 1943.

44. Moulton, F. R.: Dental caries and fluorine, Washington, D. C., 1946, American Association for the Advancement of Science.

45. Muhler, J. C., and Radike, A. W.: Effect of a dentifrice containing stannous fluoride on adults. II. Results at the end of two years of unsupervised use, J.A.D.A. 55:196, 1957.

46. Muhler, J. C.: Present status of topical fluoride therapy, J. Dent. Child. 26:173, 1959.

47. Nasmyth, A.: Researches on the development, structures and diseases of the teeth, London, 1839, John Churchill.

48. Orban, B.: Histology of enamel lamellae and tufts, J.A.D.A. 15:305, 1928.

49. Pautard, F. G. E.: An x-ray diffraction pattern from human enamel matrix, Arch. Oral Biol. 3:217, 1961.

50. Pickerill, H. P.: The prevention of dental caries and oral sepsis, New York, 1924, Paul B. Hoeber, Inc.

51. Piez, K. A.: The nature of the protein matrix of human enamel, J. D. Res. **39**:712, 1960.

52. Piez, K. A., and Likins, R. C.: The nature of collagen. II. Vertebrate collagens. In Sognnaes, R. F. (editor): Calcification in biological systems, Washington, D. C., 1960, American Association for the Advancement of Science, p. 411.

53. Posner, A. S., and Stephenson, S. R.: Isomorphous substitution in enamel apatite, J.A.D.A. **46**:257, 1953.

54. Retzius, A.: Microscopic investigation of the structure of the teeth, Arch. Anat. & Physiol., p. 486, 1837.

55. Robinson, H. B. G., Boling, L. R., and Lischer, B.: In Cowdry, E. V. (editor): Problems of ageing, ed. 2, Baltimore, 1942, Williams & Wilkins Co.

56. Rönnholm, E.: The amelogenesis of human teeth as revealed by electron microscopy. II. The development of the enamel crystallites, J. Ultrastructure Res. **6**:249, 1962.

57. Rushton, M. A.: On the fine contour lines of the enamel of milk teeth, D. Rec. **53**:170, 1933.

58. Rushton, M. A.: The birefringence of deciduous tooth enamel formed before and after birth, Brit. D. J. **67**:1, 1939.

59. Savory, A., and Brudevold, F.: The distribution of nitrogen in human enamel, J. D. Res. **38**:436, 1959.

60. Schmidt, W. J., and Keil, A.: Die gesunden und die erkrankten Zahngewebe des Menschen und der Wirbeltiere im Polarisationsmikroskop (Normal and pathological tooth structure of humans and vertebrates in the polarization microscope), München, 1958, Carl Hanser Verlag.

61. Schour, I.: The neonatal line in the enamel and dentin of the human deciduous teeth and first permanent molar, J.A.D.A. **23**:1946, 1936.

62. Schour, I., and Hoffman, M. M.: Studies in tooth development. I. The 16 microns rhythm in the enamel and dentin from fish to man, J. D. Res. **18**:91, 1939.

63. Scott, D. B., and Wyckoff, R. W. G.: Typical structures on replicas of apparently intact tooth surfaces, Pub. Health Rep. **61**:1397, 1946.

64. Scott, D. B., Kaplan, H., and Wyckoff, R. W. G.: Replica studies of changes in tooth surfaces with age, J. D. Res. **28**:31, 1949.

65. Scott, D. B., and Wyckoff, R. W. G.: Studies of tooth surface structure by optical and electron microscopy, J.A.D.A. **39**:275, 1949.

66. Scott, D. B., Ussing, M. J., Sognnaes, R. F., and Wyckoff, R. W. G.: Electron microscopy of mature human enamel, J. D. Res. **31**:74, 1952.

67. Scott, D. B.: The electron microscopy of enamel and dentin, J. New York Acad. Sc. **60**:575, 1955.

68. Scott, D. B.: Studies of the crystal structure of enamel by electron microscopy and electron diffraction, Proceedings of the 25th Year Celebration of the University of Rochester Dental Research Fellow Program, p. 175, 1957.

69. Scott, D. B.: The crystalline component of dental enamel, Fourth International Conference on Electron Microscopy, Berlin, 1960, Springer-Verlag.

70. Shaw, J. H.: Fluoridation as a public health measure, Washington, D. C., 1954, American Association for the Advancement of Science.

71. Skillen, W. C.: The permeability of enamel in relation to stain, J.A.D.A. **11**:402, 1924.

72. Smreker, E.: Ueber die Form der Schmelzprismen menschlicher Zähne und die Kittsubstanz des Schmelzes (On the form of enamel prisms of human teeth, and the cement substance of the enamel), Arch. f. mikr. Anat. **66**:312, 1905.

73. Sognnaes, R. F.: The organic elements of the enamel. III. The pattern of the organic framework in the region of the neonatal and other incremental lines of the enamel, J. D. Res. **28**:558, 1949.

74. Sognnaes, R. F.: The organic elements of the enamel. IV. The gross morphology and the histological relationship of the lamellae to the organic framework of the enamel, J. D. Res. **29**:260, 1950.

75. Sognnaes, R. F.: Microstructure and histochemical characteristics of the mineralized tissues, J. New York Acad. Sc. **60**:545, 1955.

76. Sognnaes, R. F., Shaw, J. H., and Bogoroch, R.: Radiotracer studies of bone, cementum, dentin and enamel of rhesus monkeys, Am. J. Physiol. **180**:408, 1955.

77. Spiers, R. L.: The nature of surface enamel, Brit. D. J. **107**:209, 1959.

78. Stack, M. V.: Organic constituents of enamel, J.A.D.A. **48**:297, 1954.

79. Thewlis, J.: The structure of teeth as shown by x-ray examination, Medical Research Council, Special Report Series No. 238, London, 1940, Her Majesty's Stationery Office.

80. Trautz, O. R., Klein, E., Fessenden, E., and Addelston, H. K.: The interpretation of the x-ray diffractograms obtained from human dental enamel, J. D. Res. **32**:420, 1953.

81. Turner, E. P.: The integument of the enamel surface of the human tooth, D. Practitioner & D. Record **8**:341, 1958.

82. Ussing, Marie J.: The development of the epithelial attachment, Acta odont. scandinav. **13**:123, 1955; reprinted J. West. Soc. Periodont. **3**:71, 1955.

83. Vallotton, C. F.: An acquired pigmented pellicle of the enamel surface, J. D. Res. **24**:161, 1945.

84. Wainwright, W. W., and Lemoine, F. A.: Rapid diffuse penetration of intact enamel and dentin by carbon[14]-labeled urea, J.A.D.A. **41**:135, 1950.

85. Watson, M. L.: The extracellular nature of enamel in the rat, J. Biophys. & Biochem. Cytol. **7**:489, 1960.

86. Wislocki, G. B., and Sognnaes, R. F.: Histochemical reactions of normal teeth, Am. J. Anat. **87**:239, 1950.

87. Wolf, J.: Plastische Histologie der Zahngewebe (Plastic histology of dental tissues), Deutsche Zahn-, Mund- u. Kieferheilk. **7**:265, 1940.

88. Wolf, J.: Reparative Vorgänge an der Oberflache naturlicher und kunstlich hervorger-ufener Schmelzdefekte (Reparative processes on the surface of natural and artificially created enamel defects), Deutsche Zahn-, Mund- u. Kieferheilk. **8**:222, 1941.

89. Yoon, S. H., Brudwold, F., Gardner, D. E., and Smith, F. A.: Distribution of fluoride in teeth from areas with different levels of fluoride in the water supply, J. D. Res. **39**:845, 1960.

Development

90. Allan, J. H.: Investigations into the mineralization pattern of human dental enamel, J. D. Res. **38**:1096, 1959.

91. Beams, H. W., and King, R. L.: The Golgi apparatus in the developing tooth with special reference to polarity, Anat. Rec. **57**:29, 1933.

92. Chase, S. W.: The development, histology and physiology of enamel and dentin, J. D. Res. **27**:87, 1948.

93. Crabb, H. S. M.: The pattern of mineralization of human dental enamel, Proc. Royal Soc. Med. **52**:118, 1959.

94. Crabb, H. S. M., and Darling, A. I.: The gradient of mineralization in developing enamel, Arch. Oral Biol. **2**:308, 1960.

95. Deakins, M.: Changes in the ash, water, and organic content of pig enamel during calci-fication, J. D. Res. **21**:429, 1942.

96. Deakins, M., and Burt, R. L.: The deposition of calcium, phosphorus, and carbon dioxide in calcifying dental enamel, J. Biol. Chem. **156**:77, 1944.

97. Dean, H. T.: Chronic endemic dental fluorosis, J.A.M.A. **107**:1269, 1936.

98. Diamond, M., and Applebaum, E.: The epithelial sheath: histogenesis and function, J. D. Res. **21**:403, 1942.

99. Engel, M. B., and Furuta, W.: Histochemical studies of phosphates: distribution in de-veloping teeth of albino rat, Proc. Soc. Exper. Biol. & Med. **50**:5, 1942.

100. Engel, M. B.: Some changes in the connective tissue ground substance associated with the eruption of the teeth, J. D. Res. **30**:322, 1951.

101. Fearnhead, R. W.: Mineralization of rat enamel, Nature **189**:509, 1960.

102. Frank, R. M., Sognnaes, R. F., and Kern, R.: Calcification of dental tissue with special

reference to enamel ultrastructure. In Sognnaes, R. F. (editor): Calcification in biological systems, Washington, D. C., 1960, American Association for the Advancement of Science.

103. Frank, R. M., and Sognnaes, R. F.: Electron microscopy of matrix formation and calcification in rat enamel, Arch. Oral Biol. 1:339, 1960.
104. Glasstone, S.: Development of tooth germs in vitro, J. Anat. 70:260, 1936.
105. Glimcher, M. J., Friberg, V. A., and Levine, P. T.: The isolation and amino acid composition of the enamel proteins of erupted bovine teeth, Biochem. J. 93:202, 1964.
106. Gustafson, A.-G.: A morphologic investigation of certain variations in the structure and mineralization of human dental enamel, Odont. Tskr. 67:361, 1959.
107. Hahn, W. E.: The capacity of developing tooth germ elements for self-differentiation when transplanted, J. D. Res. 20:5, 1941.
108. Hals, E.: Fluorescence microscopy of developing and adult teeth, Oslo, 1953, Norwegian Academic Press.
109. Hammarlund-Essler, E.: A microradiographic, microphotometric and x-ray diffraction study of human developing enamel, Tr. Royal Schools Dent., Stockholm and Umea 4: 15, 1958.
110. Harders-Steinhäuser, M.: Die Erhärtung des Zahnschmelzes nach polarisationsoptischen Untersuchungen (Mineralization of the enamel studied with the polarization microscope), Z. f. zellforsch. u. mikroskop. Anat. 28:274, 1938.
111. Held, H.: Ueber die Bildung des Schmelzgewebes (On the formation of enamel), Ztschr. f. mikr.-anat. Forsch. 5:668, 1926.
112. Jump, E. B.: Vascularity of the human enamel organ, J. D. Res. 17:505, 1938.
113. Kérébel, B., and Grimbert, L.: Histogénèse de l'émail (Histogenesis of the enamel), Rev. Franc. d'Odonto-Stomatol. 7:1, 1958.
114. Kotanyi, E.: Histologische Befunde an retinierten Zähnen (Histologic findings on embedded teeth), Ztschr. f. Stomatol. 22:747, 1924.
115. Kreshover, S. J., and Hancock, J. A., Jr.: The pathogenesis of abnormal enamel formation in rabbits inoculated with vaccinia, J. D. Res. 35:685, 1936.
116. Lenz, V. H.: Elektronenmikroskopische Untersuchungen der Schmelzgenese (Electron microscopic studies of enamel formation), Deutsche zahnärztl. Z. 13:991, 1958.
117. Marsland, E. A.: A histological investigation of amelogenesis in rats, Brit. D. J. 91:252, 1951; 92:109, 1952.
118. Maximow, A. A., and Bloom, W.: A textbook of histology, ed. 7, Philadelphia, 1957, W. B. Saunders Co.
119. Morningstar, C. H.: Effect of infection of the deciduous molar on the permanent tooth germ, J.A.D.A. 24:786, 1937.
120. Nuckolls, J., Leicester, H. M., and Dienstein, B.: Amelogenesis, J. Am. Coll. Dentists 14:118, 1947.
121. Nylen, M. U., Eanes, E. D., and Omnell, K.-Å.: Crystal growth in rat enamel, J. Cell. Biol. 18:109, 1963.
122. Nylen, M. U., and Scott, D. B.: An electron microscopic study of the early stages of dentinogenesis, Pub. 613, U. S. Public Health Service, Washington, D. C., 1958, U. S. Government Printing Office.
123. Nylen, M. U., and Scott, D. B.: Electron microscopic studies of odontogenesis. J. Indiana State D. A. 39:406, 1960.
124. Orban, B.: Zur Histologie des Schmelzes und der Schmelzdentingrenze (Histology of enamel and dentino-enamel junction), Vrtljschr. f. Zahnheilk. 42:336, 1926.
125. Orban, B., Sicher, H., and Weinmann, J. P.: Amelogenesis (a critique and a new concept), J. Am. Coll. Dentists 10:13, 1943.
126. Pannese, E.: Observations on the ultrastructure of the enamel organ. I. Stellate reticulum and stratum intermedium, J. Ultrastructure Res. 4:372, 1960.
127. Pindborg, J. J., and Weinmann, J. P.: Morphologic and functional correlations in the enamel organ of the rat incisor during amelogenesis, Acta anat. 36:367, 1959.

128. Quigley, M. B.: Electron microscopy of developing enamel matrix in the Syrian hamster, J. D. Res. 38:180, 1959.
129. Reith, E. J.: The ultrastructure of ameloblasts from the growing end of rat incisors, Arch. Oral Biol. 2:253, 1960.
130. Reith, E. J.: The ultrastructure of ameloblasts during matrix formation and the maturation of enamel, J. Biophys. & Biochem. Cytol. 9:825, 1961.
131. Reith, E. J.: The ultrastructure of ameloblasts during early stages of maturation of enamel, J. Cell. Biol. 18:691, 1963.
132. de Renyi, G. S.: Central bodies in the cells of the inner enamel epithelium, Am. J. Anat. 53:413, 1933.
133. Rönnholm, E.: An electron microscopic study of the amelogenesis in human teeth. I. The fine structure of the ameloblasts, J. Ultrastructure Res. 6:229, 1962.
134. Rönnholm, E.: The amelogenesis of human teeth as revealed by electron microscopy. II. The development of the enamel crystallites, J. Ultrastructure Res. 6:249, 1962.
135. Rönnholm, E.: The amelogenesis of human teeth as revealed by electron microscopy. III. The structure of the organic stroma of human enamel during amelogenesis, J. Ultrastructure Res. 6:368, 1962.
136. Sarnat, B. G., and Schour, I.: Enamel hypoplasia (chronologic enamel aplasia) in relation to systemic disease, J.A.D.A. 28:1989, 1941; 29:67, 1942.
137. Saunders, J. B. De C. M., Nuckolls, J., and Frisbie, H. E.: Amelogenesis, J. Am. Coll. Dentists 9:107, 1942.
138. Scott, D. B., Nylen, M. U., and Takuma, S.: Electron microscopy of developing and mature calcified tissues, Rev. Belge de Sci. Dent. 14:329, 1959.
139. Scott, D. B.: The crystalline component of dental enamel, Fourth International Conference on Electron Microscopy, Berlin, 1960, Springer-Verlag.
140. Scott, D. B., and Nylen, M. U.: Changing concepts in dental histology, Ann. New York Acad. Sc. 85:133, 1960.
141. Scott, D. B., and Nylen, M. U.: Organic-inorganic interrelationships in enamel and dentin—a possible key to the mechanism of caries, Internat. D. J. 12:417, 1962.
142. Sognnaes, R. F., Scott, D. B., Ussing, M. J., and Wyckoff, R. W. G.: Electron microscopy of the enamel of teeth in various stages of development, J. D. Res. 31:85, 1952.
143. Suga, S.: Amelogenesis—some histological and histochemical observations, Internat. D. J. 9:394, 1959.
144. Travis, D. F., and Glimcher, M. J.: The structure and organization of and the relationship between the organic matrix and the inorganic crystals of embryonic bovine enamel, J. Cell. Biol. 23:447, 1964.
145. Ussing, M. J.: The development of the epithelial attachment, Acta odont. scandinav. 13:123, 1955; reprinted J. West. Soc. Periodont. 3:71, 1955.
146. Wasserman, F.: Enamel formation under normal and experimental conditions, J. D. Res. 20:254, 1941.
147. Wasserman, F.: Analysis of the enamel formation in the continuously growing teeth of normal and vitamin C deficient guinea pigs, J. D. Res. 23:463, 1944.
148. Watson, M. L., and Avery, J. K.: The development of the hamster lower incisor as observed by electron microscopy, Am. J. Anat. 95:109, 1954.
149. Watson, M. L.: The extracellular nature of enamel in the rat, J. Biophys. & Biochem. Cytol. 7:489, 1960.
150. Weinmann, J. P., Wessinger, G. D., and Reed, G.: Correlation of chemical and histological investigations on developing enamel, J. D. Res. 21:171, 1942.
151. Weinmann, J. P.: Developmental disturbances of the enamel, Bur 43:20, 1943.
152. Weinmann, J. P., Svoboda, J. F., and Woods, R. W.: Hereditary disturbances of enamel formation and calcification, J.A.D.A. 32:397, 1945.
153. Witkop, C. J., Jr.: Dental genetics 1959, J.A.D.A. 60:564, 1960.

PHYSICAL PROPERTIES
CHEMICAL COMPOSITION
STRUCTURE
        Dentinal tubules
        Odontoblastic processes
        Peritubular dentin
        Intertubular dentin
        Mineral component
        Incremental lines
        Interglobular dentin
        Tomes' granular layer

INNERVATION
AGE AND FUNCTIONAL CHANGES
        Vitality of dentin
        Secondary dentin
        Reparative dentin
        Transparent (sclerotic) dentin
        Dead tracts

DEVELOPMENT
        Life cycle of odontoblasts
        Dentinogenesis
        Predentin formation
        Mineralization

Chapter IV

Dentin*

The dentin constitutes the bulk of the tooth. As a living tissue it consists of specialized cells, the odontoblasts, and an intercellular substance. Although the bodies of the odontoblasts are arranged on the pulpal surface of the dentin, the entire cell biologically and morphologically has to be considered the cell of the dentin. In its physical and chemical qualities the dentin closely resembles bone. The main morphologic difference between bone and dentin is that some of the osteoblasts forming the bone are enclosed in the intercellular substance as osteocytes, whereas the dentin contains only cytoplasmic processes of the odontoblasts.

PHYSICAL PROPERTIES

In teeth of young individuals the dentin usually is light yellowish in color. Unlike enamel, which is very hard and brittle, dentin is subject to slight deformation and is highly elastic. It is somewhat harder than bone but is considerably softer than enamel. The smaller content of mineral salts in dentin renders it more radiolucent than enamel.

Under polarized light dentin exhibits a slight positive birefringence. Actually, the organic matrix fibrils are optically positive, and the inorganic crystals are optically negative. The observed birefringence represents a net effect.[20,49]

CHEMICAL COMPOSITION

Dentin consists of 30 per cent organic matter and water and 70 per cent inorganic material. The organic substance consists of collagenous fibrils and a

---

*First draft submitted by Gerrit Bevelander; revised by David B. Scott and Marie U. Nylen.

ground substance of mucopolysaccharides.[27,38] The inorganic component has been shown by roentgen ray diffraction to consist of hydroxyapatite, as in bone, cementum, and enamel. Organic and inorganic substances can be separated by decalcification or incineration. In the process of decalcification the organic constituents can be retained and maintain the shape of the dentin. Incineration removes the organic constituents. The inorganic substances shrink but retain the shape of the organ and become very brittle and porous.

STRUCTURE

As indicated earlier, the bodies of the odontoblasts are arranged in a layer on the pulpal surface of the dentin, and only their cytoplasmic processes are embedded in the mineralized matrix. Each cell gives rise to one process, which traverses the entire thickness of the dentin in a narrow channel called the dentinal tubule. Inasmuch as the inner surface of the dentin is lined completely with odontoblasts, tubules are found throughout.

Dentinal tubules. The course of the dentinal tubules is somewhat curved,

Fig. 74. Ground section of a human incisor. Observe the course of the dentinal tubules.

resembling an S in shape (Fig. 74). Starting at right angles from the pulpal surface, the first convexity of this doubly curved course is directed toward the apex of the tooth. In the root and in the area of incisal edges and cusps, the tubules are almost straight. Over their entire lengths the tubules exhibit minute, relatively regular secondary curvatures that are sinusoid in shape.

The ratio between surface areas at the outside and inside of the dentin is about 5:1. Accordingly, the tubules are farther apart in the peripheral layers and are more closely packed near the pulp. In addition, they are wider near the pulpal cavity (2 to 3 microns) and become narrower at their outer ends (1 micron). The ratio between the numbers of tubules per unit area on the pulpal and outer surfaces of the dentin is about 4:1. Near the pulpal surface of the dentin, the number per square millimeter is said to vary between 30,000 and 75,000.[36] There are more tubules per unit area in the crown than in the root.

Odontoblastic processes. The odontoblastic processes are cytoplasmic extensions of the odontoblasts (Figs. 75 and 80) occupying a space in the dentin matrix known as the dentinal tubule. The processes are thickest near the cell bodies, tapering toward the outer surface of the dentin (Fig. 76). They divide

Calcified dentin

Uncalcified dentin (predentin)

Odontoblastic processes

Bodies of odontoblasts

Fig. 75. Odontoblastic processes (Tomes' fibers), lying in dentinal tubules, extend from the perikaryon of the odontoblasts into the dentin.

Fig. 76. Well-fixed decalcified section of dentin. **A,** Close to the pulp. **B,** Close to the outer surface. No shrinkage between the dentinal fibers and the dentinal tubules. The entire tubule is filled by the fiber. Note the size and number of dentinal tubules in **A** and **B.** (×2,000.)

Fig. 77. Branching of dentinal tubules close to the dentinoenamel junction.

near their ends into several terminal branches. (See Fig. 77.) Along their course they send out thin secondary processes, enclosed in fine tubules, which seem to unite with similar lateral extensions from neighboring odontoblastic processes (Fig. 78). These may be compared to the anastomosing processes of osteocytes.

Fig. 78. Secondary branches of dentinal tubules anastomosing with those of neighboring as well as distant tubules. (Courtesy Dr. Gerrit Bevelander.)

Fig. 79. Splitting of dentinal tubules into branches. (Courtesy Dr. Gerrit Bevelander.)

Some terminal branches of the odontoblastic processes extend into the enamel (see Chapter III). Occasionally a process splits into two almost equally thick branches. This division can occur at any distance from the pulp. (See Fig. 79.) In reality, all of these divisions and anastomoses are the result of splitting and fusion of the cell extensions during dentinogenesis, as the odontoblasts recede from the dentinoenamel or dentinocemental junction.

Fig. 80. Four types of microscopic preparations, illustrating the peritubular dentin. *OP,* Odontoblastic process. *PD,* Peritubular dentin. **A,** An undemineralized ground section, photographed by transmitted light. The peritubular zone appears translucent. (×1,000.) **B,** A contact roentgen ray photomicrograph of an undemineralized ground section. The high degree of mineralization in the peritubular zone is evident from its radiopacity. (×1,000.) **C,** An electron photomicrograph of a surface replica from an undemineralized ground section. The peritubular zone appears solid. (×5,000.) **D,** An electron photomicrograph of a demineralized section. The organic matrix in the peritubular zone is comparatively sparse. (×5,000.)

Peritubular dentin. The structural interrelations in dentin are visualized best in cross sections. When undemineralized ground sections are observed by transmitted light, a ring-shaped transparent zone surrounding the odontoblastic process can be differentiated from the remaining darker matrix (Fig. 80, A).[16] This transparent zone, which forms the wall of the dentinal tubule, has been termed peritubular dentin,[22] and the regions external to it, intertubular dentin. Studies with soft roentgen rays[5,8,13,41] and with the electron microscope[22,26,59,60,66] have shown convincingly that the peritubular dentin is more highly mineralized than the intertubular dentin (Fig. 80, B). A very delicate organic matrix has been demonstrated in the peritubular dentin[22,25,57,58,66] (Fig. 80, C and D), but this usually is lost in demineralized sections, and then the odontoblastic process appears to be surrounded by an empty space.

Fig. 81. Collagenous fibrils of the dentin (decalcified transverse section; Mallory-Azan). (From Orban, B.: J.A.D.A. **16:**1547, 1929.)

The interface between the peritubular and the intertubular dentin stands out very clearly in ground sections (Fig. 80, *A*), and in earlier years it was thought that this sharply defined boundary was due to a special structure known as the sheath of Neumann. Electron microscopic studies have so far failed to confirm the presence of such a sheath.[55,56] On the contrary, the organic fibrils of the peritubular dentin appear to intermix with the fibrils of the intertubular dentin.[17,25,66] It is possible that the optical effect is due to the marked difference in the degree of mineralization between the peritubular and the intertubular dentin. Differences in staining reactions between the boundary area and the

Fig. 82. A, A cross section of undecalcified human dentin, showing the crisscross arrangement of the collagenous matrix fibrils. Also note the densely calcified peritubular dentin. (Electron photomicrograph, ×9,000.) **B,** Fibrils of the intertubular matrix at higher magnification showing the typical crossbanding of collagen. (Electron photomicrograph, ×40,000.)

dentin on either side indicate, however, that this boundary area does have special properties, although its true nature is not understood.[40]

Intertubular dentin. The main body of the dentin is constituted by the intertubular dentin. Although it is highly mineralized, over one-half of its volume is taken up by the organic matrix. This matrix consists of large numbers of fine collagen fibrils enveloped in an amorphous ground substance. (See Figs. 81 and 82, *A*.) The fibrils are from 0.05 to 0.2 micron in diameter, and they show the crossbanding at 640Å intervals, which is typical of collagen (Fig. 82, *B*).[54,55] They are quite densely packed together, often in the form of bundles, and they run in crisscross fashion parallel to the dentin surface, at right or oblique angles to the tubules (Figs. 81 and 82, *A*). The external, first-formed portions of the dentin beneath both the enamel and the cementum contain variable amounts of coarse fibril bundles, which are arranged at right angles to the dentinal surface and give the layer a different microscopic appearance.[33] This is called mantle dentin,[74] in distinction from the subsequently formed main portion, which is known as circumpulpal dentin.

Mineral component. Roentgen ray diffraction studies have shown that the apatite crystals that comprise the mineral component of dentin have average lengths of about 0.04 micron.[67] Due to their minuteness and to the masking effect of the organic elements, crystals have been very difficult to discern microscopically in mature dentin.[26] When they have been observed under the electron microscope, they have appeared as flat platelets, up to 0.1 micron long.[29]

Polarized light studies have shown that the mineralization of dentin is largely

Fig. 83. Incremental lines in the dentin. Imbrication or incremental lines of von Ebner. Ground section.

the result of crystallization around and between the collagen fibrils,[21,49] although electron microscopic investigations have indicated that the fibrils themselves may mineralize.[65,73] Within and around individual collagen fibrils, the crystals appear to be oriented with their long axes paralleling the fibril direction.[49,65] Since the fibrils form a network, the overall distribution pattern of the crystals in dentin is far more complex than in enamel.

Incremental lines. The imbrication or incremental lines of von Ebner appear as fine lines, which in cross sections run at right angles to the dentinal tubules (Fig. 83). They correspond to the Retzius lines in the enamel and likewise reflect variations in structure and mineralization during formation of the dentin. The course of the lines indicates the growth pattern of the dentin. The distance between the lines corresponds to the daily rate of apposition, which in the crown varies from 4 to 8 microns[52,53] and becomes decreasingly less as root formation progresses.[51] (See Fig. 84.)

Occasionally, some of the incremental lines are accentuated due to disturbances in the mineralization process. Such lines, readily demonstrated in ground

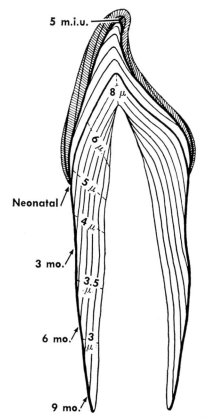

Fig. 84. Diagrammatic illustration of the incremental, appositional pattern (upper deciduous central incisor). 5 *m.i.u.*, 5 months in utero. (From Schour, I., and Massler, M.: J.A.D.A. **23**: 1946, 1936.)

Lines of
Owen

Lines of
Owen

Fig. 85. Accentuated incremental lines in the dentin: contour lines of Owen.

Prenatal dentin

Neonatal line

Postnatal dentin

Pulp

Fig. 86. Postnatally formed dentin is separated from the prenatally formed dentin by an accentuated incremental line, the neonatal line. (From Schour, I., and Poncher, H. G.: Am. J. Dis. Child. **54**:757, 1937.)

sections, are known as the contour lines of Owen. (See Fig. 85.) Studies with soft roentgen rays have shown that these lines represent hypocalcified bands.[1,2,7]

In the deciduous teeth and in the first permanent molars, where the dentin is formed partly before and partly after birth, the prenatal and postnatal dentin are separated by an accentuated contour line, the so-called neonatal line (Fig. 86).[50] This line is the result of incomplete calcification, due to metabolic disturbances at the time of adjustment of the newborn infant to the abrupt changes in environment and nutrition.

Interglobular dentin. Mineralization of the dentin sometimes begins in small globular areas that normally fuse to form a uniformly calcified dentin layer (see discussion of dentinogenesis). If fusion does not take place, unmineralized or hypomineralized regions remain between the globules. These are termed interglobular dentin. The dentinal tubules pass uninterrupted through the uncalcified areas (Fig. 87). Interglobular dentin is found chiefly in the crown, near

Fig. 87. Interglobular dentin (decalcified section). The dentinal tubules pass uninterrupted through the uncalcified and hypocalcified areas.

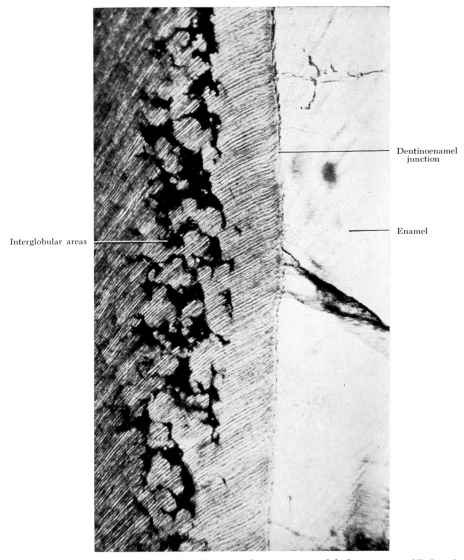

Interglobular areas

Dentinoenamel junction

Enamel

Fig. 88. Interglobular dentin as seen in a dry ground section. Interglobular areas are filled with air and appear black in transmitted light. (Courtesy Dr. Gerrit Bevelander.)

the dentinoenamel junction, and it follows the incremental pattern of the tooth.

In dry ground sections the interglobular dentin is sometimes lost and replaced by air. Then the interglobular "spaces" appear black (Fig. 88).

Tomes' granular layer. In the ground sections a thin layer of dentin adjacent to the cementum almost invariably appears granular (Fig. 89). This is known as Tomes' granular layer, and it is thought to be made up of minute areas of interglobular dentin. The configuration is found only in the root, and it does not

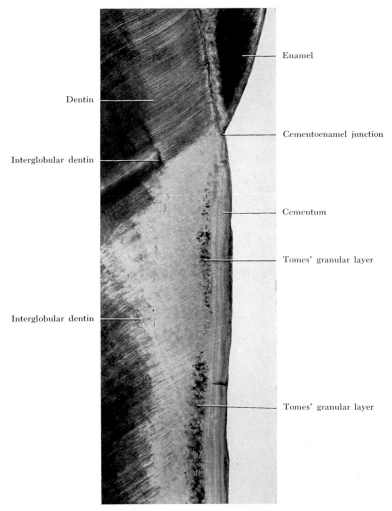

Fig. 89. Tomes' granular layer lies in the peripheral zone of the root dentin. Ground section.

follow the incremental pattern. It is thought to represent an interference with mineralization of the entire surface layer of the root dentin prior to the beginning of cementum formation.

INNERVATION

Despite the obvious clinical observation that dentin is highly sensitive to a diversity of stimuli, the anatomic basis for this sensitivity is still controversial. The literature contains many accounts of the presence of nerve fibers in the dentinal tubules, but these findings have repeatedly been shown to be artifacts. The difficulties of histologic technique are the cause for the lack of definitive information.[9,36,72]

The pulp contains numerous unmyelinated and myelinated nerve fibers. The former end on the pulpal blood vessels, whereas the latter can be followed into the subodontoblastic layer. Here they lose their myelin sheath and can be followed into the odontoblastic layer itself. In this layer most of the fibers apparently end in contact with the cell body or perikaryon of the odontoblasts. Occasionally, part of a nerve fiber seems to be embedded in the predentin or the dentin, curving back into the odontoblastic layer or, more rarely, ending in the dentin. Intratubular nerve fibers could not be established.[48]

The sensitivity of the dentin can be explained by changes in the odontoblastic processes, possibly causing changes of surface tension and surface electrical charges on the odontoblast body that in turn provide a stimulus for the nerve endings in contact with the surface of the cell body.

AGE AND FUNCTIONAL CHANGES

Vitality of dentin. Since the odontoblast, the perikaryon, as well as the process, is an integral part of the dentin, there is no doubt of dentin being a vital tissue. Also, if vitality is understood to be the capacity of the tissue to react to physiologic and pathologic stimuli, dentin must be considered a vital tissue.

The effects of aging or pathologic influences are expressed by the deposition

Demarcation line

Secondary dentin

Primary dentin

Fig. 90. The dentinal tubules bend sharply as they pass from the primary into the secondary dentin. Dentinal tubules are somewhat irregular in the secondary dentin. Ground section. Pulpal surface at the right.

of new layers of dentin (irregular or reparative dentin) and through alteration of the original dentin (transparent or sclerotic dentin). While the renewed formation of dentin is explained easily on the basis of dentinogenetic activity of the odontoblasts, the mechanisms by which the primary dentin is modified are not well understood. It is generally thought, however, that the permeation of chemical substances into mature dentin occurs by intracellular transport within the odontoblastic processes and by diffusion in the calcified matrix.[62] Since the entire dentin is in a moderate state of hydration, diffusion is most likely mediated by the fluid component. The latter probably is present simply as an integral constituent of the odontoblastic cytoplasm, the collagenous matrix fibrils, the organic ground substance, and even the inorganic crystals. The term "dental lymph" has been applied by some to this component,[14,15,23,24] but the consequent implication that it is a circulating medium has seemed unwarranted. The dentin owes to this

Pulp

Reparative dentin

Demarcation line

Dentin

Fig. 91. Reparative dentin stimulated by penetration of caries into the dentin. Dentinal tubules are irregular and less numerous than in regular dentin. Decalcified section.

Fig. 92. Root transparency in a tooth from a middle-aged individual. Note the glasslike character of the apical dentin, which permits almost unobstructed visualization of the underlying grid. (Courtesy Dr. A. E. W. Miles.)

tissue fluid its turgor that plays an important role in securing the connection between dentin and enamel.

Secondary dentin. Under normal conditions, formation of dentin may continue throughout life. Frequently, the dentin formed in later life is separated from that previously formed by a darkly stained line. In such cases the dentinal tubules bend more or less sharply at this line (Fig. 90). In other cases the newly formed dentin shows irregularities of varying degree. The tubules are often wavy and less numerous for a unit area of the dentin. The dentin, forming pulpward of the line of demarcation, is called secondary dentin. This dentin is deposited on the entire pulpal surface of the dentin. However, its formation does not proceed at an even rate in all areas. This is observed best in premolars and molars, where more secondary dentin is produced on the floor and on the roof of the pulpal chamber than on the side walls (see Chapter V).

The change in the structure from primary to secondary dentin may be caused

---

Fig. 93. Transparent dentin under a carious area viewed by **A,** transmitted light, **B,** reflected light, and **C,** grenz rays. Normal dentinal tubules are filled with air in dried ground sections and appear dark in transmitted light, **A,** and white in reflected light, **B.** Transparent dentin shows the opposite behavior because the tubules are filled with calcium salts. In a grenz-ray picture, **C,** transparent dentin appears more white because of its higher degree of radiopacity. (**C** courtesy Dr. E. Applebaum, Columbia University.)

A

Dentinal tubules
filled with air

Carious dentin

Transparent dentin

B

Dentinal tubules
filled with air

Carious dentin

Transparent dentin

C

Dentin

Carious dentin

Transparent dentin

Fig. 93. For legend see opposite page.

by the progressive crowding of the odontoblasts, which finally leads to the elimination of some and to the rearrangement of the remaining odontoblasts.[61]

Reparative dentin. If, by extensive wear, erosion, caries, or operative procedures, odontoblastic processes are exposed or cut, the entire cell is more or less severely damaged. Such damaged odontoblasts may either continue to form a hard substance or may degenerate, and then they are replaced by migration to the dentinal surface of undifferentiated cells from the deeper layers of the pulp. Damaged or newly differentiated odontoblasts are stimulated to a defense reaction in which hard tissue seals off the area of injury. This hard tissue is best called reparative dentin.[75] Here, the course of the tubules is frequently twisted, and their number is greatly reduced (Fig. 91). Some areas of reparative dentin contain few or no tubules. Dentin-forming cells are often included in the rapidly produced intercellular substance. Such cells degenerate and vacate the spaces that they formerly occupied. Frequently, reparative dentin is separated from primary or secondary dentin by a deeply staining line.

Reparative dentin

Reparative dentin

A

B

Fig. 94. Dead tracts in the dentin of a vital tooth, due to attrition and exposure of a group of dentinal tubules. Corresponding to the dead tract reparative dentin formation. *P,* Pulp. Dead tracts appear dark in transmitted light, **A,** and white in reflected light, **B.**

Transparent (sclerotic) dentin. Stimuli of different nature not only induce additional formation of reparative dentin but also lead to changes in the dentin itself. Calcium salts may be deposited in or around degenerating odontoblastic processes and may obliterate the tubules. The refractive indices of dentin in which the tubules are occluded are equalized, and such areas become transparent. Transparent dentin can be observed in teeth of elderly people, especially in the roots (Fig. 92). On the other hand, zones of transparent dentin develop around the dentinal part of enamel lamellae of Type B (Fig. 52) and under slowly progressing caries (Fig. 93). In such cases the blocking of the tubules may be considered as a defensive reaction of the dentin. Roentgen ray absorption tests[69] and permeability studies[12] have shown that such areas are denser, and hardness tests[28] have demonstrated that they are harder than normal dentin.[69,70]

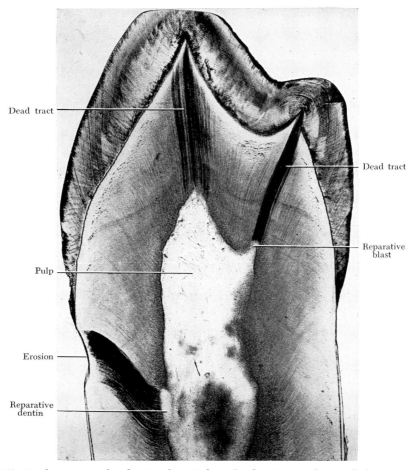

Fig. 95. Dead tracts in the dentin of a vital tooth, due to crowding and degeneration of odontoblasts in narrow pulpal horns and exposure of dentinal tubules in erosion. Well-fixed ground section (not dry!).

Transparent dentin can be demonstrated only in ground sections. It appears light in transmitted (Fig. 93, *A*) and dark in reflected light (Fig. 93, *B*) because the light passes through the transparent dentin but is reflected from the normal dentin. Dentin, decalcified by caries, normal dentin, and transparent dentin can be differentiated by the examination of ground section with soft roentgen rays, grenz rays.[2]

Dead tracts. In dried ground sections of normal dentin the odontoblastic processes disintegrate, and the empty tubules are filled with air. They appear black in transmitted and white in reflected light (Fig. 93, *A* and *B*). Disintegration of odontoblastic processes may also occur in teeth containing a vital pulp as a result of the injury of caries, attrition, abrasion, cavity preparation, or erosion (Figs. 94 and 95). Degeneration of odontoblasts is observed frequently in the narrow pulpal horns (Fig. 95) due to crowding of odontoblasts. Reparative dentin seals these tubules at their pulpal end. In all these cases dentinal tubules are filled with gaseous substances. In ground sections such groups of tubules appear black in transmitted and white in reflected light. Dentin areas characterized by degenerated odontoblastic processes have been called dead tracts.[24] They are areas of decreased sensitivity.[24,68]

DEVELOPMENT

Life cycle of odontoblasts. The odontoblasts, which have been described previously in this chapter as integral parts of mature dentin structure, are highly specialized connective tissue cells that differentiate from the peripheral cellular layer of the dental papilla. Prior to differentiation of the odontoblasts, the inner dental epithelium is separated from the dental papilla by a very thin, continuous basement membrane.[37,58] The cells of the papilla are spindle shaped, relatively uniform in size, and generally separated by rather large intercellular spaces. Some of the cells, however, come in contact with each other and with the basement membrane. At the beginning of differentiation, which takes place only in the presence of the inner enamel epithelium, the peripheral cells of the dental papilla assume a short columnar shape and become aligned in a single layer along the basement membrane. The nuclei are already basally placed at this early stage in odontoblast formation, and they remain in this position permanently. The distal ends of the cells are villose, and several projections from each cell extend to the basement membrane. As differentiation progresses, the cells grow to several times their original length, whereas their width remains quite constant. Concomitantly, pronounced changes occur in the cytoplasm of the odontoblasts. These take the form of marked increases in the concentration of organelles, granular components, and globular elements.[37,44,73] (See Fig. 96.) It is currently thought that such cytoplasmic alterations reflect a rise in cellular activity. This is taken as evidence that the odontoblasts participate actively in the formation of the dentinal matrix, a concept which has found additional support in histochemical and isotope studies.[30,34,63]

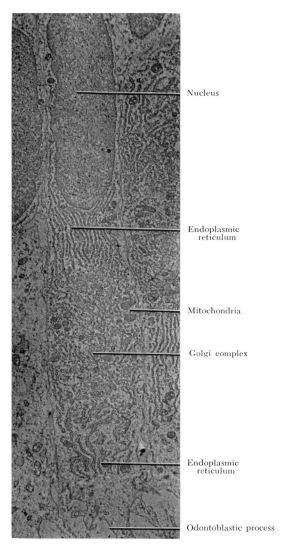

Nucleus

Endoplasmic
reticulum

Mitochondria

Golgi complex

Endoplasmic
reticulum

Odontoblastic process

Fig. 96. An electron photomicrograph of a typical odontoblast (×7,000). The cytoplasm resembles that of the ameloblasts, except that the mitochondria are scattered throughout the cell
and there are fewer granules and vacuoles. Compare with Fig. 62.

The odontoblasts begin to recede from the basement membrane with the
formation of the first dentin layer, and their distal ends become funnel shaped.
As more dentin is laid down, the cells continue to draw back, so that they are
always located in a layer along the pulpal surface of the most recently formed
predentin. As the cells recede, they leave behind single extensions, the odontoblastic processes, which become embedded in the matrix.

The fully differentiated odontoblasts decrease in size during further dentin
formation but otherwise retain their structural characteristics until dentin matrix

formation is completed. At this point the odontoblasts enter a quiescent state. Unless they are stimulated by external influences to produce reparative dentin, their activity is restricted to an ordinarily very slow formation of secondary dentin.

Dentinogenesis. Dentinogenesis takes place in a two-phase sequence, the first of which is the elaboration of an uncalcified organic matrix called predentin. The second phase, mineralization, does not begin until a fairly wide band of predentin has been laid down. Mineralization proceeds at a rate which roughly parallels that of matrix formation. Thus, until the matrix is completed, the width of the predentin layer remains relatively constant.

The formation and calcification of dentin begin at the tips of the cusps or incisal edges and proceed inward by a rhythmic apposition of conic layers, one

Fig. 97. Thickening of the basement membrane between pulp and inner dental epithelium. Development of Korff's fibers. (Courtesy Dr. Gerrit Bevelander.)

within the other. When the dentin of the crown has been laid down, the apical layers assume the shape of elongated, truncated cones (Fig. 84).[50] With completion of the root dentin, primary dentin formation comes to an end.

Predentin formation. The first sign of predentin development is the appearance of bundles of fibrils between the differentiating odontoblasts (Fig. 97). Near the basement membrane, where the cells are now funnel shaped, the fibrils diverge in a fanlike arrangement (Figs. 97 and 98). These fibrillar bundles are known as Korff's fibers, and their origin and role in dentinogenesis have been the subject of much discussion.[11,31,32,44,46] Because they stain black with silver (argyrophil reaction), it was concluded that they are precollagenous, but more recent studies with the electron microscope have revealed that at their first appearance the fibrils already demonstrate all the structural characteristics of collagen itself.[44] (See Fig. 99.)

Korff's fibers are a major constituent of the first-formed matrix, due to the fanlike arrangement of the fibrils near the basement membrane. This relatively narrow layer comprises the mantle predentin. In addition to Korff's fibers, with fibrils from 0.1 to 0.2 micron in diameter, the remainder of the mantle predentin is made up of smaller collagen fibrils, around 0.05 micron in diameter. The latter fibrils, which form a network, predominate throughout all of the succeeding circumpulpal predentin layers, whereas Korff's fibers, now compact bundles of parallel fibrils, become a minor component (Fig. 100, *B*).

Electron microscope studies have shown that the smaller collagen fibrils of the predentin are formed in the immediate vicinity of the distal ends of the

Korff's
fibers

Odonto-
blasts

Fig. 98   Fig. 99

Fig. 98. Fanlike arrangement of Korff's fibers in mantle predentin.
Fig. 99. An electron photomicrograph showing at higher magnification the fibrils making up Korff's fibers. Note the cross-bandings which identify these fibrils as collagen. (×10,000.)

Fig. 100. **A,** The predentin and dentin layers in a developing rodent tooth, as seen by phase contrast. Observe the relations of all the layers of the odontogenic complex, from ameloblasts to odontoblasts. (×350.) **B,** The circumpulpal predentin layer, as seen under the electron microscope. Note the odontoblastic process, the compact Korff's fiber bundles, and the net-work of fine matrix fibrils. (×6,000.) **C,** The dentin layer, as seen under the electron microscope. Note the increased density in contrast to the predentin as a result of mineralization. (×6,000.)

odontoblasts.[37,44,73] This finding is in agreement with the general concept that collagen fibril synthesis in connective tissues takes place through the extracellular aggregation of molecules secreted by fibril-forming cells.

Mineralization. After several microns of predentin have been laid down, mineralization of the layers closest to the dentinoenamel junction begins in small islands that subsequently fuse and form a continuous, calcified layer.[65] With further predentin formation, mineralization usually advances pulpward as a

Fig. 101. Linear and globular calcification of dentin.

linear front roughly paralleling the odontoblastic layer. (Fig. 100, *A* and *C*.) Sometimes advancing mineralization occurs, however, in globular areas that subsequently fuse. On occasion, both globular and linear calcification are seen in combination (Fig. 101).

Inception and advance of mineralization are accompanied by a number of changes in the ground substance of the organic matrix. Histochemical and radio-autographic investigation show that a mucopolysaccharide is deposited into the matrix and that it becomes especially prominent in the peritubular areas.[35,76]

The phenomena actually involved in mineralization within collagenous matrices are still under investigation. There seems to be little doubt that the mucopolysaccharide ground substance plays a most important part in mineralization, but it has not yet been determined if it serves to initiate or promote the process or rather to regulate it. It is likewise quite evident that the molecular configurations of the collagen fibrils influence the geometric distribution of the crystals that are laid down.[45]

The basic mineralization sequence in dentin appears to be as follows. The earliest crystal deposition is in the form of very fine plates of hydroxyapatite on the surfaces of the collagen fibrils and in the ground substance (Fig. 102, A). Subsequently, crystals seem to be laid down within the fibrils themselves.[65,73] The crystals associated with the collagen fibrils are arranged in an orderly fashion, with their long axes paralleling the fibril axes, and in rows conforming to the 640Å striation pattern. Within the globular islands of mineralization,

A

B

Fig. 102. **A,** A section of human dentin in an early stage of mineralization. Small crystals can be seen scattered in the intertubular matrix, whereas they are more densely packed in the peritubular region. (Electron photomicrograph, ×35,000.) **B,** The crystals in the intertubular matrix at a later stage in mineralization. (Electron photomicrograph, ×70,000.) Nearly maximal crystal size has been attained. Compare the dimensions of these crystals to those of the enamel crystals shown in Fig. 71.

crystal deposition appears to take place radially from common centers, in a so-called spherulite form.[20,49]

The general calcification process is gradual, but the peritubular region becomes highly mineralized at a very early stage (Fig. 102, A).[65] While there is obviously some crystal growth as dentin matures, the ultimate crystal size remains very small, the greatest length being on the order of 0.1 micron (Fig. 102, B).[29]

The cells of the exposed dentin should not be insulted by strong drugs, undue operative trauma, unnecessary thermal changes, or irritating filling materials. Contact of exposed dentin with saliva should be avoided. It should be borne in mind that, by exposing 1 square millimeter of dentin, about 30,000 odontoblastic processes are exposed and thus 30,000 living cells are damaged. The surface may be treated with adstringent drugs, such as phenol or silver nitrate,[42,77] to coagulate the protoplasm of the exposed odontoblastic processes. It is advisable to cover the exposed dentin surface by a nonirritating insulating substance.

The rapid penetration and spreading of caries in the dentin are due to the high content of organic substances in the dentin matrix. The enamel may be undermined at the dentinoenamel junction, even when caries in the enamel is confined to a small area. The dentinal tubules form a passage for invading bacteria that may thus reach the pulp through a thick dentinal layer.

The sensitivity of the dentin varies considerably in different layers. In most cases it is greater close to the outer surface of the dentin and diminishes in the deeper layers. The sensitivity of the dentin, therefore, is not a warning signal to avoid exposure of the pulp. The operations in the dentin can be rendered less painful by avoiding heat and pressure by the use of cooling and of sharp instruments. The sensitivity of the dentin has been explained by the hypothesis that any injury or alteration of the odontoblast leads to changes in the surface charges of the cell body and that these changes stimulate the nerve endings on these cells (p. 147). If this hypothesis is correct, then the greater sensitivity of the dentin near the dentinoenamel junction could be related to the branching of the odontoblastic processes in this zone and, therefore, to the larger surface area of exposed cytoplasm of each cell.

REFERENCES

1. Amprino, R., and Camanni, F.: Historadiographic and autoradiographic researches on hard dental tissues, Acta Anat. **28**:217, 1956.
2. Applebaum, E., Hollander, F., and Bodecker, C. F.: Normal and pathological variations in calcification of teeth as shown by the use of soft x-rays, D. Cosmos **75**:1097, 1933.
3. Arwill, T.: Innervation of the teeth, Stockholm, 1958, Ivar Haeggströms Boktryckeri AB.
4. Battistone, G. C., and Burnett, G. W.: The amino acid composition of human dentinal protein, J. D. Res. **35**:255, 1956.
5. Baud, C. A., and Held, A. J.: Silberfärbung, Röntgenmikrographie und Mineralgehalt der Zahnhartgewebe (Silver impregnation, microradiography and mineral content of calcified tooth structure), Deutsche zahnärztl. Z. **11**:309, 1956.

6. Berggren, H.: Experimental studies on the permeability of enamel and dentine, Swed. D. J. **40**(No. 1B):1, 1947.

7. Bergman, G., and Engfeldt, B.: Studies on mineralized dental tissues. II. Microradiography as a method for studying dental tissue and its application to the study of caries, Acta odont. scandinav. **12**:99, 1954.

8. Bergman, G., and Engfeldt, B.: Studies on mineralized dental tissues. VI. The distribution of mineral salts in the dentine with special reference to the dentinal tubules, Acta odont. scandinav. **13**:1, 1955.

9. Berkelbach van der Sprenkel, H.: Zur Neurologie des Zahnes (The neurology of the tooth), Ztschr. f. mikr.-anat. Forsch. **38**:1, 1935.

10. Bernick, S.: Innervation of the human tooth, Anat. Rec. **101**:81, 1948.

11. Bevelander, G.: The development and structure of the fiber system of dentin, Anat. Rec. **81**:79, 1941.

12. Bevelander, G., and Amler, M. H.: Radioactive phosphate absorption by dentin and enamel, J. D. Res. **24**:45, 1944.

13. Blake, G. C.: The peritubular translucent zones in human dentine, Brit. D. J. **104**:57, 1958.

14. Bodecker, C. F., and Lefkowitz, W.: Concerning the "vitality" of calcified dental tissues, J. D. Res. **16**:463, 1937.

15. Bodecker, C. F., and Gies, Wm. J.: Concerning the character of the age changes in enamel and dentin and their relation to the vital dental pulp, J. Am. Coll. Dentists **9**:381, 1942.

16. Bradford, E. W.: Interpretation of ground sections of dentine, Brit. D. J. **90**:303, 1951.

17. Bradford, E. W.: The interpretation of decalcified sections of human dentin, Brit. D. J. **98**:153, 1955.

18. Bradford, E. W.: The maturation of the dentine, Brit. D. J. **105**:212, 1958.

19. Bradford, E. W.: The dentine, a barrier to caries, Brit. D. J. **109**:387, 1960.

20. Cape, A. T., and Kitchin, P. C.: Histologic phenomena of tooth tissues as observed under polarized light, J.A.D.A. **17**:193, 1930.

21. Ebner, V. v.: Ueber die Entwicklung der leimgebenden Fibrillen im Zahnbein (Development of collagenous fibrils in the dentin), Sitzungsb. d. k. Akad. d. Wissensch. Vienna **115**:281, 1906; and Anat. Anz. **29**:137, 1906.

22. Fearnhead, R. W.: Histological evidence for the innervation of human dentine, J. Anat. **91**:267, 1957.

23. Fish, E. W.: The circulation of lymph in dentin and enamel, J.A.D.A. **14**:1, 1927.

24. Fish, E. W.: An experimental investigation of enamel, dentin and the dental pulp, London. 1932, John Bale Sons & Danielsson, Ltd.

25. Frank, R. M.: Contributions à l'étude au microscope electronique des tissus calcifiés normaux et pathologiques (Contributions to the electron microscope study of normal and pathologic calcified tissues), Strasbourg, 1957, Sutter Waerth.

26. Frank, R. M.: Electron microscopy of undecalcified sections of human adult dentine, Arch. Oral Biol. **1**:29, 1959.

27. Hess, W. C., Leo, D. Y., and Peckham, S. C.: The lipid content of enamel and dentin, J. D. Res. **35**:273, 1956.

28. Hodge, H. C.: Microhardness studies of transparent dentine, Brit. D. J. **63**:181, 1937.

29. Johansen, E., and Parks, H. F.: Electron microscopic observations on the three dimensional morphology of apatite crystallites of human dentine and bone, J. Biophys. & Biochem. Cytol. **7**:743, 1960.

30. Kerébel, B., and Grimbert, L.: Rôle des odontoblastes (Role of the odontoblasts), Rev. Mensuelle Suisse d'Odontologie **68**:729, 1958.

31. Korff, K. v.: Die Entwicklung der Zahnbein Grundsubstanz der Saugetiere (The development of the dentin matrix in mammals), Arch. f. mikr. Anat. **67**:1, 1905.

32. Korff, K. v.: Wachstum der Dentingrundsubstanz verschiedener Wirbeltiere (Growth of the dentin matrix of different vertebrates), Ztschr. f. mikr.-anat. Forsch. **22**:445, 1930.

33. Kramer, I. R. H.: The distribution of collagen fibrils in the dentine matrix, Brit. D. J. **91**:1, 1951.

34. Leblond, C. P.: Elaboration of dentinal collagen in odontoblasts as shown by radio-

autography after injection of labeled glycine and proline, Ann. Histochem. J. **8**:43, 1963.

35. Leblond, C. P., Bélanger, L. F., and Greulich, R. C.: Formation of bones and teeth as visualized by radioautography, Ann. New York Acad. Sc. **60**:629, 1955.

36. Lehner, J., and Plenk, H.: Die Zähne (The teeth). In von Möllendorff, W. (editor): Handbuch der mikroskopischen Anatomie des Menschen, vol. 5, pt. 3, Berlin, 1936, Julius Springer, p. 449.

37. Lenz, H.: Elektronenmikroskopische Untersuchungen der Dentinentwicklung (Electron microscopic studies of dentin development), Deutsche Zahn-, Mund- u. Kieferheilk. **30**: 367, 1959.

38. Losee, F. L., Leopold, R. F., and Hess, W. C.: Dentinal protein, J. D. Res. **30**:565, 1951.

39. Manley, E. B.: Traumatic effect of the drill during cavity preparation, Brit. D. J. **70**:329, 1941.

40. Martens, P. J., Bradford, E. W., and Frank, R. M.: Tissue changes in dentine, Internat. D. J. **9**:330, 1959.

41. Miller, J.: The micro-radiographic appearance of dentine, Brit. D. J. **97**:7, 1954.

42. Muntz, J. A., Dorfman, A., and Stephan, R. M.: In vitro studies on sterilization of carious dentin, J.A.D.A. **30**:1893, 1943.

43. Nalbandian, J., Gonzales, F., and Sognnaes, R. F.: Sclerotic age changes in root dentin of human teeth as observed by optical, electron, and x-ray microscopy, J. D. Res. **39**: 598, 1960.

44. Nylen, M. U., and Scott, D. B.: An electron microscopic study of the early stages of dentinogenesis, Pub. 613, U. S. Public Health Service, Washington, D. C., 1958, U. S. Government Printing Office.

45. Nylen, M. U., and Scott, D. B.: Basic studies in calcification, J. D. Med. **15**:80, 1960.

46. Orban, B.: The development of the dentin, J.A.D.A. **16**:1547, 1929.

47. Piez, K. A., and Likens, R. C.: The nature of collagen; II. Vertebrate collagens. In Sognnaes, R. F. (editor): Calcification in biological systems, Washington, D. C., 1960, American Association for the Advancement of Science.

48. Powers, M. M.: The staining of nerve fibers in teeth, J. D. Res. **31**:383, 1952.

49. Schmidt, W. J., and Keil, A.: Die gesunden und die erkrankten Zahngewebe des Menschen und der Wirbeltiere im Polarisationsmikroskop (Normal and pathological tooth structure of humans and vertebrates in the polarization microscope), München, 1958, Carl Hanser Verlag.

50. Schour, I., and Massler, M.: The neonatal line in enamel and dentin of the human deciduous teeth and first permanent molar, J.A.D.A. **23**:1946, 1936.

51. Schour, I., and Poncher, H. G.: The rate of apposition of human enamel and dentin as measured by the effects of acute fluorosis, Am. J. Dis. Child. **54**:757, 1937.

52. Schour, I., and Hoffman, M. M.: The rate of apposition of enamel and dentin in man and other animals, J. D. Res. **18**:161, 1939.

53. Schour, I., and Massler, M.: Studies in tooth development: the growth pattern of the human teeth, J.A.D.A. **27**:1778, 1918, 1940.

54. Scott, D. B., and Wyckoff, R. W. G.: Electron microscopy of human dentin, J. D. Res. **29**:556, 1950.

55. Scott, D. B.: Recent contributions in dental histology by the use of the electron microscope, Internat. D. J. **4**:64, 1953.

56. Scott, D. B.: The electron microscopy of enamel and dentin, J. New York Acad. Sc. **60**:575, 1955.

57. Scott, D. B., Nylen, M. U., and Takuma, S.: Electron microscopy of developing and mature calcified tissues, Rev. Belge de Sci. Dent. **14**:329, 1959.

58. Scott, D. B., and Nylen, M. U.: Changing concepts in dental histology, Ann. New York Acad. Sc. **85**:133, 1960.

59. Shroff, F. R., Williamson, K. I., and Bertaud, W. S.: Electron microscope studies of dentin, Oral Surg., Oral Med., & Oral Path. **7**:662, 1954.

60. Shroff, F. R.: Further electron microscope studies on dentin: the nature of the odontoblast process, Oral Surg., Oral Med., & Oral Path. **9**:432, 1956.

61. Sicher, H.: The biology of dentin, Bur **46**:121, 1946.

62. Sognnaes, R. F., Shaw, J. H., and Bogoroch, R.: Radiotracer studies on bone, cementum, dentin and enamel of rhesus monkeys, Am. J. Physiol. **180**:408, 1955.

63. Sognnaes, R. F.: Microstructure and histochemical characteristics of the mineralized tissues, J. New York Acad. Sc. **60**:545, 1955.

64. Stanley, H. R., Jr., and Swerdlow, H.: Reaction of the human pulp to cavity preparation: results produced by eight different grinding techniques, J.A.D.A. **58**:49, 1959.

65. Takuma, S.: Preliminary report on the mineralization of human dentin, J. D. Res. **39**:964, 1960.

66. Takuma, S.: Electron microscopy of the structure around the dentinal tubule, J. D. Res. **39**:973, 1960.

67. Thewlis, J.: The structure of teeth as shown by x-ray examination, Medical Research Council, Special Report Series No. 238, London, 1940, Her Majesty's Stationery Office.

68. Thomas, B. O. A.: Protective metamorphosis of the dentin: its relationship to pain, J.A.D.A. **31**:459, 1944.

69. Van Huysen, G., Hodge, H. C., Warren, S. L., and Bishop, F. W.: Quantitative roentgen-ray study of certain pathological changes in dentin, D. Cosmos **75**:729, 1933.

70. Van Huysen, G., Bale, W. F., and Hodge, H. C.: Comparative study of the roentgen-ray absorption properties of normal and pathological dentin, D. Cosmos **77**:146, 1935.

71. Van Huysen, G., and Gurley, W. B.: Histologic changes in the teeth of dogs following preparation of cavities at various depths, J.A.D.A. **26**:87, 1939.

72. Wasserman, F.: The innervation of teeth, J.A.D.A. **26**:1097, 1939.

73. Watson, M. L., and Avery, J. K.: The development of the hamster lower incisor as observed by electron microscopy, Am. J. Anat. **95**:109, 1954.

74. Weidenreich, F.: Ueber den Bau und die Entwicklung des Zahnbeines in der Reihe der Wirbeltiere (Structure and development of the dentin of the vertebrates), Ztschr. f. Anat. u. Entwcklngsgesch. **76**:218, 1925.

75. Weider, F. R., Schour, I., and Mohamed, C. I.: Reparative dentin following cavity preparation and fillings in the rat molars, Oral Surg., Oral Med., & Oral Path. **9**:221, 1956.

76. Wislocki, G. B., and Sognnaes, R. E.: Histochemical reactions of normal teeth, Am. J. Anat. **87**:239, 1950.

77. Zander, H. A., and Burrill, D.: Penetration of silver nitrate solution into dentin, J. D. Res. **22**:85, 1943.

FUNCTION
    Formative
    Nutritive
    Sensory
    Defensive

ANATOMY
    Pulp chamber
    Root canal
    Apical foramen

DEVELOPMENT
STRUCTURAL ELEMENTS
    Fibroblasts and fibers
    Odontoblasts
    Defense cells
    Blood vessels
    Lymph vessels
    Nerves

REGRESSIVE CHANGES
    Pulpstones
    Calcifications
    Fibrosis

CLINICAL CONSIDERATIONS

Chapter V

Pulp*

FUNCTION

Formative. The dental pulp is of mesodermal origin and contains most of the cellular and fibrous elements that are present in loose connective tissue. The primary function of the dental pulp is the production of dentin.

Nutritive. The pulp furnishes nourishment to the dentin through the odontoblasts with their odontoblastic processes. The nutritional elements are contained in the tissue fluid.

Sensory. The nerves of the pulp contain both sensory and motor fibers. The sensory fibers, responsible for the sensitivity of pulp and dentin, mediate the sensation of pain and pain only. However, their main function seems to be the initiation of reflexes for the control of the circulation in the pulp. The motor leg of the reflex arch is provided by the visceral motor fibers that end on the muscles of the pulpal blood vessels.

Defensive. The pulp is well protected against external injuries as long as it is surrounded by an intact wall of dentin. However, if exposed to irritation, whether of mechanical, thermal, chemical, or bacterial nature, it can produce an effective defense reaction. The defensive reaction may be expressed in the formation of reparative dentin (see Chapter IV) if the irritation is mild or as an inflammatory reaction in more severe irritation. While the rigid dentinal wall has to be considered as a protection to the pulp, it also endangers its existence under certain conditions. During inflammation of the pulp, the hyperemia and the exudate often lead to the accumulation of an excess of fluid and colloidal material outside of the capillaries. A disbalance of this character, limited by un-

---

*First draft submitted by Balint J. Orban; revised by John J. O'Malley.

yielding surfaces, tends to be self-perpetuating and commonly is followed by the total destruction of the pulp.

ANATOMY

Pulp chamber. The dental pulp occupies the pulp cavity, which consists of the coronal pulp chamber and the root canals. The pulp is continuous with the periapical tissues through the apical foramen or foramina. In young individuals the shape of the pulp chamber follows, roughly, the outline of the outer surface of the dentin. The extensions into the cusps of the tooth are called pulpal horns. At the time of eruption the pulp chamber is large, but it becomes smaller with advancing age, due to continuous deposition of dentin[15] (Fig. 103). The decrease in the size of the pulp cavity in molars does not occur at the same rate on all walls of the pulp chamber. Formation of dentin progresses fastest on the floor[*] of the pulp chamber. Some is formed at the occlusal wall or roof and less is formed on the side walls of the pulp chamber, so that the pulp dimension is reduced mainly in an occlusal direction. The chamber may be narrowed further and its shape may become irregular by formation of reparative dentin. The formation of pulpstones (Fig. 103, *B*) may also reduce the size and change the shape of the formerly wide pulp cavity, occasionally even occluding it.

Root canal. Advancing age induces similar changes in the root canals. During root formation, the apical root end is a wide opening, limited by the epithelial diaphragm (Fig. 104, *A*). The dentinal walls taper, and the shape of the pulp canal is like a wide, open tube. As growth proceeds, more dentin is formed, so that when the root of the tooth has matured, the root canal is considerably narrower. In the course of root formation, Hertwig's epithelial root sheath breaks up into epithelial rests, and cementum is laid down on the dentin surface (Fig. 104, *B*). The cementum will influence the size and shape of the apical foramen in the fully formed tooth. Root canals are not always straight and single but vary by the occurrence of accessory canals, as seen in corrosion specimens[12] or after filling of the root canals with India ink and clearing (Fig. 105).

At any distance from the apex of the tooth (Fig. 106A), side branches of the root canal may be present. In multirooted teeth these are observed at, or close to, the floor of the pulp chamber (Figs. 106B and 106C). A possible explanation for the development of all side branches of the pulp canals may be a defect in Hertwig's epithelial root sheath during development of the root at the site of a larger supernumerary blood vessel.

Apical foramen. There are variations in shape, size, and location of the apical foramen.[8] A regular, straight apical opening is rare (Fig. 104, *B*). Occasionally the cementum can be traced from the outer surface of the dentin into the pulpal canal. Sometimes the apical opening is found on the lateral side of the apex

---

[*]Regardless of the position of a tooth in the maxilla or the mandible, the occlusal wall is called the roof, and the cervical wall, the floor.

Pulp
stone

A

B

C

Fig. 103. **A** and **B**, Age changes in the pulp chamber of the first permanent molar. Decalcified sections. Enamel lost. **A,** From an individual 8 years of age. **B,** From an individual 55 years of age. Reduction of the pulp chamber in height is greater than in the mesiodistal diameter. Pulp-stones narrowing the entrance into the root canals in **B. C,** Mandibular third molar. Pulp exposed by grinding away the lingual wall. Note the shape of the dentin at the end of the incompletely formed roots. (**A** and **B** from Kronfeld, R.: Dental histology and comparative dental anatomy, Philadelphia, 1937, Lea & Febiger; **C** courtesy D. Permar.)

Fig. 104. Development of the apical foramen. **A,** Undeveloped root end. Wide opening at end of the root, partly limited by the epithelial diaphragm. **B,** Apical foramen fully formed. Root canal straight. Apical foramen surrounded by cementum. (From Coolidge, E. D.: J.A.D.A. **16:** 1456, 1929.)

(Fig. 107, *B*), although the root itself is not curved. Frequently there are two or more distinct apical foramina separated by a partition of dentin and cementum, or cementum only.

The location and the shape of the apical foramen may also undergo changes, due to functional influences upon the teeth.[21] A tooth may be tipped due to horizontal pressure, or it may migrate mesially, causing the apex to deviate in the opposite direction. Under these conditions the tissues entering the pulp through the apical foramen exert pressure on one wall of the foramen, causing resorption. At the same time, cementum is laid down on the opposite side of the apical root canal, resulting in a change in the relative position of the original opening (Fig. 107, *A*).

DEVELOPMENT

The development of the dental pulp begins at a very early stage of embryonic life (in the eighth week) in the region of the incisors. In the other teeth its development begins later. The first indication is a proliferation and condensation of mesenchymal elements, known as the dental papilla, at the basal end of the dental organ. (See Fig. 108.) Due to the rapid proliferation of the epithelial elements, the tooth germ changes into a bell-shaped organ, and the future pulp is well defined in its outline. In a silver-impregnated section the arrangement of the fibers in the embryonic dental papilla is clearly visible. (See Fig. 108.) In the future pulp area the fibers are fine and are arranged irregularly and much more densely than in the surrounding tissue.

The fibers in the embryonic pulp are argyrophil. There are no mature collagenous fibers in the embryonic pulp except where the fibers follow the course of the blood vessels.[9,10,17] As the development of the tooth germ progresses, the pulp becomes increasingly vascular, and the cells develop into star-shaped connective tissue cells, fibroblasts. (Fig. 109, *A*.) The cells are more numerous in the periphery of the pulp. Between the epithelium and the pulp cells is a cell-free layer. This contains numerous fibers, forming the basement or limiting membrane (see Chapter IV, section on development).

Little is known about the time and mode of penetration of the pulp by nerve fibers.

STRUCTURAL ELEMENTS

The pulp is a specialized loose connective tissue. It consists of cells, fibroblasts, and an intercellular substance. The latter, in turn, consists of fibers and a ground substance. In addition, defense cells and the bodies of the cells of the dentin, the odontoblasts, are part of the dental pulp. The fibroblasts of the pulp and the defense cells are identical to those found elsewhere in loose connective tissue. The fibers of the pulp are in part argyrophil, in part mature collagenous fibers. Elastic fibers are absent. The ground substance of the pulp seems to be of a much higher consistency than that in the loose connective tissue outside the

Fig. 105. Drawings of teeth after filling of the root canals with India ink and clearing. **A,** Upper incisors. **B,** Upper canines. **C,** Lower incisors. **D,** Lower canines. (From Aprile, E. C. de, and Aprile, H.: Rev. Odontologia **35**:686, 1947.)

Fig. 105, cont'd. E, Upper premolars. **F,** Upper molars. **G,** Lower premolars. **H,** Lower molars.
(From Aprile, E. C. de, and Aprile, H.: Rev. Odontologia **35:**686, 1947.)

Fig. 106A   Fig. 106B

Fig. 106A. Sections through teeth with accessory canals. Close to the apex.
Fig. 106B. Sections through teeth with accessory canals. Close to the bifurcation.

pulp. The turgidity of the substance in any loose connective tissue is the result of a constant, but dynamic, equilibrium between a water-soluble and a water-insoluble phase. In the fully developed pulp the balance of the two phases is such that the ground substance is gelatinous. The histochemistry of the pulp is discussed in greater detail in Chapter XV. For the present, it can be stated that the pulp is no different in its essential composition and reactivity from any other loose connective tissue.[33]

Fibroblasts and fibers. In the course of development the relative number of cellular elements in the dental pulp decreases, whereas the intercellular substance increases (Fig. 109, *B*). With advancing age there is a progressive reduction in the number of fibroblasts, accompanied by an increase in the number of fibers (Fig. 109, *C*). In the embryonic and immature pulp the cellular elements are predominant. In the mature tooth the fibrous constituents are predominant. In a fully developed tooth the cellular elements decrease in number toward the apical region, and the fibrous elements become more numerous (Fig. 112).

A microscopic specimen of a mature pulp, stained with hematoxylin and

Fig. 106C. Roentgenogram of lower molar with accessory canal filled. (From Johnston, H. B., and Orban, B.: J. Endodontia 3:21, 1948.)

Resorption of dentin

Apposition of cementum

Apical foramen

Apex

A   B

Fig. 107. Variations of the apical foramen. **A,** Shift of the apical foramen by resorption of dentin and cementum on one surface and apposition of cementum on the other. **B,** Apical foramen on the side of the apex. (From Coolidge, E. D.: J.A.D.A. **16:**1456, 1929.)

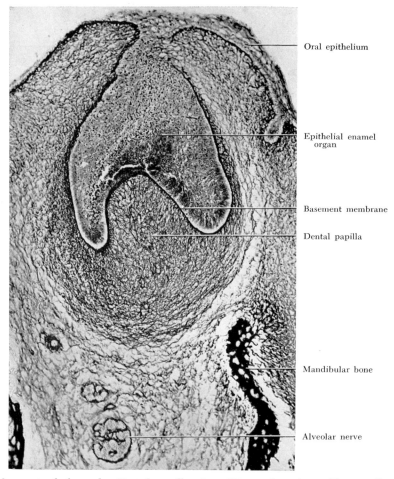

Oral epithelium

Epithelial enamel organ

Basement membrane

Dental papilla

Mandibular bone

Alveolar nerve

Fig. 108. Development of the pulp. Dental papilla of a 2½-month embryo. The papilla contains a rich network of fine argyrophil fibers. Basement membrane between the mesenchyme and epithelium. Silver impregnation. (Courtesy Dr. P. Gruenwald.)

eosin, does not present a complete picture of the structure of the pulp because not all of the fibrous elements are stained by means of this method (Fig. 110, *A*). A great abundance of fibers is revealed by silver impregnation (Fig. 110, *B*), especially the so-called Korff's fibers between the odontoblasts.

The Korff's fibers originate from among the pulp cells as thin fibers, thickening at the periphery of the pulp to form relatively thick bundles that pass between the odontoblasts and attach to the predentin. They stain black with silver, hence the term argyrophil fibers. The remaining part of the pulp contains a dense, irregular network of collagenous fibers.

Odontoblasts. The most significant change in the dental pulp during development is the differentiation of the connective tissue cells adjacent to the dental epithelium into odontoblasts. Dentin development begins in approximately the

Dental
epithelium

Blood vessel

Blood vessel

Blood vessel

Nerve fibers

Fig. 109. Age changes of the dental pulp. Cellular elements decrease and fibrous intercellular substance increases with advancing age. **A,** Newborn infant. **B,** Infant 9 months of age. **C,** Adult.

fifth embryonic month soon after the odontoblasts have differentiated. The development of odontoblasts starts at the highest point in the pulpal horn and progresses apically.

Odontoblasts are highly differentiated connective tissue cells. Their body is columnar in shape, with an oval nucleus (Fig. 111). Each cell extends as a cytoplasmic process into a tubule in the dentin. At the dentinal surface the cell

A

Dentin —

Bodies of
odontoblasts

Dentin —

Argyrophil
fibers of
Korff

Capillary

Capillary

Collagenous
fibers

B

Fig. 110. Cellular and fibrous elements in the pulp. **A,** Cellular elements stained with hematoxylin and eosin. **B,** Fibrous elements stained by silver impregnation. Both specimens are from the same tooth.

bodies of the odontoblasts are separated from each other by condensations, the so-called terminal bars. In a section the terminal bars appear as fine dots or lines. The odontoblasts are connected with each other and with the adjacent cells of the pulp by intercellular bridges. The cell bodies of some odontoblasts are long, others short, the nuclei being irregularly placed.

The form and arrangement of the bodies of the odontoblasts are not uniform throughout the pulp. They are more cylindrical and longer in the crown (Fig. 112, *A*) and become cuboid in the middle of the root (Fig. 112, *B*). Close to the apex of an adult tooth the odontoblasts are flat and spindle shaped and can be recognized as odontoblasts only by their extensions into the dentin. In areas close to the apical foramen the dentin is irregular (Fig. 112, *C*).

The odontoblasts are responsible for the formation of the dentin and mediate

Predentin

Dentin

Odontoblastic
process

Terminal bars

Odontoblastic
process

Bodies of
odontoblasts

Pulp

Bodies of
odontoblasts

Fig. 111. Bodies of odontoblasts.

its nutrition. Histogenetically and biologically they have to be regarded as the cells of the dentin. They play a part in the sensitivity of the dentin (see Chapter IV).

In the crown of the pulp a cell-free layer can be found just inside the layer of odontoblasts (Fig. 113). This layer is known as the zone of Weil or subodontoblastic layer, and it contains a network of nerve fibers, the subodontoblastic plexus. Most unmyelinated nerve fibers are a continuation of the myelinated fibers of the deeper layers and continue to their terminal arborization in the odontoblastic layer. The zone of Weil can be found but rarely in young teeth.

Defense cells. In addition to fibroblasts and odontoblasts there are other cellular elements in the human pulp, usually associated with small blood vessels and capillaries. They are important for the defense activity of the pulp, especially in inflammatory reaction.[26] In the normal pulp these cells are in a resting state.

One group of these cells is that of the histiocytes or adventitial cells or,

Fig. 112. Variation of odontoblasts in different regions of one tooth. **A,** High columnar odontoblasts in the pulp chamber. **B,** Low columnar odontoblasts in the root canal. **C,** Flat odontoblasts in the apical region.

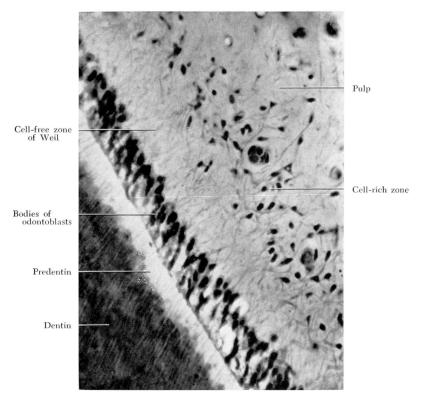

Cell-free zone
of Weil

Bodies of
odontoblasts

Predentin

Dentin

Pulp

Cell-rich zone

Fig. 113. Cell-free subodontoblastic zone of Weil.

according to Maximow's nomenclature,[19,20] the "resting wandering cells." These cells generally are located along the capillaries. Their cytoplasm has a notched, irregular, branching appearance, and the nuclei are dark and oval. They may have diverse forms in the human pulp but usually can be recognized easily. (See Fig. 114.) Intravital staining methods have revealed that histiocytes are able to store dyes. During an inflammatory process the histiocytes withdraw their cytoplasmic branches, assume a rounded shape, migrate to the site of inflammation, and develop into macrophages.

Another cell type, the reserve cell of the loose connective tissue, was described by Maximow as undifferentiated mesenchymal cell (Fig. 114). These cells are also associated with capillaries and have oval, elongated nuclei similar to those of fibroblasts or endothelial cells and long, faintly visible cytoplasmic bodies. They are in close proximity to the capillary wall. These cells can be differentiated from endothelial cells only by their location outside the capillary wall. They are pluripotential; i.e., they can, under the proper stimulus, develop into any type of connective tissue element. In an inflammatory reaction they may form macrophages or plasma cells. After loss of odontoblasts they migrate to the dentinal wall through the zone of Weil and differentiate into cells that produce the reparative (irregular) dentin.

Fig. 114. Defense cells in the pulp.

Vein

Artery

A

B

Fig. 115. Blood vessels of the pulp. **A,** Larger vessels in the center of the pulp. **B,** Dense capillary network in the periphery of the pulp. Arteries narrow, with thick walls and even outline. Veins wide with thin walls and irregular outline.

A third type of cell that plays an important part in defense reactions is the ameboid wandering cell or the lymphoid wandering cell (Fig. 114, *C*). These cells are migrating elements that probably escape from the bloodstream. Their cytoplasm is sparse and shows fine extensions, pseudopodia, suggesting a migratory character. The dark nucleus fills almost the entire cell and is often slightly indented. In chronic inflammatory reactions they migrate to the site of injury. The function of these cells is not as yet fully known.

Blood vessels. The blood supply of the pulp is abundant. The blood vessels of the dental pulp enter through the apical foramen. Usually one artery and one or two veins are found at the foramen. The artery, carrying the blood into the pulp, branches out into a rich network of blood vessels soon after entering the root canal. The veins gather blood from the capillary network and carry it back through the apical foramen into larger vessels. (See Fig. 115.) The arteries are clearly identified by their straight course and thicker walls, whereas the thin-walled veins are wider and frequently have an irregular outline. The capillaries

Fig. 116. Branching artery in the pulp. Circular muscle coating.

form loops close to the odontoblasts, near the surface of the pulp, and may even reach into the odontoblastic layer.

The larger vessels in the pulp, especially the arteries, have a typical circular muscular coating (Fig. 116). These muscular elements can be traced to the finer branches. Along the capillaries are found branching cells, the pericytes (Rouget's cells). It has been claimed that they are modified muscular elements.[20]

Occasionally it is difficult to differentiate between pericytes and undifferentiated mesenchymal cells. However, some sections show both types of cells, thus making it possible to distinguish between the two (Fig. 117). The nuclei of the pericytes can be distinguished as round or slightly oval bodies outside the endothelial wall of the capillary. A very thin cytoplasm can be seen between the nuclei and the endothelium. The endothelial cells can be recognized because they lie in the wall of the capillary. The undifferentiated reserve cells lie outside the pericytes and have fingerlike projections. If no pericytes are present, the undifferentiated mesenchymal reserve cells are in close proximity to the endothelial wall. (See Fig. 114.)

Fig. 117. Pericytes of capillaries in the pulp. Note the differences in location and nuclear shape between endothelial cells, pericytes, and undifferentiated reserve cells.

Lymph vessels. Lymph vessels are present in the dental pulp. Special methods are required to render them visible. The common histologic technique does not reveal them. The presence of lymph vessels has been demonstrated by the application into the pulp of dyes that are carried into the regional lymph nodes.[11, 23, 24] Injection methods have also been tried successfully.[22, 30]

Nerves. The nerve supply of the dental pulp is abundant. Thick nerve bundles enter the apical foramen and pass into the crown portion of the pulp, where they split into numerous fiber groups and ultimately into single fibers and their branches (Fig. 118). Usually the nerve bundles follow the blood vessels, and

Fig. 118. Nerve fibers in the pulp.

the finer branches can be seen along the smaller vessels and capillaries.

Most nerve fibers that enter the pulp are myelinated. They mediate the sensation of pain. The unmyelinated nerve fibers belong to the sympathetic nervous system and are the nerves of the blood vessels, reflectorily regulating their lumen.

The bundles of myelinated fibers follow closely the arteries, dividing coronally into smaller and smaller branches. Individual fibers form a network beneath the subodontoblastic zone of Weil, the parietal plexus. From there the individual fibers pass through the subodontoblastic zone and, losing their myelin sheath, begin to branch. Their terminal arborization occurs in the odontoblastic layer (see Chapter IV).

It is a peculiar feature that whatever stimulus reaches the pulp will always elicit only pain sensation. There is no possibility in the pulp to differentiate between heat, cold, touch, pressure, or chemicals—the result is always pain. The cause of this behavior is the fact that only one type of nerve endings, free nerve endings, are found in the pulp. The free nerve endings are specific for the reception of pain. Pulpal pain, as a rule, is not localized to the diseased tooth. This is in strong contrast to the sharp localization of periodontal pain.

REGRESSIVE CHANGES

Pulpstones. Certain formations in the dental pulp, such as pulpstones or denticles, are on the borderline of pathologic changes. Their discussion in this chapter is justified, however, because of their frequent occurrence. Pulpstones are often found in teeth which appear to be quite normal in all other respects. They have been found not only in functioning teeth but also in embedded teeth.

Pulpstones are classified, according to their structure, as true denticles, false denticles, and diffuse calcifications (Fig. 119). True denticles consist of dentin, showing traces of dentinal tubuli and odontoblasts (Fig. 119, A). They are comparatively rare and usually are found close to the apical foramen. A theory has been advanced[27] that the development of this type of pulpstones is caused by remnants of Hertwig's epithelial root sheath that invade or become enclosed in the pulp because of some local disturbance during development. These epithelial remnants may induce cells of the pulp to form true denticles. It is an accepted fact that cells of the dental epithelium are necessary for the differentiation of odontoblasts and the onset of dentin formation.[7]

False denticles do not show the structure of true dentin. They consist, instead, of concentric layers of calcified tissue (Fig. 119, B). In the center of these concentric calcified structures there usually are remnants of necrotic and calcified cells. Calcification of thrombi in blood vessels, phleboliths, may also be the nidus for false denticles. Once calcification has begun, more layers of calcium phosphate are laid down on the surface of the pulpstones, thereby increasing their size. The surrounding pulp tissue may be quite normal (Fig. 119, B). No patho-

True denticle

Bodies of odontoblasts

Dentin

False denticle

False denticle

Diffuse calcifications

Dentin

Fig. 119. Denticles (pulpstones). **A,** True denticle. **B,** False denticle. **C,** Diffuse calcifications.

logic changes can be detected in the cells or intercellular fibrous matrix. Sometimes pulpstones of this character fill the pulp chamber almost completely. They increase in number and size with advancing age. Overdoses of vitamin D may cause formation of numerous denticles.[1]

Calcifications. Diffuse calcifications (Fig. 119, *C*) are irregular calcific deposits in the pulp tissue, usually following collagenous fiber bundles or blood vessels. Sometimes they develop into large bodies. At other times they persist as fine spicules. They are amorphous, having no specific structure, and usually are the final outcome of a hyalin degeneration of the pulp tissue. The pulp, in its coronal portion, may be quite normal without any sign of inflammation or other pathologic changes. These diffuse calcifications usually are located in the root canal, seldom in the pulp chamber. Advancing age favors their development.

Pulpstones are classified not only according to their structure, but also according to their location in relation to the dentinal wall. Free, attached, and

Free denticle

Attached denticle

Embedded denticle

Fig. 120. Free, attached, and embedded denticles.

embedded denticles can be distinguished (Fig. 120). The free denticles are entirely surrounded by pulp tissue, attached denticles are partly fused with the dentin, and embedded denticles are entirely surrounded by dentin. All are formed free in the pulp, and some become attached or embedded as formation of the dentin progresses.

Pulpstones are frequently found close to nerve bundles, as shown in Fig. 121. Occasionally this may bring about a disturbance if the pulpstones come close enough to the nerves to exert pressure. This may entail pain in the jaw in which the affected tooth is located, rendering a satisfactory diagnosis difficult because teeth are also seen in which the pulp is laden with pulpstones without producing pain. Conceivably, in those teeth presenting pulpstones and painful symptoms, the existence of the calcifications may be secondary to an injury which initially caused the formation of pulpstone and eventually has led to a

Pulpstone

Nerve

Pulpstone

Fig. 121. Pulpstones in close proximity to a nerve.

final deterioration and inflammation of the surviving pulp. The close proximity of pulpstones to blood vessels may cause atrophy of the pulp if the growing pulpstones exert pressure upon the vessels. It is improbable that the pulsation of the blood in the arteries, close to pulpstones, causes sufficient movement of the stone to irritate nerves and cause pain. Pulp calcifications are more common in older teeth. Diffuse calcium deposits may be found in and around the pulpal vessels or close to nerves, especially in the roots of older teeth. Well-outlined calcified bodies are more frequently found in the coronal portion of the pulp. In 29 teeth from individuals between 10 and 30 years of age, Hill[13] found pulp calcifications in 66 per cent; in 62 teeth from individuals between 30 and 50 years of age, 80 to 82.5 per cent showed calcification in the pulp; and in 31 teeth from individuals over 50 years of age, 90 per cent had pulp calcification.

Fibrosis. It has been pointed out that with advancing age the cellular elements of the pulp decrease in number, whereas the fibrous components increase. In older individuals this shift in tissue elements can be considerable, and fibrosis may thus develop in the pulp.

CLINICAL CONSIDERATIONS

For all operative procedures it is important to bear in mind the shape of the pulp chamber and its extensions into the cusps, the pulpal horns. The wide pulp chamber in the tooth of a young person will make a deep cavity preparation hazardous, and it should, if possible, be avoided. In some rare instances the pulpal horns project high into the cusps, and in some cases this may explain the exposure of a pulp when it is least anticipated.[28] (See Fig. 122.) Sometimes a roentgenogram will help to determine the size of a pulp chamber and the extent of the pulpal horns.

If it becomes necessary to open a pulp chamber for treatment, its size and variation in shape must be taken into consideration. With advancing age the pulp chamber becomes smaller and, due to excessive dentin formation at the roof and floor of the chamber, it is sometimes difficult to locate the root canals. In such cases it is advisable, when opening the pulp chamber, to advance toward the distal root in the lower molar and toward the lingual root in the upper molar. In this region one is most likely to find the opening of the pulp canal without risk of perforating the floor of the pulp chamber. In the anterior teeth the coronal part of the pulp chamber may be filled with secondary dentin, making it difficult to locate the root canal. Pulpstones lying at the opening of the root canal may cause considerable difficulty when an attempt is made to locate the canals. (Fig. 103, *B.*)

The shape of the apical foramen and its location may play an important part in the treatment of root canals, especially in root canal filling. When the apical foramen is narrowed by cementum, it is more readily located because further progress of the broach will be stopped at the foramen. If the apical opening is at the side of the apex, as shown in Fig. 107, *A*, not even the roentgenograms

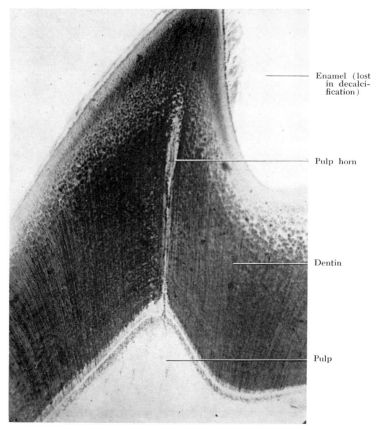

Enamel (lost
in decalci-
fication)

Pulp horn

Dentin

Pulp

Fig. 122. Pulp horn reaching far into the cusp of a molar. (From Orban, B.: J.A.D.A. 28: 1069, 1941.)

will reveal the true length of the root canal, and this may lead to misjudging the length of the canal and the root canal filling.

The problem of accessory canals in root canal work plays an important part in making the outcome of the endodontic treatment questionable if complete sterilization of the canal is not obtained. Side branches of the pulp are rarely seen in the roentgenograms and usually are overlooked in the treatment and filling of the root canal.

There is another condition in which accessory canals may play an important part, especially if they are located in the bifurcation, or high up near the cementoenamel junction (Fig. 106, *B*). In periodontal diseases, e.g., where pocket formation progresses, accessory canals may be exposed, and infection of the pulp may follow. This may account for some causes of pulp necrosis in periodontal diseases, not only in molars but also in single-rooted teeth.

For a long time it was believed that an exposed pulp meant a lost pulp. The fact that defense cells have been recognized in the pulp has changed this concept.[26] Extensive experimental work has shown that exposed pulps can be preserved if proper pulp capping or pulp amputation procedures are applied.[29,32] This is especially so in noninfected, accidentally exposed pulps in young individuals. In many instances dentin is formed at the site of the exposure, forming a dentin barrier or bridge, and the pulp may remain vital. Pulp capping of primary teeth has been shown to be remarkably successful.

REFERENCES

1. Aprile, E. C. de, and Aprile, H.: Topografia de los conductos radiculares, Rev. Odontologia **35**:686, 1947.
2. Becks, Hermann: Dangerous effects of vitamin D overdosage on dental and paradental structures, J.A.D.A. **29**:1947, 1942.
3. Bodecker, C. F.: The soft fiber of tomes, J. Nat. D. A. **9**:281, 1922.
4. Bodecker, C. F., and Applebaum, E.: Metabolism of the dentin, D. Cosmos **73**:995, 1931.
5. Bodecker, C. F., and Lefkowitz, W.: Concerning the "vitality" of the calcified dental tissues, J. D. Res. **16**:463, 1937.
6. Boling, L. R.: Blood supply of dental pulp, J. D. Res. **20**:247, 1941.
7. Brunn, A. v.: Die Ausdehnung des Schmelzorganes und seine Bedeutung für die Zahnbildung (The extension of the enamel organ and its significance in the formation of teeth), Anat. Anz. **1**:259, 1886.
8. Coolidge, E. D.: Anatomy of root apex in relation to treatment problems, J.A.D.A. **16**: 1456, 1929.
9. Ebner, V. v.: Ueber die Entwicklung der leimgebenden Fibrillen im Zahnbein (The development of collagenous fibrils in dentin), Anat. Anz. **29**:137, 1906.
10. Ebner, V. v.: Histologie der Zähne (Histology of the teeth, Scheff's handbook of dentistry), ed. 4, Vienna, 1922, A. Hoelder.
11. Fish, E. W.: An experimental investigation of enamel, dentin and the dental pulp, London, 1932, John Bale Sons & Danielsson, Ltd.
12. Hess, W., and Zurcher, E.: The anatomy of the root canals, London, 1925, John Bale Sons & Danielsson, Ltd.
13. Hill, T. J.: Pathology of the dental pulp, J.A.D.A. **21**:820, 1934.
14. Johnston, H. B., and Orban, B.: Interradicular pathology as related to accessory root canals, J. Endodontia **3**:21, 1948.
15. Kronfeld, R.: Dental histology and comparative dental anatomy, Philadelphia, 1937, Lea & Febiger.
16. Langeland, K.: Effect of various procedures on the human dental pulp, Oral Surg., Oral Med. & Oral Path. **14**:210, 1961.
17. Lehner, J., and Plenk, H.: Die Zähne (The teeth). In von Möllendorff, W. (editor): Handbuch der mikroskopischen Anatomie des Menschen, vol. 5, pt. 3, Berlin, 1936, Julius Springer, p. 449.
18. Magnus, G.: Ueber den Nachweis der Lymphgefässe in der Zahnpulpa (Demonstration of lymph vessels in the dental pulp), Deutsche Monatschr. f. Zahnh. **40**:661, 1922.
19. Maximow, A. A.: Morphology of the mesenchymal reactions, Arch. Path. & Lab. Med. **4**:557, 1927.
20. Maximow, A. A., and Bloom, W.: Textbook of histology, ed. 4, Philadelphia, 1942, W. B. Saunders Co.
21. Meyer, W.: Ist das Foramen apicale stationär? (Is the apical foramen stationary?) Deutsche Monatschr. f. Zahnh. **45**:1016, 1927.
22. Noyes, F. B., and Dewey, K.: Lymphatics of the dental region, J.A.M.A. **71**:1179, 1918.
23. Noyes, F. B.: Review of the work of lymphatics of dental origin, J.A.D.A. **14**:714, 1927.
24. Noyes, F. B., and Ladd, R. L.: The lymphatics of the dental region, D. Cosmos **71**: 1041, 1929.
25. Okumura, T.: Anatomy of the root canals, J.A.D.A. **14**:632, 1927.
26. Orban, B.: Contribution to the histology of the dental pulp, J.A.D.A. **16**:965, 1929.

27. Orban, B.: Epithelial rests in the teeth, Proc. Am. Assoc. D. Schools, 5th Annual Meeting, Washington, D. C., 1929, p. 121.
28. Orban, B.: Biologic considerations in restorative dentistry, J.A.D.A. **28**:1069, 1941.
29. Restarski, J. S.: Preserving vitality of pulps exposed by caries in young children, Illinois D. J. **9**:2, 1940.
30. Schweizer, G.: Die Lymphgefässe des Zahnfleisches und der Zähne (Lymph vessels of the gingiva and teeth), Arch. f. mikr. Anat. **69**:807, 1907; **74**:927, 1909.
31. Wassermann, F.: The innervation of teeth, J.A.D.A. **26**:1097, 1939.
32. Zander, H. A.: Reaction of the pulp to calcium hydroxide, J. D. Res. **18**:373, 1939.
33. Zerlotti, E.: Histochemical study of the connective tissue of the dental pulp, Arch. Oral Biol. **9**:149, 1964.

INTRODUCTION

PHYSICAL CHARACTERISTICS

CHEMICAL COMPOSITION

CEMENTOGENESIS
    Cementoblasts
    Cementoid tissue

STRUCTURE
    Acellular cementum
    Cellular cementum

CEMENTOENAMEL JUNCTION

CEMENTODENTINAL JUNCTION

FUNCTION

HYPERCEMENTOSIS

CLINICAL CONSIDERATIONS

Chapter VI

Cementum*

INTRODUCTION

Cementum is the hard dental tissue covering the anatomic roots of the human teeth. It was first demonstrated microscopically in 1835 by two pupils of Purkinje.[5] It begins at the cervical portion of the tooth at the cementoenamel junction and continues to the apex. Cementum furnishes a medium for the attachment of the fibers that bind the tooth to the surrounding structures. It can be defined as a specialized, calcified tissue of mesodermal origin, a modified type of bone covering the anatomic root of the teeth.

PHYSICAL CHARACTERISTICS

The hardness of adult or fully formed cementum is less than that of dentin.[11,24] It is light yellowish in color and is easily distinguished from the enamel by its lack of luster and its darker hue. It is somewhat lighter in color than dentin. By means of vital staining and other experiments, the cementum has been proved to be permeable.[25]

CHEMICAL COMPOSITION

Adult cementum consists of about 45 to 50 per cent inorganic substances and 50 to 55 per cent organic material and water. The inorganic substances consist mainly of calcium phosphates. The molecular structure is hydroxylapatite, as in enamel, dentin, and bone. The chief constituents of the organic material are collagen and mucopolysaccharides.

CEMENTOGENESIS

When the dentin of the root has begun to form under the organizing influence of the epithelial root sheath, it is separated by epithelium from the surround-

---

*First draft submitted by Emmerich Kotanyi; revised by the editor.

ing connective tissue. However, the continuity of the epithelial root sheath soon is broken either by partial degeneration of the epithelium or by active proliferation of the connective tissue. Thus, contact of the connective tissue with the surface of the dentin is established (Fig. 123). The epithelial sheath persists as a network of epithelial strands that lie fairly close to the root surface. The remnants of the epithelial sheath are known as epithelial rests of Malassez[15] (see Chapter VII). When the separation of the epithelium from the surface of the root dentin has been accomplished, cells of the periodontal connective tissue, now in contact with the root surface, form cementum.

Cementoblasts. Before cementum is formed, cells of the loose connective

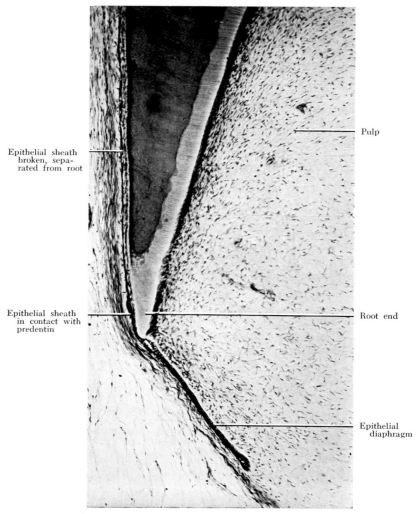

Epithelial sheath broken, separated from root

Epithelial sheath in contact with predentin

Pulp

Root end

Epithelial diaphragm

Fig. 123. Hertwig's epithelial root sheath at end of forming root. At the side of the root the sheath is broken up, and cementum formation begins. (From Gottlieb, B.: J. Periodont. 13:13, 1942.)

Fig. 124. Epithelial sheath is broken and separated from root surface by connective tissue.

tissue that are in contact with the root surface differentiate into cuboidal cells, the cementoblasts (Fig. 124). These cells produce the cementum in two consecutive phases. In the first phase uncalcified cementoid tissue is laid down. In the second phase the cementoid tissue is transformed into calcified cementum. This is similar to the process of bone and dentin formation.

In elaborating the cementoid tissue, the cementoblasts use the collagen material of the argyrophil connective tissue fibers (Figs. 125 and 126) to integrate the collagen material into the cementoid substance as collagen fibrils. At the same time the mucopolysaccharides of the connective tissue are changed chemically and polymerized into the ground substance.

The second phase is characterized by a change in the molecular structure of the ground substance, most probably a depolymerization and its combination with calcium phosphates that are deposited as apatite crystals along the fibrils.[26]

Argyrophil fibers

Argyrophil fibers

Dentin

Attachment of fibers

Fig. 125. Argyrophil collagenous fibers of the periodontal connective tissue attached to the dentin (silver impregnation).

Collagenous fibers

Dentin

Cementum

Fig. 126. Collagenous fibers and the mucopolysaccharides of the periodontal connective tissue are utilized in the formation of cementum.

Dentin

Cementoblasts

Cementum

Periodontal
ligament

Cementoid
tissue

Cementoblast

Fig. 127. Cementoid tissue on the surface of calcified cementum. Cementoblasts between fibers.

The changes of the ground substance that occur in the second phase of cementogenesis are in all probability responsible for the different behavior of cementoid tissue and cementum. Cementoid tissue, like osteoid tissue and pre-dentin, is highly resistant to destruction by osteoclastic activity, whereas cementum, bone, and dentin are readily resorbable.

Cementoid tissue. Since growth of the cementum is a rhythmic process under normal conditions, a thin layer of cementoid tissue is only seen on the surface of the cementum (Figs. 127 and 128) while a new layer is apposed. This cementoid tissue is lined by cementoblasts. Connective tissue fibers from the periodontal ligament pass between the cementoblasts into the cementum. These fibers are embedded in the cementum and serve as an attachment for the tooth to the

Fig. 128. Cementum lacuna and canaliculi filled with air (ground section).

surrounding bone. Their embedded portions are known as Sharpey's fibers. These were described accurately by G. V. Black,[2] in 1887, as an essential part of the suspensory apparatus.

STRUCTURE

From a morphologic standpoint two kinds of cementum can be differentiated: acellular and cellular. The term acellular cementum is unfortunate. As a living tissue, cells are an integral part of cementum at all times. However, some layers of cementum do not *include* cells, the spiderlike cementocytes, while other layers do contain such cells in their lacunae. In other layers the cementocytes are arranged along the surface of the cementum as "cementoblasts." It is at any time impossible to say whether such cells are cementocytes maintaining the integrity (vitality) of the cementum or whether they actively produce cementum. In connective tissue the same difficulty is encountered when one wants to differentiate fibroblasts from fibrocytes. The cells of the dentin are at the same time odontoblasts and odontocytes. Only in bone is it easy to recognize osteoblasts and osteocytes by their different shape and location. Therefore, it must be understood that cementum always consists of cells and their product, fibrils or fibers, and ground substance.

Acellular cementum. Acellular cementum may cover the root dentin from the cementoenamel junction to the apex, but it is often missing on the apical third of the root. Here the cementum may be entirely of the cellular type. The acellular cementum is thinnest at the cementoenamel junction (20 to 50 microns) and thickest toward the apex (150 to 200 microns). The apical foramen is surrounded by cementum. Sometimes the cementum extends to the inner wall of the dentin for a short distance, forming a lining of the root canal.

Acellular cementum seems to consist only of the calcified intercellular substance and contains the embedded Sharpey's fibers because its cells line its surface. The intercellular substance is composed of two elements, the collagenous fibrils and the calcified ground substance. The fibrils in the matrix are perpendicular to the embedded Sharpey's fibers and parallel to the cementum surface. The fibrils are less numerous than in lamellated bone and about as numerous as those of "bundle" bone. Due to identical optical qualities, i.e., the same refractive index, the fibrils are masked by the interfibrillar ground substance and can be made visible only by special staining methods, e.g., by means of silver impregnation. In dried ground sections, Sharpey's fibers are disintegrated. The spaces and channels that they formerly occupied are filled with air and appear as dark lines.

Dentin

Periodontal ligament

Acellular cementum

Alveolar bone

Fig. 129. Incremental lines in the acellular cementum.

Cellular cementum. The cells included in cellular cementum, cementocytes, are similar to osteocytes. They lie in spaces designated as lacunae. Frequently the cell body has the shape of a plum stone, with numerous long processes radiating from the cell body. These processes may branch, and they frequently anastomose with those of a neighboring cell. Most of the processes are directed toward the periodontal surface of the cementum.

The cells are irregularly distributed throughout the thickness of the cellular cementum. The cavities can be observed best in ground sections of dried teeth, where they appear as dark, spiderlike figures (Fig. 128). The dark appearance is due to the fact that the spaces are filled with air. These spaces also can easily be filled with dyes.

Both acellular and cellular cementum are separated by incremental lines into layers that indicate periodic formation (Figs. 129 and 131). While the cementum remains relatively thin, Sharpey's fibers can be observed crossing the entire thickness of the cementum. With further apposition of cementum, a larger part of the fibers is incorporated in the cementum. At the same time, the portion of the fibers lying in the deeper layers of the cementum becomes obscure. The

Dentin

Cementum

Fibers of periodontal ligament

Fig. 130. The fibers of the periodontal ligament continue into the surface layer of the cementum.

Periodontal ligament

Cementoid tissue

Alveolar bone

Dentin

Acellular cementum

Cellular cementum

Acellular cementum

Fig. 131. Cellular cementum on the surface of acellular cementum, and again covered by acellular cementum (incremental lines). The lacunae of the cellular cementum are empty, indicating that this part of the cementum is necrotic.

Periodontal ligament

Cementoid tissue

Dentin

Cellular cementum

Fig. 132. Cellular cementum forming the entire thickness of the apical cementum. (From Orban, B.: Dental histology and embryology, Philadelphia, 1929, P. Blakiston's Son & Co.)

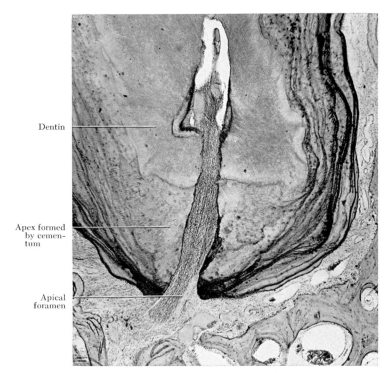

Dentin

Apex formed
by cemen-
tum

Apical
foramen

Fig. 133. Cementum thickest at the apex, contributing to the length of the root.

attachment proper is confined to the most superficial or recently formed layer of cementum (Fig. 130). This would seem to indicate that the thickness of the cementum does not enhance functional efficiency by increasing the strength of attachment of the individual fibers. Continuous growth of cementum is essential for the continuous eruptive movements of the functioning tooth, but it serves mainly to maintain a young and vital surface layer of the cementum, whose life span is restricted. Often the cells in the deeper layers of the cementum have degenerated, and the lacunae are empty (Fig. 130).

The location of acellular and cellular cementum is not definite. Layers of acellular and cellular cementum may alternate in almost any arrangement. The acellular cementum, which is normally laid down on the surface of the dentin, occasionally may be found on the surface of cellular cementum. (See Fig. 131.) Cellular cementum usually is formed on the surface of acellular cementum. (Fig. 131), but it may comprise the entire thickness of the apical cementum (Fig. 132). It is always thickest around the apex and, by its growth, contributes to the lengthening of the root (Fig. 133).

CEMENTOENAMEL JUNCTION

The relation between cementum and enamel at the cervical region of the teeth is variable.[21] In about 30 per cent of the examined teeth the cementum meets the cervical end of the enamel in a sharp line (Fig. 134, A). Here, the cementum, as well as the enamel, tapers into a knife-edge. In other teeth, about 60 per cent, the cementum overlaps the cervical end of the enamel for a short distance (Fig. 134, B). Developmentally, this can occur only when the dental epithelium that normally covers the entire enamel degenerates in its cervical end, permitting the connective tissue, which is responsible for the deposition of cementum, to come in contact with the enamel surface.

In about 10 per cent of all teeth various other aberrations of the cemento-enamel junction may be observed. Occasionally, the dental epithelium which covers the cervical part of the root does not separate from the dentin surface at the proper time,[6] remains attached to the dentin of the root for variable distances (Fig. 135, A), and prevents the formation of cementum. In such cases there is no cementoenamel junction, but a zone of the root is devoid of cementum and covered by dental epithelium. In other instances cementum is

Fig. 134. Variations at the cementoenamel junction. **A,** Cementum and enamel meet in a sharp line. **B,** Cementum overlaps enamel.

A   B

Fig. 135. Variations at the cementoenamel junction. **A,** Dental epithelium remained attached to the dentin surface, preventing cementum formation. **B,** Dental epithelium breaking continuity of cementum near the cementoenamel junction.

formed at the cementoenamel junction for a short distance only, and apically Hertwig's epithelial root sheath remains in contact with the dentin in a limited area (Fig. 135, *B*). Enamel spurs, pearls, or drops may be formed by this epithelium.[6]

CEMENTODENTINAL JUNCTION

The surface of the dentin upon which the cementum is deposited is normally smooth in permanent teeth. The cementodentinal junction in deciduous teeth, however, is sometimes scalloped. The attachment of the cementum to the dentin, in either case, is quite firm, although the nature of this attachment is not fully understood.

Sometimes the dentin is separated from the cementum by an intermediate

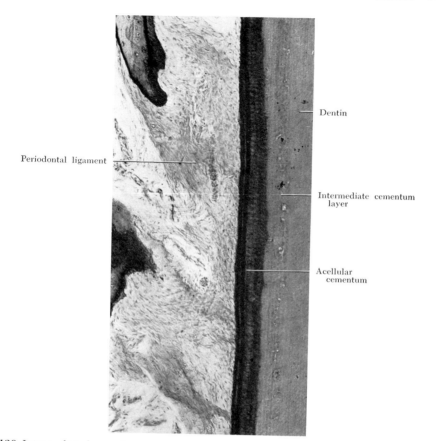

Dentin

Periodontal ligament

Intermediate cementum layer

Acellular cementum

Fig. 136. Intermediate layer of cementum.

layer, known as the intermediate cementum layer, which does not exhibit the characteristic features of either dentin or cementum (Fig. 136). This layer contains large and irregular cells. Its development may be due to localized, premature disintegration of Hertwig's epithelial sheath after its cells have induced the differentiation of odontoblasts but before the production of dentinal intercellular substance had begun. It is found mostly in the apical two-thirds of the root. Sometimes it is a continuous layer. Sometimes it is found only in isolated areas.[18]

FUNCTION

The functions of cementum are as follows: (1) to anchor the tooth to the bony socket by attachment of fibers, (2) to compensate by its growth for loss of tooth substance due to occlusal wear, and (3) to contribute by its growth to the continuous occlusomesial eruption of the teeth.

The continued deposition of cementum is of great biologic importance.[6,8,13] In contrast to the alternating resorption and new formation of bone, cementum is not resorbed under normal conditions. If a layer ages or, functionally speaking, loses its vitality, the periodontal connective tissue and cementoblasts must produce a new layer of cementum on the surface to keep the attachment apparatus intact. In bone the loss of vitality can be recognized by the fact that the bone cells degenerate, and the bone lacunae are empty. Aging in acellular cementum cannot be so readily ascertained, but in cellular cementum the cells in the deepest layers may degenerate, and the lacunae may be empty (Fig. 130). In the surface layers the lacunae contain normal cementocytes. The nuclei of degenerating cells in the deeper layers are pyknotic and the cells are shrunken. Near the surface the cells fill the entire space of the cementum lacunae (Fig. 131), and the nuclei stain dark.[7,8]

The repeated apposition of a new layer of cementum presents the aging of the tooth as an organ. In other words, a tooth is, biologically speaking, only as old as the last layer of cementum laid down on its root. This "biologic age" of a tooth may be considerably less than its chronologic age.

Alveolar bone

Periodontal ligament

Hypertrophic cementum

Dentin

Hypertrophic cementum

Fig. 137. Pronglike excementoses.

HYPERCEMENTOSIS

Hypercementosis is an abnormal thickening of the cementum. It may be diffuse or circumscribed, it may affect all teeth of the dentition, or it may be confined to a single tooth, and it may even affect only parts of one tooth. If the overgrowth improves the functional qualities of the cementum, it is termed a cementum hypertrophy. If the overgrowth occurs in nonfunctional teeth or if it is not correlated with increased function, it is termed hyperplasia.

In localized hypertrophy a spur or pronglike extension of cementum may be formed (Fig. 137). This condition frequently is found in teeth that are exposed to great stress. The pronglike extensions of cementum provide a larger surface area for the attaching fibers, thus securing a firmer anchorage of the tooth to the surrounding alveolar bone.[7]

Localized hypercementosis may sometimes be observed in areas in which enamel drops have developed on the dentin. The hyperplastic cementum, cover-

Hyperplastic cementum   Dentin

Enamel drop

Hyperplastic cementum

Fig. 138. Irregular hyperplasia of cementum on the surface of an enamel drop.

Excementosis

Cementum

Excementosis

Alveolar bone

Fig. 139. Excementoses in bifurcation of a molar. (From Gottlieb, B.: Oesterr. Ztschr. f. Stomatol. 19:515, 1921.)

ing the enamel drops (Fig. 138), occasionally is irregular and sometimes contains round bodies which may be calcified epithelial rests. The same type of embedded calcified round bodies frequently are found in localized areas of hyperplastic cementum. (See Fig. 139.) Such knoblike projections are designated as excementoses. They, too, develop around disintegrated, degenerated epithelial rests.[6]

Extensive hyperplasia of the cementum of a tooth is found occasionally in connection with chronic periapical inflammation. Here the hyperplasia is circumscribed and surrounds the root like a cuff.

A thickening of the cementum is often observed on teeth that are not in function. The hyperplasia may extend around the entire root of the nonfunctioning teeth or may be localized in small areas (see Chapter VII). Hyperplasia of cementum in nonfunctioning teeth is characterized by the absence of Sharpey's fibers.

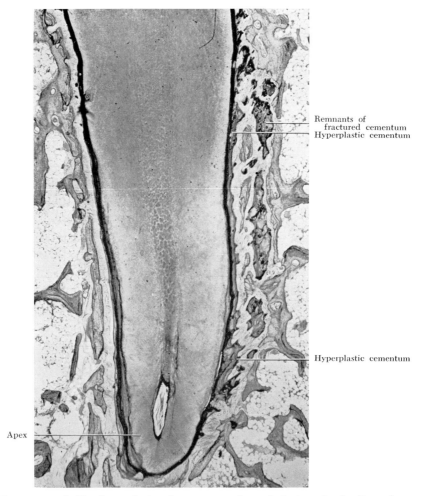

Remnants of
   fractured cementum
Hyperplastic cementum

Hyperplastic cementum

Apex

Fig. 140. Extensive spikelike hyperplasia of cementum formed during the healing of a cemental tear.

The cementum is thicker around the apex of all teeth and in the furcation of multirooted teeth than it is on other areas of the root. This thickening can be observed in embedded as well as in newly erupted teeth.[13]

In some cases an irregular overgrowth of cementum can be found with spike-like extensions and calcification of Sharpey's fibers, accompanied by numerous cementicles. This type of cementum hyperplasia can occasionally be observed on many teeth of the same dentition and is, at least in some cases, the sequela of injuries to the cementum (Fig. 140).

CLINICAL CONSIDERATIONS

The fact that cementum appears to be more resistant to resorption than bone renders orthodontic treatment possible. When a tooth is moved by means of an orthodontic appliance, bone is resorbed on the side of pressure, and new bone is formed on the side of tension. On the side toward which the tooth is moved, pressure is equal on the surfaces of bone and cementum. Resorption of bone, as well as of cementum, may be anticipated. However, in careful orthodontic treatment, cementum resorption, if it occurs, usually is localized and shallow, possibly because the cementum is often covered by a layer of cementoid tissue that is highly resistant to resorption. Moreover, resorptions are repaired readily if the intensity of pressure is reduced and if the surrounding connective tissue remains intact.

The difference in the resistance of bone and cementum to "pressure" may be caused by the fact that bone is richly vascularized while cementum is avascular. Thus degenerative processes are much more easily affected by interference with circulation in bone, while cementum with its slow metabolism (as in other avascular tissues) is not damaged by a pressure equal to that exerted on bone.

Excessive lateral stress may compress the periodontal connective tissue between bone and cementum and cause bleeding, thrombosis, and necrosis. After resorption of the damaged tissues, accompanied by bone resorption, repair may take place.[4,9,16,23]

A　　　　　　　　　　　B　　　　　　　　　　　C

Fig. 141. Repair of resorbed cementum. **A,** Repair by acellular cementum, *x.* **B,** Repair by cellular cementum, *x.* **C,** Repair first by cellular, *x,* and later by acellular, *xx,* cementum. *D,* Dentin. *R,* Line of resorption. *P,* Periodontal ligament.

Resorption of cementum may continue into the dentin. After resorption has ceased, the damage usually is repaired, either by formation of acellular (Fig. 141, *A*) or cellular (Fig. 141, *B*) cementum or by alternate formation of both (Fig. 141, *C*). In most cases of repair there is a tendency to reestablish the former outline of the root surface. However, if only a thin layer of cementum is deposited on the surface of a deep resorption, the root outline is not reconstructed, and a baylike recess remains. In such areas sometimes the periodontal space is restored to its normal width by formation of a bony projection, so that a proper functional relationship will result. The outline of the alveolar bone, in these cases, follows that of the root surface. (See Fig. 142.) In contrast to anatomic repair, this change is called functional repair.[17]

If teeth are subjected to a severe blow, smaller or larger fragments of cementum may be severed from the dentin. The tear occurs frequently at the cementodentinal junction, but it may also be in the cementum or dentin. Trans-

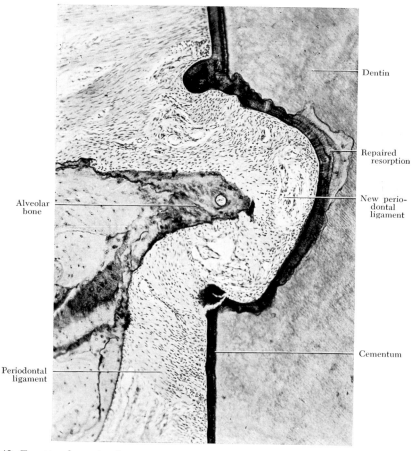

Fig. 142. Functional repair of cementum resorption by bone apposition. Normal width of the periodontal ligament reestablished.

verse fractures of the root may heal by formation of new cementum uniting the fragments.

Frequently, hyperplasia of cementum is secondary to periapical inflammation or extensive occlusal stress. The fact is of practical significance because the extraction of such teeth may necessitate the removal of bone. This also applies to extensive excementoses, as shown in Fig. 139. These can anchor the tooth so tightly to the socket that the jaw or parts of it may be fractured in an attempt to extract the tooth. This possibility indicates the necessity for taking roentgenograms before any extraction. Small fragments of roots left in the jaw after extraction of teeth may be surrounded by cementum and remain in the jaw without causing any disturbance.

If the cementum does not cover the cervical part of the root, recession of the gingiva will expose the highly sensitive dentin in the cervical area. When calculus is removed, it is impossible to avoid the removal of the thin cementum covering the cervical region of the exposed root. As the individual gets older, more cementum is gradually exposed and subject to the abrasive action of dentifrices. Since the cementum is the softest of the hard dental tissues, a considerable amount of cementum may be removed by these mechanical means.[12] The denuded dentin is then highly sensitive to thermal, chemical, or mechanical stimuli. The hypersensitivity can often be relieved with astringent chemicals that coagulate the protoplasmic odontoblastic processes.

REFERENCES

1. Becks, H.: Systemic background of paradentitis, J.A.D.A. **28:**1447, 1941.
2. Black, G. V.: A study of histological characters of the periosteum and peridental membrane, D. Rev. 1886-1887; and W. T. Keener Co., Chicago, 1887.
3. Box, H. K.: The dentinal cemental junction (Bull. No. 3), Canad. D. Res. Found., May, 1922.
4. Coolidge, E. D.: Traumatic and functional injuries occurring in the supporting tissues of human teeth, J.A.D.A. **25:**343, 1938.
5. Denton, G. H.: The discovery of cementum, J. D. Res. **18:**239, 1939.
6. Gottlieb, B.: Zementexostosen, Schmelztropfen und Epithelnester (Cementexostosis, enamel drops and epithelial rests), Oesterr. Ztschr. f. Stomatol. **19:**515, 1921.
7. Gottlieb, B.: Tissue changes in pyorrhea, J.A.D.A. **14:**2178, 1927.
8. Gottlieb, B.: Biology of the cementum, J. Periodont. **13:**13, 1942.
9. Gottlieb, B., and Orban, B.: Die Veränderungen der Gewebe bei übermässiger Beanspruchung der Zähne (Experimental traumatic occlusion), Leipzig, 1931, Georg Thieme.
10. Gottlieb, B., and Orban, B.: Biology and pathology of the tooth (translated by M. Diamond), New York, 1938, The Macmillan Co.
11. Kitchin, P. C.: The prevalence of tooth root exposure, J. D. Res. **20:**565, 1941.
12. Kitchin, P. C., and Robinson, H. B. G.: The abrasiveness of dentifrices as measured on the cervical areas of extracted teeth, J. D. Res. **27:**195, 1948.
13. Kronfeld, R.: Die Zementhyperplasien an nicht funktionierenden Zähnen (Cementum hyperplasia on nonfunctioning teeth), Ztschr. f. Stomatol. **25:**1218, 1927.
14. Kronfeld, R.: The biology of cementum, J.A.D.A. **25:**1451, 1938.
15. Malassez, M. L.: Sur le rôle des débris epitheliaux paradentaires (The epithelial rests around the root of the teeth), Arch. de Physiol. **5:**379, 1885.
16. Oppenheim, A.: Human tissue response to orthodontic intervention, Am. J. Orthodont. & Oral Surg. **28:**263, 1942.

17. Orban, B.: Resorption and repair on the surface of the root, J.A.D.A. **15:**1768, 1928.
18. Orban, B.: Dental histology and embryology, Philadelphia, 1929, P. Blakiston's Son & Co.
19. Sicher, H., and Weinmann, J. P.: Bone growth and physiologic tooth movement, Am. J. Orthodont. & Oral Surg. **30:**109, 1944.
20. Skillen, W. G.: Permeability: A tissue characteristic, J.A.D.A. **9:**187, 1922.
21. Sorrin, S., and Miller, S. C.: The practice of pedodontia, New York, 1928, The Macmillan Co.
22. Stones, H. H.: The permeability of cementum, Brit. D. J. **56:**273, 1934.
23. Stuteville, O. H.: Injuries caused by orthodontic forces, Am. J. Orthodont. & Oral Surg. **24:**103, 1938.
24. Tainter, M. L., and Epstein, S.: A standard procedure for determining abrasion, J. Am. Coll. Dentists **9:**353, 1942.
25. Thomas, N. G., and Skillen, W. G.: Staining the granular layer, D. Cosmos **62:**725, 1920.
26. Weinmann, J. P., and Sicher, H.: Bone and bones; fundamentals of bone biology, ed. 2, St. Louis, 1955, The C. V. Mosby Co.

Chapter VII

Periodontal ligament*

INTRODUCTION

FUNCTION

DEVELOPMENT

STRUCTURAL ELEMENTS
      Evolution of the periodontal ligament
      Fiber bundles
      Fibroblasts
      Osteoblasts and osteoclasts
      Cementoblasts
      Interstitial tissue
      Blood vessels
      Lymphatics
      Nerves
      Epithelial structures
      Cementicles

PHYSIOLOGIC CHANGES
      Measurements and changes in
        dimensions during life
      Physiologic changes

CLINICAL CONSIDERATIONS

INTRODUCTION

The periodontal ligament is the connective tissue that surrounds the root of the tooth and attaches it to the bony alveolus. It is continuous with the connective tissue of the gingiva. Various terms have been given to this tissue: peridental membrane, pericementum, dental periosteum, and alveolodental membrane. This tissue is called a membrane although it does not resemble other fibrous membranes, like fasciae, capsules of organs, perichondrium, or periosteum. It has some structural and functional similarities to these tissues, but it is different in that it serves not only as pericementum for the tooth and periosteum for the alveolar bone but also mainly as the suspensory ligament for the tooth. Therefore, the term periodontal *ligament* is most appropriate.

FUNCTION

The functions of the periodontal ligament are formative, supportive, protective, sensory, and nutritive. The formative function is fulfilled by the cementoblasts and the osteoblasts, which are essential in building cementum and bone, and by the fibroblasts, which form the fibers of the ligament. The supportive function is that of maintaining the relation of the tooth to the surrounding hard and soft tissues. Limiting the masticatory movements of the tooth, the periodontal ligament protects the tissues at the sites of pressure. This is achieved by connective tissue fibers that comprise the bulk of the ligament. Functions that are sensory and nutritive to the cementum and alveolar bone are carried out by the nerves and the blood vessels in the periodontal ligament.

---

*First draft submitted by Helmuth A. Zander; revised by the editor.

DEVELOPMENT

The periodontal ligament is derived from the dental sac that envelops the developing tooth germ. Around the tooth germ three zones can be seen: an outer zone containing fibers related to the bone, an inner zone of fibers adjacent to the tooth, and an intermediate zone of unoriented fibers between the other two (Fig. 143). During the formation of cementum, fibers of the inner zone become attached to the surface of the root. As the tooth moves toward the oral cavity, gradually a functional orientation of the fibers takes place.[20] Instead of loose and irregularly arranged fibers, fiber bundles extend from the bone to the tooth. When the tooth has reached the plane of occlusion and the root is fully formed, this functional orientation is complete. However, due to changes in functional stresses and the eruptive and drifting movements of the teeth, changes in the structural arrangement of the periodontal ligament occur throughout life.

STRUCTURAL ELEMENTS

The main tissue elements in the periodontal ligament are the principal fibers, all of which are attached to the cementum.[2,3] The fiber bundles extend from the cementum to the alveolar wall, or across the crest of the interdental septum to the cementum of the adjacent tooth, or into the gingival tissue. The principal fibers of the periodontal ligament are white collagenous connective tissue fibers,

Fig. 143. Three zones in the periodontal ligament of a developing tooth.

and they cannot be lengthened. There are no elastic fibers in the periodontal ligament. The apparent elasticity of the periodontal ligament is due to the arrangement of the principal fiber bundles. They follow a wavy course from bone to cementum, thereby allowing slight movements of the tooth during mastication. Near the bone the fibers seem to form larger bundles before their insertion into it. Although the bundles run directly from bone to cementum, the single fibers do not span the entire distance. The bundles are "spliced or braided" and chemically bound together from shorter fibers in an intermediate plexus midway between cementum and bone. (Fig. 144A.) The presence of an intermediate plexus is common to the periodontal ligament of all mammalian teeth because they move occlusomesially by continuous eruption during their functional period. These movements necessitate a continued adaptive readjustment of the suspensory ligament. This rearrangement does not occur by the embedding of new fibers in bone and cementum, as previously assumed, but by the formation of new chemical links, in all probability by mucopolysaccharides, between the al-

Fig. 144A. Periodontal ligament of premolars of a monkey. Interdental and alveolar bundles of principal fibers may be seen. The fibers are intertwined between cementum and bone in an intermediate plexus.

veolar and the dental fibers in the intermediate plexus. How conspicuous or inconspicuous this plexus is depends on the rate of eruptive movements. In the rat incisor that has a daily eruptive rate of one-third of one millimeter, this plexus is quite wide and conspicuous.[28,29] In man, in whom eruptive movements and mesial drift are quite slow, the intermediate plexus is inconspicuous. However, during the time of fast eruptive movement before the teeth get into function, an intermediate plexus in human teeth has been observed.[20] The interdental or transseptal ligaments also consist of fibers that are shorter than the ligaments themselves. In contrast to alveolodental and interdental ligaments, the fibers of the gingival ligament seem to extend directly from the cementum into the gingiva.

Evolution of the periodontal ligament. There is a fundamental difference in the attachment of reptilian and mammalian teeth. In the ancestral reptiles the teeth are ankylosed to the bone. In mammals they are suspended in their sockets by ligaments. The evolutionary step from reptile to mammal included a series of coordinated changes in the jaws. The central point of these changes is the radical "reconstruction" of the mandible. In the reptiles the mandible consists of a series of bones, united by sutures. Only the uppermost bone, the dentary, carries the ankylosed teeth. The mandibular articulation is formed by a separate bone of the mandible, the articulare, and a separate bone of the cranium, the quadratum. During the period of transition from advanced types of reptiles to the first mammals, the dentary attains larger proportions, while the other man-

Fig. 144B   Fig. 144C

Fig. 144B. Periodontal ligament of a rat molar. Note the "braiding" of the periodontal fibers in the intermediate plexus. Silver impregnation. (×400.) (Courtesy Dr. Ino Sciaky, Jerusalem.)
Fig. 144C. Higher magnification of an area of **144B.** (×800.) (Courtesy Dr. Ino Sciaky, Jerusalem.)

dibular bones are reduced in size. Finally, only the dentary forms the mammalian mandible. The other bony components of the reptilian mandible are either lost or changed into two of the ossicles of the middle ear: the articulare survives as the malleus and the quadratum as the incus. Before this change could take place, the dentary, growing a condylar process, formed a "new" temporomandibular articulation that, for a time, functioned together with the old articulare-quadratum joint. Such "double-jointed" forms are now known.

The change from the many-bone reptilian to the single-boned mammalian mandible brings with it a radical change in the mode of growth. In the reptile the growth of the mandible is "sutural" in the same manner as the growth of the cranium. In the mammal the newly acquired cartilage of the condyle takes over as the most important growth center of the mandible. In the reptile, growth of the mandibular body in height occurs in the mandibular sutures, whereas in the mammal it occurs by growth at the free margins of the alveolar process. In the reptile the mandibular (and maxillary) teeth "move" with the bones to which they are fused. In the mammal the teeth have to "move" as units independent of the bones.

This evolutionary—one is almost tempted to say revolutionary—change necessitates the replacement of ankylosis by a syndesmosis, the ligamentous suspension of the tooth. Thus, and only thus, the mammalian tooth can keep pace with the growing jaws. Of course, this is not the only, although perhaps the most significant, change of the dentition.

The "growth movements" or the eruptive movements of the tooth in both vertical and horizontal direction need, of course, continual changes of the supporting tissues, cementum, bone, and suspensory ligaments, i.e., alveolodental, interdental, and gingival ligaments. Therefore, alveolodental and interdental ligaments consist, as do all other ligaments, of fibers that are shorter than the ligament itself. Only by this arrangement, by the physicochemical "splicing" of shorter fibers to form a ligament, can ligaments adjust to growth in length. In the dental ligaments, however, the adjustive changes are manifold. Some alveolodental fibers have to lengthen, for instance, to allow horizontal tooth movements, "drifting" of teeth (mesial in man, distal in the rat). In a closed dentition with contact wear, the interdental ligaments have to shorten. In axial movement the functional arrangement of the alveolodental ligament has to undergo continual changes. All adjustments occur in a middle zone of these ligaments that has been called the intermediate plexus.

This plexus in which the fibers arising in the cementum on one side and in the bone on the other are "spliced" is characteristic for *all* mammalian teeth. However, its dimensions are correlated to the speed of eruptive movements.

The presence of an intermediate plexus and its significance for the rearrangement of fibers of the periodontal ligament make it clear that the continued apposition of cementum serves mainly the maintenance of the vitality of the cementum,

Fig. 145. Gingival fibers of the periodontal ligament pass from the cementum into the gingiva.

Fiber bundles. The bundles of collagenous fibers are so arranged that they can be divided into the following ligaments: (1) gingival ligament, (2) interdental ligament, and (3) alveolodental ligaments.*

The fibers of the *gingival ligament* (Fig. 145) attach the gingiva to the cementum. The fiber bundles pass outward from the cementum into the free and attached gingiva. Usually they break up into a meshwork of smaller bundles and individual fibers, interlacing terminally with the fibrous tissue and the circular fibers of the gingiva.

The *transseptal, or interdental, ligaments* (Fig. 146) connect adjacent teeth. The ligaments, but not the single fibers, run from the cementum of one tooth over the crest of the alveolus to the cementum of the neighboring tooth.

The *alveolodental ligament* (Fig. 147) attaches the tooth to the bone of the alveolus. It consists of five groups of bundles.

    1. *Alveolar crest group:* The fiber bundles of this group radiate from the crest of the alveolar process and attach themselves to the cervical part of the cementum.

    2. *Horizontal group:* The bundles run at right angles to the long axis of the tooth, from the cementum to the bone.

---

*Many ligaments are subdivided into several ligaments: the bifurcate ligament in the foot consists of the calcaneonavicular and the calcaneocuboid ligaments, the coracoclavicular ligament in the shoulder consists of the conic and the trapezoid ligaments, etc.

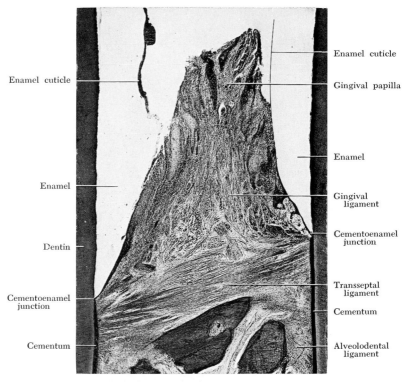

Enamel cuticle

Enamel cuticle

Gingival papilla

Enamel

Enamel

Gingival ligament

Cementoenamel junction

Dentin

Transseptal ligament

Cementoenamel junction

Cementum

Cementum

Alveolodental ligament

Fig. 146. Transseptal ligament connects adjacent teeth.

3. *Oblique group:* The bundles run obliquely. They are attached in the cementum somewhat apically from their attachment to the bone. These fiber bundles are most numerous and constitute the main support of the tooth against masticatory forces.

4. *Apical group:* The bundles are irregularly arranged and radiate from the apical region of the root to the surrounding bone (Fig. 148).

5. *Interradicular group:* From the crest of the interradicular septum, bundles extend to the furcation of multirooted teeth.

The arrangement of the bundles in the different groups is well adapted to fulfill the functions of the periodontal ligament. No matter from which direction a force is applied to the tooth, it is counteracted by some or all of the fiber groups. The alveolar principal fibers, as a whole, may be regarded as a ligament, alveolodental ligament, by which the tooth is attached to the alveolar bone. Its function is primarily to transform pressure exerted upon the tooth into traction on cementum and bone.[25]

The periodontal ligament, as other ligaments, has also a protective function, limiting the masticatory movements of the tooth. In the areas toward which the roots move, the numerous veins are emptied for a short time during mastication, thus dissipating any pressure on the cellular elements. Therefore, normal masti-

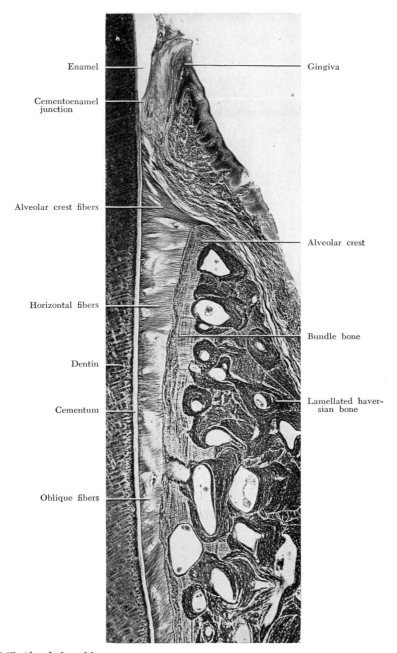

Enamel

Cementoenamel
junction

Alveolar crest fibers

Horizontal fibers

Dentin

Cementum

Oblique fibers

Gingiva

Alveolar crest

Bundle bone

Lamellated haver-
sian bone

Fig. 147. Alveolodental ligament.

Periodontal
ligament

Apex

Periodontal
ligament

Fig. 148. Apical fibers of the periodontal ligament. (From Orban, B.: Dental histology and embryology, Philadelphia, 1929, P. Blakiston's Son & Co.)

catory forces do not lead to the differentiation of osteoclasts in "pressure areas." The structure of the periodontal ligament changes continuously to meet the requirements of the continuously moving tooth.[9,22]

Fibroblasts. Most cells of the periodontal ligament are typical fibroblasts. They are long, slender, stellate connective tissue cells whose nuclei are large and oval in shape. These cells lie between the fibers, and they are active in the formation and maintenance of the principal fibers and especially in the dissolution of old and the establishment of new fiber connections in the intermediate plexus.

Osteoblasts and osteoclasts. As is true of bone elsewhere in the body, the bone of the alveolus is constantly resorbed and rebuilt. Resorption of bone is brought about by the osteoclasts. Formation of new bone is initiated by the activity of the osteoblasts.

Where bone formation is in progress, osteoblasts are found along the surface of the wall of the bony socket, the periodontal ligament fibers passing between them. These cells usually are irregularly cuboid in shape, with large single nuclei containing large nucleoli and fine chromatin particles. The fibers of the periodontal ligament are secured to the bone by the formation of bone around the ends of the fibers. Osteoclasts are mostly multinucleated and are believed to originate by fusion of undifferentiated mesenchymal cells in the periodontal ligament. They are found only during the process of active bone resorption. Presumably the osteoclasts produce enzymes that dissolve the organic components of bone and probably produce chelating agents capable of bringing the calcium salts into solution.[32] Where their cytoplasm is in contact with bone, hollows or depressions called Howship's lacunae, or resorption lacunae, are formed. When bone resorption ceases, the osteoclasts disappear. These cells are also active when resorption of the roots of teeth occurs (see Chapters VIII and XII).

Fig. 149. Interstitial spaces in the periodontal ligament contain loose connective tissue and carry glomerulus-like arranged blood vessels and nerves. (From Orban, B.: J.A.D.A. **16:** 405, 1929.)

Cementoblasts. Cementoblasts, cementocytes, are connective tissue cells found on the surface of cementum between the fibers. They are large cuboidal cells with spheroid or ovoid nuclei, which are active in the formation of cementum (see Chapter VI). The cells have irregular, fingerlike projections that fit around the fibers that extend from the cementum.

Interstitial tissue. The blood vessels, lymphatics, and nerves of the periodontal ligament are contained in spaces between the principal fiber bundles (Fig. 149). They are surrounded by loose connective tissue in which fibroblasts, histiocytes, undifferentiated mesenchymal reserve cells, and lymphocytes are found. Many arteriovenous anastomoses exist in these glomerulus-like arrangements of blood vessels.[11]

Blood vessels. The blood supply of the periodontal ligament is derived from three sources: (1) blood vessels of the periapical area arise from the blood

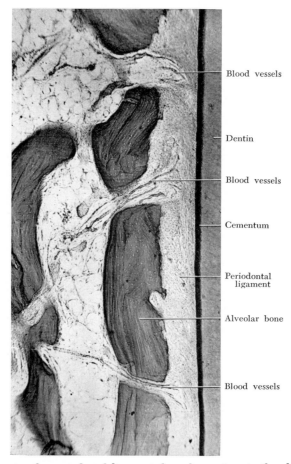

Blood vessels

Dentin

Blood vessels

Cementum

Periodontal ligament

Alveolar bone

Blood vessels

Fig. 150. Blood vessels enter the periodontal ligament through openings in the alveolar bone. (From Orban, B.: Dental histology and embryology, Philadelphia, 1929, P. Blakiston's Son & Co.)

vessels for the pulp; (2) vessels branching from the interalveolar arteries pass into the periodontal tissues through openings in the wall of the alveolus (Fig. 150) and are the main source of blood supply; and (3) arteries of the gingiva anastomose across the alveolar crest with those of the periodontal tissues. The capillaries form a rich network in the periodontal ligament.[30] Veins form glomus-like convolutions in the interstitial spaces that are emptied in the masticatory movements of the teeth and are speedily refilled from arteriovenous anastomoses when masticatory movements are reversed.

Lymphatics. A network of lymphatic vessels, following the path of the blood vessels, provides the lymph drainage of the periodontal ligament. The flow is from the ligament toward and into the adjacent alveolar bone.[18,26]

Nerves. The nerves of the periodontal ligament follow the path of the blood vessels, both from the periapical area and from the interdental and interradicular

Epithelial rests

Cementum

Alveolar bone

Periodontal ligament

Epithelial rests

Fig. 151. Epithelial rests in the periodontal ligament.

arteries through the alveolar wall. A rich plexus is formed in the periodontal ligament. Three types of nerve endings are found, one terminating in a knob-like swelling, another forming loops or rings around bundles of the principal fibers, and the third, free nerve endings that are receptors of pain. The terminal branches are free of myelin sheaths. Many nerve endings are receptors for proprioceptive stimuli. Any pressure to the crown of the tooth is transmitted to the nerve endings through the medium of the periodontal ligament. The proprioceptive endings allow accurate localization of degree and direction of pressure. Proprioceptive reflexes regulate the masticatory musculature and, by inhibition of muscular activity, protect the tooth in sudden overload. Pain reflexes are a second line of defense in an emergency, as in biting upon hard particles, bone, or birdshot.

The proprioceptive and pain sensation are not impaired by removal of the

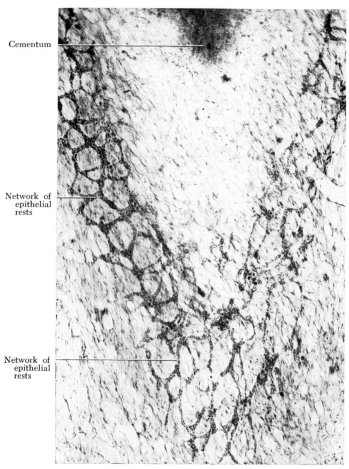

Cementum

Network of epithelial rests

Network of epithelial rests

Fig. 152. Network of epithelial rests in the periodontal ligament. (Tangential section almost parallel to root surface.)

Alveolar bone

Epithelial
rests

Cementum

Periodontal
ligament

Dentin

Blood vessel

Fig. 153. Long strand of epithelium in the periodontal ligament.

Cementoid

Cementoblast

Epithelial rests

Cementoblast

Principal fibers

Fig. 154. Pseudoglandular structure of epithelial rest in the periodontal ligament.

apical parts of the membrane, as in apicoectomy, or by removal of its gingival portion, gingivectomy, since most of the nerves of the periodontal ligament arise from the interdental nerves running in the interdental septum. As elsewhere in the body, fibers from the sympathetic system supply the blood vessels of the periodontal ligament.[1,15]

Epithelial structures. In the periodontal ligament epithelial cells are found which usually lie close to the cementum but not in contact with it (Fig. 151). They were first described by Malassez in 1884.[16] They are remnants of the epithelium of Hertwig's epithelial root sheath[5] (see Chapter II). At the time of formation of cementum, the continuous layer of epithelium lining the dentin surface breaks into strands that persist as a network parallel to the surface of the root (Fig. 152). Only in sections almost parallel to the root can the true arrangement of these epithelial strands be seen.[6] Cross or longitudinal sections

Free cementicle

Alveolar bone

Attached cementicle

Periodontal ligament

Embedded cementicle

Fig. 155. Cementicles in the periodontal ligament.

through the tooth cut through the strands of the network, and thus only isolated nests of epithelial cells appear in the sections. It is not clear whether the epithelial sheath breaks up because of degeneration of the epithelial cells, or because of active proliferation of the connective tissue, or both. The disintegration of the epithelium enables the connective tissue to approach the outer surface of the dentin and to deposit cementum on its surface. Frequently epithelial rests appear in sections as long strands (Fig. 153) or as tubules (Fig. 154). Under pathologic conditions they may proliferate and give rise to epithelial masses, associated with granulomas, cysts, or tumors of dental origin.

Cementicles. Calcified bodies, cementicles, are sometimes found in the periodontal ligament, especially in older persons. These bodies may remain free in the connective tissue, they may fuse into large calcified masses, or they may be joined with the cementum (Fig. 155). As the cementum thickens with advancing age, it may envelop these bodies. When they are adherent to the cementum, they form excementoses. The origin of these calcified bodies is not established. It is presumed that degenerated epithelial cells form the nidus for their calcification.

PHYSIOLOGIC CHANGES

Measurements and changes in dimensions during life. Several studies of the width of the periodontal ligament in human specimens have been reported.[7,8,13,14] All reports agree that the thickness of the periodontal ligament varies in different individuals, in different teeth in the same person, and in different locations on the same tooth, as is illustrated in Tables 2 and 3.

The measurements shown in the tables indicate that it is not feasible to refer to an average figure of normal width of the periodontal ligament. Measurements of a large number of cases range from 0.15 to 0.38 mm. The fact that the periodontal ligament is thinnest in the middle region of the root seems to indicate that the fulcrum of physiologic movement is in this region. The thickness of the periodontal ligament seems to be maintained by the functional movements of the

Table 2. Thickness of periodontal ligament of 154 teeth from 14 human jaws*

	Average at alveolar crest (mm.)	Average at midroot (mm.)	Average at apex (mm.)	Average for the entire tooth (mm.)
Ages 11-16 83 teeth from 4 jaws	0.23	0.17	0.24	0.21
Ages 32-50 36 teeth from 5 jaws	0.20	0.14	0.19	0.18
Ages 51-67 35 teeth from 5 jaws	0.17	0.12	0.16	0.15

*The table shows that the width of the periodontal ligament decreases with age and that it is wider at the crest and at the apex than at the midroot. (From Coolidge, E. D.: J.A.D.A. **24:**1260, 1937.)

Table 3. Comparison of periodontal ligament in different locations around the same tooth (subject 11 years of age)*

	Mesial (mm.)	Distal (mm.)	Labial (mm.)	Lingual (mm.)
Upper right central incisor, mesial and labial drift	0.12	0.24	0.12	0.22
Upper left central incisor, no drift	0.21	0.19	0.24	0.24
Upper right lateral incisor, distal and labial drift	0.27	0.17	0.11	0.15

*The table shows the variation in width of the mesial, distal, labial, and lingual sides of the same tooth. (From Coolidge, E. D.: J.A.D.A. 24:1260, 1937.)

tooth. It is thinner in functionless and embedded teeth, but cementum and bone do not fuse even in functionless teeth.

Physiologic changes. Physiologic eruptive movement of human teeth is characterized by a vertical component in compensation for occlusal wear and a mesial component in compensation for the wear at their contact areas.[31] Mesial drift seems to cause a difference in the periodontal ligament in the distal and mesial areas (Fig. 156). On the distal side of the tooth the interstitial spaces with their blood vessels, lymph vessels, and nerves appear in sections elliptic in contrast to those on the mesial side that appear round.[9] Bone resorption on the mesial side of the tooth sometimes opens marrow spaces to the periodontal ligament (Fig. 156, A). Frequently, however, the drift is so gradual that bone formation in the marrow spaces keeps pace with the resorption on the periodontal side, and the thickness of the alveolar bone is maintained. Due to the shift of the tooth, epithelial rests may become incorporated in the bone on the side from which the tooth moves.[22]

CLINICAL CONSIDERATIONS

The complex functional interrelation of the teeth and their supporting tissues brings about continuous structural changes during life. Between the two extremes of occlusal trauma and loss of function there are many intermediate stages. In loss of function the periodontal ligament becomes narrower because of decreased use of that particular tooth.[8,12,13] The regular arrangement of the principal fibers is lost, and the periodontal *ligament* is changed into a *membrane* with irregularly arranged collagenous fibers. The cementum becomes thicker but finally aplastic. It contains no Sharpey's fibers. Also, the alveolar bone is in an aplastic state and lacks Sharpey's fibers (Fig. 157, B).

For restorative dentistry the importance of these changes in structure is obvious.[21] The supporting tissues of a tooth long out of function are unable to carry the load suddenly placed upon the tooth by a restoration. This applies to bridge abutments, teeth opposing bridges or dentures, and teeth used as anchor-

Open mar-
row space

Alveolar
bone

Interstitial
space

Principal
fibers

Principal
fibers

Interstitial
space

Lamellated
bone

Bundle bone

Interstitial
space

A   B

Fig. 156. Interstitial spaces between the principal fiber bundles are round on the pressure side, **A**, and elliptic on the tension side, **B**. Marrow spaces open up on the pressure side and become interstitial spaces. *C*, Cementum. *D*, Dentin.

age for removable bridges. This may account for the inability of a patient to use a restoration immediately following its placement. Some time must elapse before the supporting tissues become again adapted to the new functional demands. An adjustment period, likewise, must be permitted following orthodontic treatment.

Acute trauma of the periodontal ligament, accidental blows, condensing of foil, or rapid mechanical separation, may produce pathologic changes such as fractures or resorption of the cementum, tears of fiber bundles, hemorrhage, and necrosis. The adjacent alveolar bone is resorbed, the periodontal ligament lengthened, and the tooth becomes loose. When trauma is eliminated, repair usually takes place. Occlusal trauma is always restricted to the intra-alveolar tissues and does not cause changes of the gingiva such as recession or pocket formation or gingivitis.

Orthodontic tooth movement depends upon bone resorption and bone formation stimulated by properly regulated pressure and tension.[19] These stimuli are transmitted through the medium of the periodontal ligament. If the move-

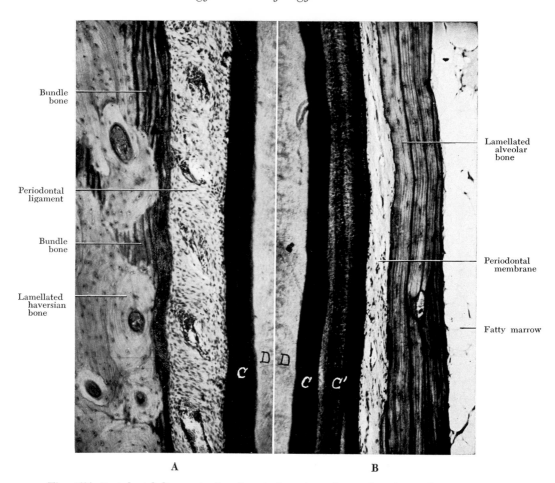

Bundle bone

Periodontal ligament

Bundle bone

Lamellated haversian bone

Lamellated alveolar bone

Periodontal membrane

Fatty marrow

A

B

Fig. 157. Periodontal *ligament* of a functioning, **A**, and periodontal *membrane* of a nonfunctioning, **B**, tooth. In the functioning tooth the periodontal ligament is wide, and principal fibers are present. Cementum, *C*, is thin. Bundle bone with Sharpey's fibers. In the nonfunctioning tooth the periodontal space is narrow, and no principal fiber bundles are present. Cementum is thick, *C* and *C'*. Alveolar bone is lamellated, containing no Sharpey's fibers. *D*, Dentin.

ment of teeth is within physiologic limits (which may vary with the individual), the initial compression of the periodontal ligament on the pressure side is compensated for by bone resorption, whereas the stretch of the bundles of the periodontal ligament on the tension side is balanced by bone apposition. The presence of an intermediate plexus in the alveolodental and interdental ligaments allows a rather speedy adjustment after orthodontic movements. The absence of an intermediate plexus in the gingival fiber bundles prolongs such a readjustment and may be responsible for the relapse, for instance, after rotation of a tooth.[24]

Under the stimulus of inflammation such as occurs in a dental granuloma, the epithelial rests of the periodontal ligament may proliferate to form a periodontal cyst around the root end of the tooth. Careful studies[10,17] have shown that 100 per cent of dental granulomas contain either proliferating or resting epithelium. Therefore, all dental granulomas must be considered as potential periodontal cysts.

REFERENCES

1. Berkelbach van der Sprenkel, H.: Zur Neurologie des Zahnes (Neurology of the tooth), Ztschr. f. mikr.-anat. Forsch **38**:1, 1935.
2. Black, G. V.: A study of the histological characters of the periosteum and peridental membrane, Chicago, 1887, W. T. Keener Co.
3. Black, G. V.: The fibers and glands of the peridental membrane, D. Cosmos **41**:101, 1899.
4. Box, K. F.: Evidence of lymphatics in the periodontium, J. Canad. D. A. **15**:8, 1949.
5. Brunn, A. v.: Ueber die Ausdehnung des Schmelzorganes und seine Bedeutung für die Zahnbildung (The extension of the enamel organ and its significance in tooth development), Arch. f. mikr. Anat. **29**:367, 1887.
6. Bruszt, P.: Ueber die netzartige Anordnung des paradentalen Epithels (The network arrangement of the epithelium in the periodontal membrane), Ztschr. f. Stomatol. **30**: 679, 1932.
7. Coolidge, E. D.: Clinical pathology and treatment of the dental pulp and periodontal tissues, Philadelphia, 1939, Lea & Febiger.
8. Coolidge, E. D.: The thickness of the human periodontal membrane, J.A.D.A. **24**:1260, 1937.
9. Gottlieb, B.: Paradental Pyorrhöe und Alveolar atrophie (Paradental pyorrhea and alveolar atrophy), Fortschr. d. Zahnheilk. **2**:363, 1926.
10. Hill, T. J.: The epithelium in dental granulomata, J. D. Res. **10**:323, 1930.
11. Ishimitsu, K.: Beitrag zur Kenntnis der Morphologie und Entwicklungsgeschichte der Glomeruli periodontii (Contribution of the knowledge of morphology and development of the periodontal glomeruli), Yokohama med. Bull. **11**:415, 1960.
12. Kellner, E.: Histologische Befunde an antagonistenlosen Zähnen (Histologic findings on teeth without antagonists), Ztschr. f. Stomatol. **26**:271, 1928.
13. Klein, A.: Systematische Untersuchungen über die Periodontalbreite (Systematic investigations on the width of the periodontal membrane), Ztschr. f. Stomatol. **26**:417, 1928.
14. Kronfeld, R.: A case of tooth fracture, with special emphasis on tissue repair and adaptation following traumatic injury, J. D. Res. **15**:429, 1935-1936.
15. Lehner, J., and Plenk, H.: Die Zähne (The teeth). In von Möllendorff, W. (editor): Handbuch der mikroskopischen Anatomie des Menschen, vol. 5, pt. 3, Berlin, 1936, Julius Springer, p. 449.
16. Malassez, M. L.: Sur l'existence de masses epithéliales dans le ligament alveolodentaire (On the existence of epithelial masses in the periodontal membrane), Compt. rend. Soc. de biol. **36**:241, 1884.
17. McCrea, M. W.: Histologic studies on the occurrence of epithelium in dental granulomata, J.A.D.A. **24**:1133, 1937.
18. Noyes, F. B.: A review of work on the lymphatics of dental origin, J.A.D.A. **14**:714, 1927.
19. Oppenheim, A.: Human tissue response to orthodontic intervention of short and long duration, Am. J. Orthodont. & Oral. Surg. **28**:263, 1942.
20. Orban, B.: Entwicklungsgeschichte und Histogenese (Embryology and histogenesis), Fortschr. d. Zahnheilk. **3**:749, 1927.
21. Orban, B.: Biologic considerations in restorative dentistry, J.A.D.A. **28**:1069, 1941.
22. Orban, B.: A contribution to the knowledge of the physiologic changes in the periodontal membrane, J.A.D.A. **16**:405, 1929.
23. Orban, B.: Dental histology and embryology, Philadelphia, 1929, P. Blakiston's Son & Co.
24. Reitan, K.: Tissue behavior during orthodontic tooth movement, Am. J. Orthodontics **46**: 881, 1960.

25. Robinson, H. B. G.: Some clinical aspects of intra-oral age changes, Geriatrics **2**:9, 1947.
26. Schweitzer, G.: Die Lymphgefässe des Zahnfleisches und der Zähne (Lymph vessels of the gingivae and teeth), Arch. f. mikr. Anat. **69**:807, 1907; **74**:927, 1909.
27. Sicher, H.: Bau und Funktion des Fixationsapparates der Meerschweinchenmolaren (Structure and function of the supporting apparatus in the teeth of guinea pigs), Ztschr. f. Stomatol. **21**:580, 1923.
28. Sicher, H.: The axial movement of continuously growing teeth, J. D. Res. **21**:201, 1942.
29. Sicher, H.: The principal fibers of the periodontal membrane, Bur **55**:2, 1954.
30. Weinmann, J. P.: Progress of gingival inflammation into the supporting structures of the teeth, J. Periodont. **12**:71, 1941.
31. Weinmann, J. P.: Bone changes related to eruption of the teeth, Angle Orthodontist **11**:83, 1941.
32. Weinmann, J. P., and Sicher, H.: Bone and bones, ed. 2, 1955, The C. V. Mosby Co.

Chapter VIII

Maxilla and mandible (alveolar process)*

DEVELOPMENT OF THE MAXILLA
AND THE MANDIBLE
   Maxilla
   Mandible

DEVELOPMENT OF THE ALVEOLAR PROCESS

STRUCTURE OF THE ALVEOLAR PROCESS

PHYSIOLOGIC CHANGES IN
THE ALVEOLAR PROCESS

INTERNAL RECONSTRUCTION OF BONE

CLINICAL CONSIDERATIONS

DEVELOPMENT OF THE MAXILLA AND THE MANDIBLE

In the beginning of the second month of fetal life the skull consists of three parts:

1. The chondrocranium, which is cartilaginous, comprises the base of the skull with the otic and nasal capsules.
2. The desmocranium, which is membranous, forms the lateral walls and roof of the brain case.
3. The appendicular or visceral part of the skull consists of the cartilaginous skeletal rods of the branchial arches.

The bones of the skull develop either by endochondral ossification, replacing the cartilage, or by intramembranous ossification in the mesenchyme. Intramembranous bone may develop in close proximity to cartilaginous parts of the skull, or directly in the desmocranium, the membranous capsule of the brain. (See Plate 2.)

The endochondral bones are the bones of the base of the skull: ethmoid bone; inferior concha (turbinate bone); body, lesser wings, basal part of greater wings, and the lateral plate of pterygoid process of the sphenoid bone; petrosal part of the temporal bone; basilar, lateral, and lower part of the squamous portion of the occipital bone. The following bones develop in the desmocranium: frontal bones; parietal bones; squamous and tympanic parts of the temporal bone; parts of the greater wings and the medial plate of the pterygoid process of the sphenoid bone; the upper part of the squamous portion of the occipital bone. All the bones of the upper face develop by intramembranous ossification, most of them close to the cartilage of the nasal capsule. The mandible develops as

*First draft submitted by Harry Sicher and Joseph P. Weinmann; revised by the editor.

intramembranous bone, lateral to the cartilage of the mandibular arch. This cartilage, Meckel's cartilage, is in its proximal parts the primordium for two of the auditory ossicles: the incus (anvil) and the malleus (hammer). The third auditory ossicle, the stapes (stirrup), develops from the proximal part of the skeleton in the second branchial arch, which then gives rise to the styloid process, the stylohyoid ligament, and part of the hyoid bone, which is completed by the derivatives of the third arch. The fourth and fifth arches form the skeleton of the larynx.

Maxilla. The human maxilla is homologous to two bones, the maxilla proper and the premaxilla. The latter, in most animals a separate bone, carries the incisors and forms the anterior part of the hard palate and the rim of the piriform aperture. The ossification centers of the premaxilla and maxilla may be separate for a very short time,[23] or only one center of ossification, common to

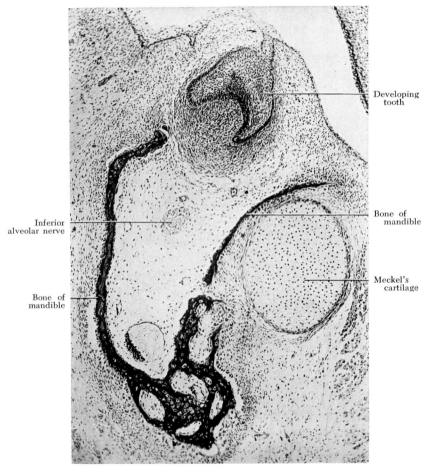

Fig. 158. Development of the mandible as intramembranous bone lateral to Meckel's cartilage (human embryo 45 mm. in length).

A

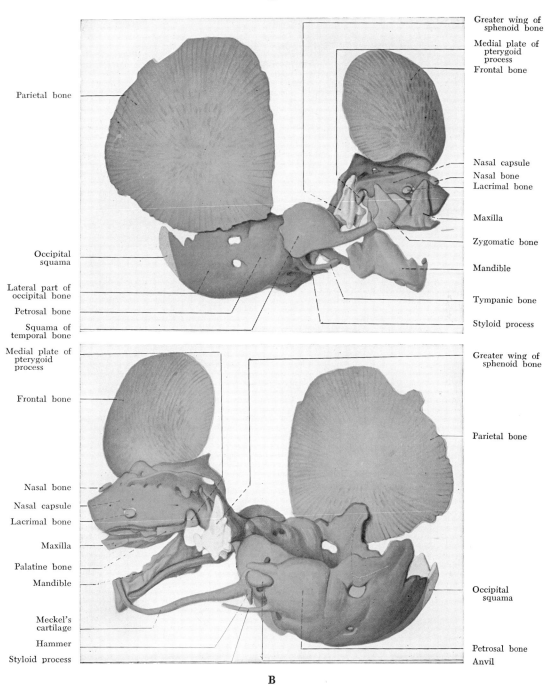

Greater wing of
sphenoid bone

Medial plate of
pterygoid
process

Frontal bone

Parietal bone

Nasal capsule
Nasal bone
Lacrimal bone

Maxilla

Zygomatic bone

Occipital
squama

Mandible

Lateral part of
occipital bone

Petrosal bone

Tympanic bone

Squama of
temporal bone

Styloid process

Medial plate of
pterygoid
process

Greater wing of
sphenoid bone

Frontal bone

Parietal bone

Nasal bone

Nasal capsule

Lacrimal bone

Maxilla

Palatine bone

Mandible

Occipital
squama

Meckel's
cartilage

Hammer

Petrosal bone

Styloid process

Anvil

B

Plate 2. Reconstruction of the skull of a human embryo 80 mm. in length. Cartilage, green. Intramembranous bones, pink. Endochondral bones, white. **A,** Right lateral view. **B,** Left lateral view after removal of left intramembranous bones. (From Sicher, H., and Tandler, J.: Anatomie für Zahnärzte [Anatomy for dentists], Vienna, 1928, Julius Springer.)

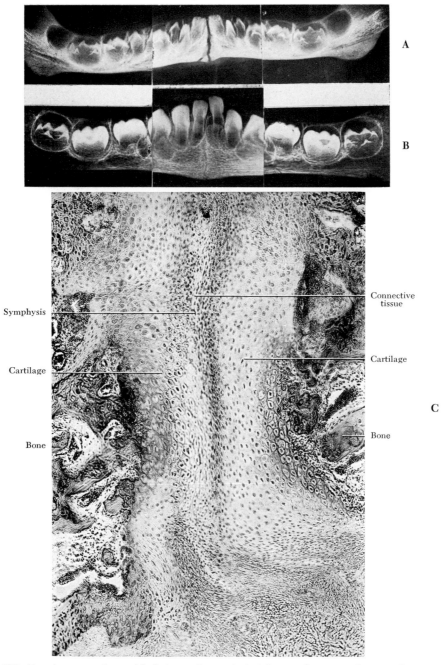

Fig. 159. Development of mandibular symphysis. **A,** Newborn infant. Symphysis wide open. Mental ossicle (roentgenogram). **B,** Child 9 months of age. Symphysis partly closed. Mental ossicles fused to the mandible (roentgenogram). **C,** Frontal section through the mandibular symphysis of a newborn infant. Connective tissue in the midline connects plates of cartilage on either side. The cartilage is later replaced by bone.

both the premaxilla and maxilla, appears. That man, therefore, may not have an independent premaxilla, even in the first developmental stages, does not change the fact that man possesses the homologue of a premaxilla. The composition of the human maxilla from premaxilla and maxilla is indicated by the incisive fissure, well visible in young skulls on the palate, extending from the incisive foramen to the alveolus of the canine.

Mandible. The mandible makes its appearance as a bilateral structure in the sixth week of fetal life as a thin plate of bone lateral to, and at some distance from, Meckel's cartilage (Fig. 158). The latter is a cylindrical rod of cartilage. Its proximal end (close to the base of the skull) is continuous with the hammer and is in contact with the anvil. Its distal end at the midline is bent upward and is in contact with the cartilage of the other side. (See Plate 2.) The greater part of Meckel's cartilage disappears without contributing to the formation of the bone of the mandible. Only a small part of the cartilage, some distance from the midline, is the site of endochondral ossification. Here the cartilage calcifies and is destroyed by chondroclasts, replaced by connective tissue and then by bone. Throughout fetal life the mandible is a paired bone. Right and left mandibles are joined in the midline by fibrocartilage in the mandibular symphysis. The cartilage at the symphysis is not derived from Meckel's cartilage but differentiates from the connective tissue in the midline. In it, small irregular bones, known as the mental ossicles, develop and at the end of the first year fuse with the mandibular body. At the same time the two halves of the mandible unite by ossification of the symphysial fibrocartilage. (See Fig. 159.)

DEVELOPMENT OF THE ALVEOLAR PROCESS

Near the end of the second month of fetal life, the maxilla, as well as the mandible, forms a groove which is open toward the surface of the oral cavity (Fig. 158). The tooth germs are contained in this groove, which also includes the alveolar nerves and vessels. Gradually, bony septa develop between the adjacent tooth germs, and much later the primitive mandibular canal is separated from the dental crypts by a horizontal plate of bone.

An alveolar process in the strict sense of the word develops only during the eruption of the teeth. It is important to realize that during growth part of the alveolar process is gradually incorporated into the maxillary or mandibular body, while it grows at a fairly rapid rate at its free borders. During the period of rapid growth, a tissue may develop at the alveolar crest that combines characteristics of cartilage and bone. It is called chondroid bone (Fig. 160).

STRUCTURE OF THE ALVEOLAR PROCESS

The alveolar process may be defined as that part of the maxilla and the mandible that forms and supports the sockets of the teeth (Fig. 161). Anatomically, no distinct boundary exists between the body of the maxilla or the mandible and their respective alveolar processes. In some places the alveolar process

Chondroid bone

Chondroid bone

Proliferation zone at alveolar crest

Resorption

Fig. 160. Vertical growth of the mandible at the alveolar crest. Formation of chondroid bone that later is replaced by typical bone.

is fused with, and partly masked by, bone which is not functionally related to the teeth. In the anterior part of the maxilla the palatine process fuses with the oral plate of the alveolar process. In the posterior part of the mandible the oblique line is superimposed laterally upon the bone of the alveolar process (Fig. 161, *D* and *E*).

As a result of its adaptation to function, two parts of the alveolar process can be distinguished. The first consists of a thin lamella of bone that surrounds the root of the tooth and gives attachment to principal fibers of the periodontal ligament. This is the alveolar bone proper. The second part is the bone that surrounds the alveolar bone and gives support to the socket. This has been called supporting alveolar bone.[13] The latter, in turn, consists of two parts: (1) compact bone, cortical plates, forming the vestibular or buccolabial and oral or lingual plates of the alveolar processes and (2) the spongy bone between these plates and the alveolar bone proper. (Fig. 161.)

The cortical plates, continuous with the compact layers of maxillary and mandibular body, are generally much thinner in the maxilla than in the man-

Fig. 161. Gross relations of alveolar processes. **A,** Horizontal section through upper alveolar process. **B,** Labiolingual section through upper lateral incisor. **C,** Labiolingual section through lower canine. **D,** Labiolingual section through lower second molar. **E,** Labiolingual section through lower third molar. (From Sicher, H., and Tandler, J.: Anatomie für Zahnärzte [Anatomy for dentists], Vienna, 1928, Julius Springer.)

Fig. 162. Diagrammatic illustration of the relation between the cementoenamel junction of adjacent teeth and the shape of the crests of the alveolar septa. (From Ritchey, B., and Orban, B.: J. Periodont. 24:75, 1953.)

dible. They are thickest in the premolar and molar regions of the lower jaw, especially on the buccal side. In the maxilla the outer cortical plate is perforated by many small openings through which blood and lymph vessels pass. In the lower jaw the cortical bone of the alveolar process is dense. In the region of the anterior teeth of both jaws the supporting bone usually is very thin. No spongy bone is found here, and the cortical plate is fused with the alveolar bone proper (Fig. 161, *B* and *C*). In such areas, notably in the premolar and molar regions of the maxilla, defects of the outer alveolar wall are fairly common. Such defects, where periodontal tissues and covering mucosa fuse, do not impair the firm attachment and function of the tooth.

The shape of the outlines of the crest of the alveolar septa in the roentgenogram is dependent upon the position of the adjacent teeth. In a healthy mouth the distance between the cementoenamel junction and the free border of the

Fig. 163. Appositional growth of the mandible by formation of circumferential lamellae. These are replaced by haversian bone; remnants of circumferential lamellae in the depth persisting as interstitial lamellae.

alveolar bone proper is fairly constant. In consequence the alveolar crest often is oblique if the neighboring teeth are inclined. In the majority of individuals the inclination is most pronounced in the premolar and molar regions, the teeth being tipped mesially. Then the cementoenamel junction of the mesial tooth is situated in a more occlusal plane than that of the distal tooth, and the alveolar crest, therefore, slopes distally (Fig. 162).

The interdental and interradicular septa contain the perforating canals of Zuckerkandl and Hirschfeld, which house the interdental and interradicular arteries, veins, lymph vessels, and nerves.

Histologically, the cortical plates consist of longitudinal lamellae and haversian systems (Fig. 163). In the lower jaw circumferential or basic lamellae reach from the body of the mandible into the cortical plates.

The study of roentgenograms permits the classification of the spongiosa of the alveolar process into two main types. In Type I the interdental and interradicular trabeculae are regular and horizontal in a ladderlike arrangement (Fig. 164, A to C). Type II shows irregularly arranged numerous and delicate interdental and interradicular trabeculae (Fig. 164, D). Both types show a variation in thickness of trabeculae and size of marrow spaces. The architecture of Type I fits well into the general idea of trajectorial pattern of spongy bone. Type II, although evidently functionally satisfactory, lacks a distinct trajectorial pattern, which seems to be compensated for by the greater number of trabeculae in any given area. From the apical part of the socket of lower molars trabeculae are sometimes seen radiating in a slightly distal direction. These trabeculae are less prominent in the upper jaw because of the proximity of the nasal cavity and the maxillary sinus. The marrow spaces in the alveolar process may contain hemopoietic marrow, but usually they contain fatty marrow. In the condylar process, in the angle of the mandible, in the maxillary tuberosity, and in other foci, hemopoietic cellular marrow is found frequently, even in adults.[4,17]

The alveolar bone proper, which forms the inner wall of the socket (Fig. 164), is perforated by many openings that carry branches of the interalveolar nerves and blood vessels into the periodontal ligament (see Chapter VII), and it is, therefore, called the cribriform plate. The alveolar bone proper consists partly of lamellated and partly of bundle bone. Some lamellae of the lamellated bone are arranged roughly parallel to the surface of the adjacent marrow spaces, whereas others form haversian systems. Bundle bone is that bone in which the principal fibers of the periodontal ligament are anchored. The term bundle bone was chosen because the bundles of the principal fibers continue into the bone as Sharpey's fibers. The bundle bone is characterized by the scarcity of the fibrils in the intercellular substance. These fibrils, moreover, are all arranged at right angles to Sharpey's fibers. The bundle bone appears much lighter in preparations stained with silver than lamellated bone because of the reduced number of fibrils (Fig. 165). In some areas the alveolar bone proper consists mainly of bundle bone. Such areas are visible in a roentgenogram by their greater radiopacity.

Fig. 164. Supporting trabeculae between alveoli. **A,** Roentgenogram of a mandible. **B,** Mesio-distal section through mandibular molars showing alveolar bone proper and supporting bone. **C,** Type I of alveolar spongiosa. Note regular horizontal trabeculae. **D,** Type II of alveolar spongiosa. Note irregularly arranged trabeculae. (Courtesy Dr. N. Brescia, Chicago, Ill.)

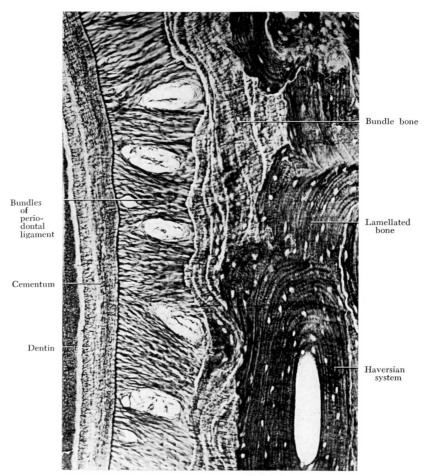

Fig. 165. Bundle bone and haversian bone on the distal alveolar wall, separated by a reversal line (silver impregnation).

PHYSIOLOGIC CHANGES IN THE ALVEOLAR PROCESS

The internal structure of bone is adapted to mechanical stresses. It changes continuously during growth and alteration of functional stresses. In the jaws structural changes are correlated to the growth, eruption, movements, wear, and loss of teeth. All these processes are made possible only by a coordination of destructive and formative activities. Specialized cells, the osteoclasts, have the function of eliminating overaged bony tissue or bone that is no longer adapted to mechanical forces, whereas osteoblasts produce new bone.

Osteoclasts are as a rule multinucleated giant cells (Fig. 166, *A*). The number of nuclei in one cell may rise to a dozen or more. However, occasionally uninuclear osteoclasts are found. The nuclei are vesicular, showing a prominent nucleolus and little chromatin. The cell body is irregularly oval or club shaped and may show many branching processes. In general, osteoclasts are found in

Fig. 166. Resorption and apposition of bone. **A,** Osteoclasts in Howship's lacunae. **B,** Osteoblasts along a bone trabecula. Layer of osteoid tissue as a sign of bone formation (high magnification).

baylike depressions in the bone that are called Howship's lacunae. They are formed by the activity of the osteoclasts. The cytoplasm that is in contact with the bone is striated. These striations have been explained as the expression of a secretory activity of these cells. The osteoclasts seem to produce proteolytic enzymes that destroy or dissolve the organic constituents of the bone matrix and chelating substances that bring about the solubility of the otherwise insoluble bone salts. A decalcification of bone in the living organism has often been claimed but has never been demonstrated.

Osteoclasts differentiate from undifferentiated mesenchymal reserve cells most probably by fusion of several cells. The stimulus that leads to the differentiation of mesenchymal cells into osteoclasts is not known. Osteoclastic resorption of bone is partly genetically patterned, partly functionally determined. Overaged bone seems to stimulate the differentiation of osteoclasts,[8] possibly by chemical changes that are the consequence of degeneration and final necrosis of the osteocytes.

New bone is produced by the activity of osteoblasts (Fig. 166, *B*). These cells also differentiate from undifferentiated mesenchymal reserve cells of the loose connective tissue. Functioning osteoblasts are arranged along the surface of the growing bone in a continuous layer.

The osteoblasts produce the intercellular substance of bone consisting of collagenous fibrils bound together by mucopolysaccharides. It is at first devoid of mineral salts and at this stage is termed osteoid tissue. While the intercellular substance is produced, some of the osteoblasts become embedded in it as osteocytes. Normally, the organic matrix calcifies immediately after formation.[3,12,23]

INTERNAL RECONSTRUCTION OF BONE

The bone in the alveolar process is identical to bone elsewhere in the body and is in a constant state of flux. During the growth of the maxilla and the mandible, bone is deposited on the outer surfaces of the cortical plates. In the mandible, with its thick, compact cortical plates, bone is deposited in the shape of basic or circumferential lamellae (Fig. 163). When the lamellae reach a certain thickness, they are replaced from the inside by haversian bone. This reconstruction is correlated to the functional and nutritional demands of the bone. In the haversian canals, closest to the surface, osteoclasts differentiate and resorb the haversian lamellae and part of the circumferential lamellae. The resorbed bone is replaced by proliferating loose connective tissue. After a time the resorption ceases and new bone is apposed onto the old. The scalloped outline of Howship's lacunae that turn their convexity toward the old bone remains visible as a darkly stained cementing line, reversal line. This is in contrast to those cementing lines that correspond to a rest period in an otherwise continuous process of bone apposition. They are called resting lines (Fig. 163). Resting and reversal lines are found between layers of bone of varying age.

Wherever a muscle, tendon, or ligament is attached to the surface of bone, Sharpey's fibers can be seen penetrating the basic lamellae. During replacement of the latter by haversian systems, fragments of bone containing Sharpey's fibers remain in the deeper layers. Thus, the presence of interstitial lamellae containing Sharpey's fibers indicates the former level of the surface.[21]

Alterations in the structure of the alveolar bone are of great importance in connection with the physiologic eruptive movements of the teeth. These movements are directed mesiocclusally. At the alveolar fundus the continual apposition of bone can be recognized by resting lines separating parallel layers of bundle bone. When the bundle bone has reached a certain thickness, it is resorbed partly from the marrow spaces and then replaced by lamellated bone or spongy trabeculae. The presence of bundle bone indicates the level at which the alveolar fundus was situated previously. During the mesial drift of a tooth, bone is apposed on the distal and resorbed on the mesial alveolar wall (Fig. 167). The distal wall is made up almost entirely of bundle bone. However, the osteoclasts in the adjacent marrow spaces remove part of the bundle bone when

Cementum

Bundle bone

Periodontal ligament

Cementum

Resorption

Lamellated bone

Periodontal ligament

Resorption

A   B

Fig. 167. Mesial drift indicated by arrow. **A,** Apposition of bundle bone on the distal alveolar wall. **B,** Resorption of bone on the mesial alveolar wall. (From Weinmann, J. P.: Angle Orthodontist **11**:83, 1941.)

it reaches a certain thickness. In its place lamellated bone is laid down (Fig. 165).

On the mesial alveolar wall of a drifting tooth, signs of active resorption are the presence of Howship's lacunae containing osteoclasts (Fig. 167). Bundle bone, however, on this side is always present in some areas but forms merely a thin layer (Fig. 168). This is due to the fact that the mesial drift of a tooth does not occur simply as a bodily movement. Thus, resorption does not involve the entire mesial surface of the alveolus at one and the same time. Moreover, periods of resorption alternate with periods of rest and repair. It is during these periods of repair that bundle bone is formed, and detached periodontal fibers are again secured. Islands of bundle bone are separated from the lamellated bone by reversal lines that turn their convexities toward the lamellated bone (Fig. 168).

During these changes compact bone may be replaced by spongy bone or spongy bone may change into compact bone. This type of internal reconstruction of bone can be observed in physiologic mesial drift or in orthodontic mesial

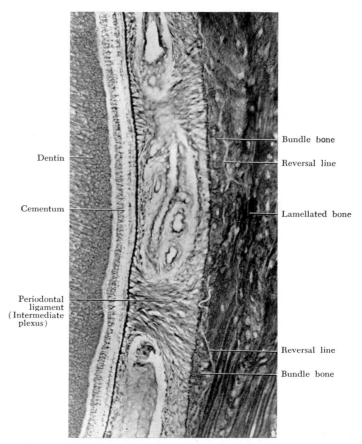

Dentin

Cementum

Periodontal
ligament
(Intermediate
plexus)

Bundle bone

Reversal line

Lamellated bone

Reversal line

Bundle bone

Fig. 168. Mesial alveolar wall consisting mostly of lamellated bone, islands of bundle bone anchoring principal fibers of the periodontal ligament.

or distal movement of teeth. In these movements an interdental septum shows apposition on one surface and resorption on the other. If the alveolar bone proper is thickened by apposition of bundle bone, the interdental marrow spaces widen and advance in the direction of apposition. Conversely, if the plate of the alveolar bone proper is thinned by resorption, apposition of bone occurs on those surfaces that face the marrow spaces. The result is a reconstructive shift of the interdental septum.

CLINICAL CONSIDERATIONS

Bone, although one of the hardest tissues of the human body, is, biologically, a highly plastic tissue. Where bone is covered by a vascularized connective tissue, it is exceedingly sensitive to pressure, whereas tension acts, generally, as a stimulus to the production of new bone. It is this biologic plasticity that enables the orthodontist to move teeth without disrupting their relations to the alveolar bone. Bone is resorbed on the side of pressure and apposed on the side

A   B

Fig. 169. Osteoporosis of the alveolar process caused by inactivity of the tooth that has no antagonist. Labiolingual sections through upper molars of the same individual. **A,** Disappearance of bony trabeculae after loss of function. Plane of the mesiobuccal root. Alveolar bone proper remains intact. **B,** Normal spongy bone in the plane of the mesiobuccal root of the functioning tooth. (From Kellner, E.: Ztschr. f. Stomatol. **18:**59, 1920.)

of tension, thus allowing the entire alveolus to shift with the tooth.

The adaptation of bone to function is quantitative as well as qualitative. Whereas increase in functional forces leads to formation of new bone, decreased function leads to a decrease in the volume of bone. This can be observed in the supporting bone of teeth that have lost their antagonists.[10] Here, the spongy bone around the alveolus shows marked rarefaction: the bone trabeculae are less numerous and very thin (Fig. 169). The alveolar bone proper, however, is generally well preserved because it continues to receive some stimuli by the tension of the periodontal tissues.

During healing of fractures or extraction wounds, an embryonic type of bone is formed, which only later is replaced by mature bone. The embryonic bone, immature or coarse fibrillar bone, is characterized by the greater number, size, and irregular arrangement of the osteocytes and the irregular course of its fibrils. The greater number of cells and the reduced volume of calcified intercellular substance render this immature bone more radiolucent than mature bone. This explains why bony callus cannot be seen in roentgenograms at a time when histologic examination of a fracture reveals a well-developed union between the fragments and why a socket after an extraction wound appears to be empty at a time when it is almost filled with immature bone. The visibility in radiograms lags two or three weeks behind actual formation of new bone.

REFERENCES

1. Becks, H.: Dangerous consequences of vitamin D overdosage on dental and paradental structures, J.A.D.A. **29:**1947, 1942.
2. Becks, H.: The effect of deficiencies of the filtrate fraction of the vitamin B complex and nicotinic acid on teeth and oral structures, J. Periodont. **13:**18, 1942.
3. Bloom, W., and Bloom, M. A.: Calcification and ossification. Calcification of developing bones in embryonic and newborn rats, Anat. Rec. **78:**497, 1940.
4. Box, H. K.: Red bone marrow in human jaws, Toronto, 1933, University of Toronto Press.
5. Breitner, C.: Bone changes resulting from experimental orthodontic treatment, Am. J. Orthodont. & Oral Surg. **26:**521, 1940.
6. Brodie, A. G.: Some recent observations on the growth of the mandible, Angle Orthodontist **10:**63, 1940.
7. Brodie, A. G.: On the growth pattern of the human head from the third month to the eighth year of life, Am. J. Anat. **68:**209, 1941.
8. Gottlieb, B.: Zur Aetiologie und Therapie der Alveolarpyorrhoe (Etiology and therapy of alveolar pyorrhea), Oesterr. Ztschr. f. Stomatol. **18:**59, 1920.
9. Ham, A. W.: Histology, ed. 2, Philadelphia, 1953, J. B. Lippincott Co.
10. Kellner, E.: Histologische Befunde an antagonistenlosen Zähnen (Histological findings on teeth without antagonists), Ztschr. f. Stomatol. **26:**271, 1928.
11. Lehner, J., and Plenk, H.: Die Zähne (The teeth). In von Möllendorff, W. (editor): Handbuch der mikroskopischen Anatomie des Menschen, vol. 5, pt. 3, Berlin, 1936, Julius Springer.
12. McLean, F. C., and Bloom, W.: Calcification and ossification. Calcification in normal growing bone, Anat. Rec. **78:**333, 1940.
13. Orban, B.: Dental histology and embryology, ed. 1, Chicago, 1928, Rogers Printing Co.
14. Orban, B.: A contribution to the knowledge of the physiologic changes in the periodontal membrane, J.A.D.A. **16:**405, 1929.
15. Ritchey, B., and Orban, B.: The crests of the interdental alveolar septa, J. Periodont. **24:**75, 1953.
16. Schaffer, J.: Die Verknöcherung des Unterkiefers (Ossification of the mandible), Arch. f. mikr. Anat. **32:**266, 1888.
17. Schoenbauer, F.: Histologische Befunde bei Kieferosteomyelitis (Histologic findings in osteomyelitis of the jaw), Ztschr. f. Stomatol. **35:**820, 1937.
18. Schour, I., and Massler, M.: Endocrines and dentistry, J.A.D.A. **30:**595, 763, 943, 1943.
19. Sicher, H., and Tandler, J.: Anatomie für Zahnärzte (Anatomy for dentists), Vienna, 1928, Julius Springer.
20. Sicher, H.: Oral anatomy, ed. 2, St. Louis, 1952, The C. V. Mosby Co.
21. Weinmann, J. P.: Das Knochenbild bei Störungen der physiologischen Wanderung der Zähne (Bone in disturbances of the physiologic mesial drift), Ztschr. f. Stomatol. **24:**397, 1926.
22. Weinmann, J. P.: Bone changes related to eruption of the teeth, Angle Orthodontist **11:**83, 1941.
23. Weinmann, J. P., and Sicher, H.: Bone and bones, ed. 2, St. Louis, 1955, The C. V. Mosby Co.

GENERAL CHARACTERISTICS
TRANSITION BETWEEN SKIN AND
  MUCOUS MEMBRANE
SUBDIVISIONS OF THE ORAL MUCOSA

Masticatory mucosa
    Gingiva
        Blood and nerve supply
    Dentogingival junction
        Development
        Structure of the epithelial attachment
        Shift of the dentogingival junction
        First stage
        Second stage
        Third stage
        Fourth stage
        Mode of attachment of epithelium
        Gingival sulcus
    Hard palate
        Incisive papilla
        Palatine rugae (transverse palatine ridges)
        Epithelial pearls

Lining mucosa
    Lip and cheek
    Vestibular fornix and alveolar mucosa
    Mucous membrane of the inferior surface of
       the tongue and of the floor of the oral
       cavity
    Soft palate

Specialized mucosa
    Dorsal lingual mucosa
    Taste buds

CLINICAL CONSIDERATIONS

Chapter IX

Oral mucous membrane*

GENERAL CHARACTERISTICS

The oral cavity, as the first part of the digestive tract, serves a variety of functions. It is both the portal of entry and the place of mastication of food. It contains the taste organs. The saliva secreted into the oral cavity not only lubricates the food to facilitate swallowing but also contains enzymes that initiate digestion. The oral cavity is lined throughout by a mucous membrane. This term designates the lining of body cavities that communicate with the outside.

The morphologic structure of the mucous membrane varies in the different areas of the oral cavity in correlation with the functions of specific zones and the mechanical influences that bear upon them. Around the teeth and on the hard palate, for example, the mucous membrane is exposed to mechanical forces in the mastication of rough and hard food, whereas on the floor of the mouth it is largely protected by the tongue. This is the reason the mucous membrane around the teeth and on the hard palate differs in structure from that of the floor of the mouth, cheeks, and lips.

The mucous membrane is attached to the underlying structures by a layer of connective tissue, the submucosa, which also varies in character in different areas. The oral mucous membrane itself is composed of two layers, the lamina

---

*First draft submitted by Balint J. Orban and Harry Sicher; revised by the editor.

Keratinous layer
Granular layer
Prickle cell layer
Basal layer
Basement membrane
Capillaries
Lamina propria
Submucous layer
Artery
Vein
Periosteum
Bone

Opening of duct
Intraepithelial nerve endings
Subepithelial nerve plexus
Nerve
Gland

Fig. 170. Diagrammatic drawing of the oral mucous membrane (epithelium, lamina propria, and submucosa).

propria and the surface epithelium. (See Fig. 170.) A basement membrane separates the lamina propria from the stratified squamous epithelium.

In man the stratified squamous epithelium is keratinized in some areas only, viz., the gingiva and the hard palate. Keratinized epithelium and nonkeratinized epithelium differ not only by the presence or the lack of a horny layer. In both types, the basal cells form a single layer of high cuboidal cells that are anchored to the basement membrane by short protoplasmic processes. In the next layers the cells are irregularly polyhedral, larger in nonkeratinized areas than in the keratinized zones. In keratinizing epithelium, intercellular spaces and, therefore, "intercellular bridges" are conspicuous but are insignificant or absent in nonkeratinizing areas, for instance, in the cheek. However, in all zones they are referred to as prickle cells, although the "prickly" appearance of isolated cells is characteristic only for cells with conspicuous "intercellular bridges."

It is known, however, that the "bridges" do not form a continuity between cells and that tonofibrils do not cross from cell to cell. Instead, the "bridges" consist of two processes of adjacent cells. Where these processes come into contact, the cells adhere to each other by specialized structures, the desmosomes. These are ultramicroscopic structures consisting of two plates at the cell surfaces cementing two cells together. The tonofibrils end at these plates. Desmosomes are also present in nonkeratinized epithelium, but the lack of "bridges" is caused by the lack of intercellular spaces, the cells contacting each other in broad surfaces. Adhesion, however, here also is provided by irregularly distributed desmosomes.

Toward the surface the polyhedral cells of the prickle cell layer everywhere flatten and at the same time widen considerably. No further changes occur in the nonkeratinizing epithelium. In areas in which the epithelium is keratinized, the cells of the prickle cell layer flatten and pass first into the granular layer and then into the keratinous layer as they move toward the surface. The cells of the granular layer contain keratohyalin granules that are basophil and stain blue in hematoxylin-eosin preparation. The nuclei of the flattened cells are pyknotic. The keratinous layer is characterized by its acidophil nature. Here most, if not all, the nuclei have disappeared. The structure of the granular and keratinous layers varies in the different regions of the oral cavity. A stratum lucidum, such as is seen in regions of the skin where cornification is abundant, is, as a rule, missing in the oral mucosa.

The lamina propria is a layer of dense connective tissue of variable thickness. Its papillae, which indent the epithelium, carry both blood vessels and nerves. Some of the latter actually pass into the epithelium. The papillae of the lamina propria vary considerably in length and width in different areas. The inward epithelial projections between the papillae are described as epithelial pegs because of their appearance in sections. In reality, however, they form a continuous network of epithelial ridges. The arrangement of the papillae increases the area of contact between lamina propria and epithelium and facilitates the exchange of material between blood vessels and epithelium. The presence of papillae permits the subdivision of the lamina propria into the outer papillary and the deeper reticular layer.

The submucosa consists of connective tissue of varying thickness and density. It attaches the mucous membrane to the underlying structures. Whether this attachment is loose or firm depends upon the character of the submucosa. Glands, blood vessels, nerves, and also adipose tissue are present in this layer. It is in the submucosa that the larger arteries divide into smaller branches, which then enter the lamina propria. Here they again divide to form a subepithelial capillary network in the papillae. The veins originating from the capillary network follow the course of the arteries. The blood vessels are accompanied by a rich network of lymph vessels. The sensory nerves of the mucous membrane traverse the submucosa. The nerve fibers are myelinated but lose their myelin sheath in the mucous membrane before splitting into their end arborizations. Sensory nerve endings of various types are found in the papillae. Some of the fibers enter the epithelium, where they terminate between the epithelial cells as free nerve endings. The blood vessels are accompanied by nonmyelinated visceral nerve fibers that supply their smooth muscles. Other visceral fibers supply the glands.

The oral cavity can be divided into two parts: the vestibulum oris (vestibule) and the cavum oris proprium (oral cavity proper). The vestibule is that part of the oral cavity which is bounded by the lips and cheeks on the outer side and by the teeth and alveolar processes on the inner side. The oral cavity proper lies within the dental arches and bones of the jaws, being limited posteriorly toward the pharynx by the anterior pillars of the fauces, or the palatoglossal arches.

TRANSITION BETWEEN SKIN AND MUCOUS MEMBRANE

The transitional zone between the skin covering the outer surface of the lip and the true mucous membrane lining the inner surface is the red zone or the vermilion border of the lip. It is present in man only (Fig. 171). The skin of the lip is covered by a keratinized epithelium of moderate thickness. The papillae of the connective tissue are few and short. Many sebaceous glands are found in connection with the hairs. Sweat glands occur between them. The epidermis is a

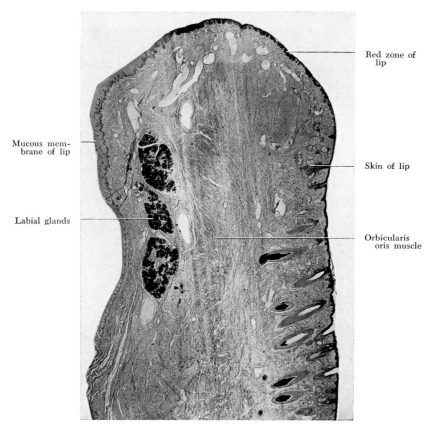

Fig. 171. Section through the lip.

keratinized stratified squamous epithelium with a rather thick keratin layer. The transitional region is characterized by numerous densely arranged long papillae of the lamina propria, reaching deep into the epithelium and carrying large capillary loops close to the surface. Thus, blood is visible through the thin parts of the translucent epithelium covering the papillae; hence the red color of the lips. Because this transitional zone contains only occasional single sebaceous glands, it is particularly subject to drying if not moistened by the tongue.

The boundary between the red zone of the lip and the mucous membrane is found where keratinization of the transitional zone ends. The epithelium of the mucous membrane of the lip is not keratinized.

SUBDIVISIONS OF THE ORAL MUCOSA

In studying any mucous membrane, the following features should be considered: (1) type of covering epithelium, (2) structure of the lamina propria, especially as to its density, thickness, and presence or lack of elasticity, (3) the type of junction between the epithelium and lamina propria, and (4) its fixation to the underlying structures, in other words, the submucous layer. A submucosa may be present or absent as a separate and well-defined layer. Looseness or density of its texture determines whether the mucous membrane is movably or immovably attached to the deeper layers. Presence or absence and location of adipose tissue or glands should also be noted.

The oral mucosa may be divided primarily into three different types. During mastication some parts are subjected to strong forces of pressure and friction. These parts, gingiva and covering of the hard palate, may be termed *masticatory mucosa*. The second type of oral mucosa is that which is merely the protective lining of the oral cavity. These areas may be termed *lining mucosa*. They comprise the mucosa of the lips and the cheeks, the mucosa of the vestibular fornix and that of the upper and lower alveolar process peripheral to the gingiva proper, the mucosa of the floor of the mouth extending to the inner surface of the lower alveolar process, the mucosa of the inferior surface of the tongue, and, finally, the mucous membrane of the soft palate. The third type of mucosa is represented by the covering of the dorsal surface of the tongue and is highly specialized; hence the term *specialized mucosa*.

The epithelium of the masticatory mucosa is, as a rule, keratinized, while that of the lining mucosa is nonkeratinized. The differences in these types of epithelium are, however, not just the presence or absence of a layer of keratin but extend into all layers of the epithelium and to the junction of the lamina propria with the epithelium and the lamina propria itself. A comparison of the palatal and buccal mucosa shows that the keratinized epithelium is thinner than the nonkeratinized epithelium. The former has a granular layer, the basal cells are larger but the average cell size is smaller, and the cells have an angular shape. Further, it is characterized by having many tonofibrils, wider intercellular spaces, and "prickles" that form intercellular "bridges." The basement membrane contains more reticular fibers, and its papillae are high and more closely spaced. From these all pervasive differences it appears that it would be best to state that the masticatory mucosa is a keratinized mucosa, while the lining mucosa is a nonkeratinized mucosa.

Masticatory mucosa

Gingiva and covering of the hard palate have in common the thickness and keratinization of the epithelium, the thickness, density, and firmness of the lamina propria, and finally, their immovable attachment to the deep structures. In the gingiva, formation of true keratin, orthokeratosis, is in a majority of individuals replaced by parakeratosis. Sometimes the epithelium is nonkeratinized although the gingiva has to be regarded as normal. In the structure of the submucosa the areas of gingiva and hard palate differ markedly. In the gingiva a well-differentiated submucous layer cannot be recognized. Instead, the dense and inelastic connective tissue of the lamina propria fuses with the periosteum of the alveolar process or is attached to the cervical region of the tooth and the marginal areas of the alveolar process.

In contrast to this, the covering of the hard palate has, with the exception of narrow areas, a distinct submucous layer. It is absent only in the peripheral zone, where the palatine tissue is identical with the gingiva, and in a narrow zone along the midline, starting in front with the palatine or incisive papilla and continuing as the palatine raphe over the entire length of the hard palate. In spite of the presence of a well-defined submucous layer in the wide lateral fields of the hard palate between the palatine raphe and palatine gingiva, the mucous membrane is immovably attached to the periosteum of maxillary and palatine bones. This attachment is accomplished by dense bands and trabeculae of fibrous connective tissue that join the lamina propria of the mucous membrane to the periosteum. The submucous space is thus subdivided into irregular intercommunicating compartments of various sizes. These are filled with adipose tissue in the anterior part and with glands in the posterior part of the hard palate. The presence of fat or glands in the submucous layer acts as a cushion comparable to that which may be found in the subcutaneous tissue of the palm of the hand and the sole of the foot.

Gingiva

The gingiva surrounding the teeth is subjected to forces of friction and pressure in the process of mastication. The character of this tissue shows that it is adapted to these forces. The gingiva is limited sharply on the outer surface of both jaws by a scalloped line, the mucogingival junction, which separates it from the alveolar mucosa (Fig. 172). The gingiva is normally pink, sometimes with a grayish tinge, dependent on the variable thickness of the stratum corneum. The alveolar mucosa is red, showing numerous small vessels close to the surface. A similar line of demarcation is found on the inner surface of the lower jaw be-

Fig. 172. Surface of the gingiva of a young adult. (Courtesy Dr. A. Ogilvie.)

tween the gingiva and the mucosa on the floor of the mouth. On the palate there is no sharp dividing line because of the dense structure and firm attachment of the entire palatal mucosa.

According to the behavior of the surface layer, four types of gingival epithelium can be distinguished. They are described as follows (Fig. 173).

1. In fully keratinized epithelium the surface layers consist of flat, tightly packed, horny scales, the transformed surface cells. Nuclei are absent.
2. In parakeratosis the surface cells seem to consist of keratin but have retained pyknotic nuclei.
3. In incomplete parakeratosis specific stains, e.g., Mallory's stain, show the surface layer divided into two layers. The deeper layer stains like keratin, but this stain is lost in the superficial layer, probably by the influence of oral fluids on the incompletely differentiated keratin of the nuclei-containing cells.
4. Where keratinization is lacking, the flat surface cells retain their nuclei.

The most frequent type is parakeratosis, about 50 per cent. The next frequent type is incomplete parakeratosis, 25 per cent. Then follows full keratinization, 15 per cent, and nonkeratinization, 10 per cent. Presence of inflammation and/or glycogen seems progressively to interfere with keratinization.

The rate of cell renewal is expressed in the mitotic index, i.e., the number of cells in mitosis of 1,000 cells counted. The index increases with age. In individuals between 50 and 70 years of age it is higher by 50 per cent than in the group between 25 and 35 years of age. In the latter it was calculated as 1.37, which is higher than the index in the epidermis. Presence or lack of a granular layer also influences the mitotic index. It is twice as high in the absence of the granular layer. There is, however, no correlation of the mitotic index to the variations of keratinization.

The gingival epithelium covers the margin of the gingiva and continues into

Fig. 173. Variations of the gingival epithelium. **A,** Orthokeratosis. **B,** Lack of keratinization. **C,** Parakeratosis.

the epithelial lining of the gingival sulcus to terminate on the surface of the tooth as the epithelial attachment (see discussion on the structure of the epithelial attachment).

The cells of the basal layer may contain pigment granules (melanin) (Fig. 174). While pigmentation is a normal occurrence in Negroes, it is often found, too, in the Caucasian race, especially in people with a dark complexion. It is most abundant in the bases of the interdental papillae. It may increase considerably in persons with Addison's disease, destruction of the adrenal cortex. The melanin pigment is stored by the basal cells of the epithelium, but these cells do not produce the pigment. The melanin is elaborated by specific cells, melanoblasts, situated in the basal layer of the epithelium (Fig. 175). These cells have long processes and are also termed dendritic cells. In the usual hematoxylin-eosin specimen these cells have a clear cytoplasm and are also known as clear cells.

Cells of human oral epithelium show, as human epidermal epithelium, a sex difference. In females the majority of the nuclei contain a large chromatin particle adjacent to the nuclear membrane.[21]

The lamina propria of the gingiva consists of dense connective tissue that is

Fig. 174. Pigment in the basal cells of the gingiva of a Negro.

Fig. 175. Dendritic melanoblasts in the basal layer of the epithelium. Biopsy of normal gingiva. (×1,000.) (From Aprile, E. C. de: Arch. hist. normal y Pat. 3:473, 1947.)

Fig. 176. Macrophages in the normal gingiva. Rio Hortega stain. (×1,000.) (From Aprile, E. C. de: Arch hist. normal y Pat. 3:473, 1947.)

not highly vascular. Macrophages are present in the perivascular loose connective tissue of the normal gingiva (Fig. 176). These cells have an important function in the defense mechanism of the body and in repair. The papillae of the connective tissue are characteristically long, slender, and numerous. The presence of these high papillae permits the sharp demarcation of the gingiva and alveolar mucosa in which the papillae are quite low (Fig. 177). The tissue of the lamina propria contains only few elastic fibers that are, for the most part, confined to the walls of the blood vessels. The gingival fibers of the periodontal ligament enter into the lamina propria, attaching the gingiva firmly to the teeth (see Chapter VII). The gingiva is also immovably and firmly attached to the periosteum of the alveolar bone. Here, a dense connective tissue, consisting of coarse collagenous bundles (Fig. 178, A), extends from the bone to the lamina propria. In con-

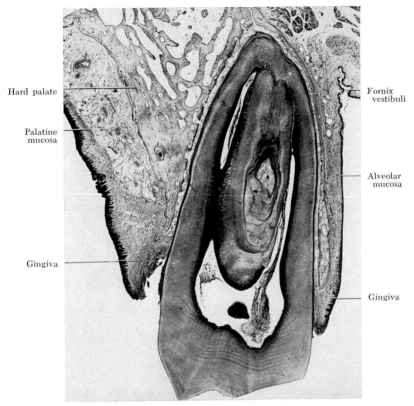

Hard palate

Palatine mucosa

Gingiva

Fornix vestibuli

Alveolar mucosa

Gingiva

Fig. 177. Structural differences between the gingiva and alveolar mucosa. Upper premolar.

trast, the submucosa underlying the alveolar mucous membrane is loosely textured (Fig. 178, *B*). The fiber bundles of the lamina propria of the alveolar mucosa are thin and regularly interwoven. The alveolar mucosa and submucosa contain numerous elastic fibers that are thin in the lamina propria and thicker in the submucosa.

Collagen fibers arranged in strong bundles arise from the cervical area of cementum (gingival group of periodontal ligament fibers), in part from the outer surface of the alveolar process. They interlace with bundles of varying direction. Circular fibers in the attached gingiva are sometimes quite conspicuous. The gingival fibers are functionally arranged in the following groups[8]:

1. *Gingival ligament:* Extends from the cervical cementum into the lamina propria of the gingiva. The fibers of the gingival ligament constitute the most numerous group of gingival fibers.
2. *Alveologingival group:* The fibers arise from the alveolar crest and extend into the lamina propria.
3. *Circular group:* A small group of fibers that circle the tooth and interlace with the other fibers.
4. *Dentoperiosteal fibers:* These fibers can be followed from the cementum

Epithelium

Lamina
propria

A

B

Submucosa

Fig. 178. Differences between the gingiva, **A,** and the alveolar mucosa, **B.** Silver impregnation of collagenous fibers. Note the coarse bundles of fibers in the gingiva and finer fibers in the alveolar mucosa.

into the periosteum of the alveolar crest and of the vestibular and oral surfaces of the alveolar bone.

Blood and nerve supply. The blood supply of the gingiva is derived chiefly from the branches of the alveolar arteries that penetrate the interdental septa.[42] The interdental alveolar arteries perforate the alveolar crest in the interdental spaces and end in the gingiva, supplying the interdental papilla and the adjacent areas of the buccal and lingual gingiva. In the gingiva these branches anas-

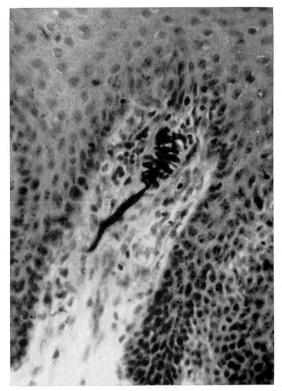

Fig. 179A. Meissner tactile corpuscle in the human gingiva. Silver impregnation after Biel-schowsky-Gros. (From Gairns, F. W., and Aitchison, J. A.: D. Rec. **70**:180, 1950.)

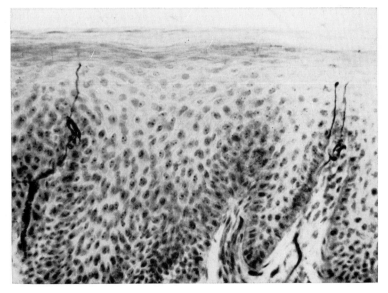

Fig. 179B. Intraepithelial "ultraterminal" extensions and nerve endings in the human gingiva. Silver impregnation after Bielschowsky-Gros. (From Gairns, F. W., and Aitchison, J. A.: D. Rec. **70**:180, 1950.)

tomose with superficial branches of arteries that supply the oral and vestibular mucosa and marginal gingiva, for instance, with branches of the lingual, buccinator, mental, and palatine arteries. There is a rich network of lymph vessels in the gingiva along the blood vessels leading to submental and submandibular lymph nodes.

The gingiva is well innervated.[10] Different types of nerve endings can be observed, such as the Meissner or Krause corpuscles, end bulbs, loops, or fine fibers that enter the epithelium as "ultraterminal" fibers. (Figs. 179A and 179B.)

The gingiva can be divided into the *free gingiva,* the *attached gingiva* (Figs. 180A and 180B),[29] and the *interdental papillae.* The dividing line between the free and the attached gingiva is the *free gingival groove,* which runs parallel to the margin of the gingiva at a distance of 0.5 to 1.5 mm. The free gingival groove, not always visible macroscopically, appears in histologic sections (Fig. 181) as a shallow V-shaped notch corresponding to the heavy epithelial ridge that divides the free and the attached gingiva. The free gingival groove develops at the level of, or somewhat apical to, the bottom of the gingival sulcus. In some cases the free gingival groove is not so well defined as in others, and then the division between the free and the attached gingiva is not clear. The free gingival groove and the epithelial ridge are probably caused by functional impacts upon the free gingiva, folding the movable free part back upon the attached and immovable zone.

The attached gingiva is characterized by high connective tissue papillae elevating the epithelium, so that the surface of the attached gingiva appears stippled (Fig. 181). Between the elevations there are shallow depressions that correspond to the center of heavier epithelial ridges and show signs of degenera-

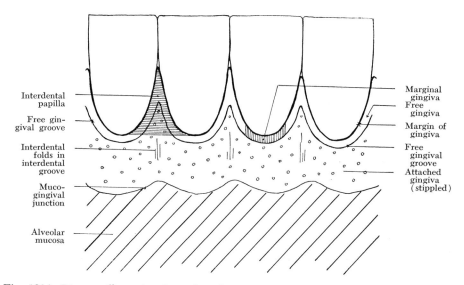

Fig. 180A. Diagram illustrating the surface characteristics of the gingiva.

tion and keratinization at their depth. The stippling is probably a functional adaptation to mechanical impacts.

While the degree of stippling (Fig. 172) and the texture of the collagenous fibers vary with different individuals, there are also differences according to age and sex. In younger female persons the connective tissue is more finely textured than that of the male. However, with increasing age, the collagenous fiber bundles become more coarse in both sexes.[44] The disappearance of stippling is an indication of edema, an expression of an involvement of the attached gingiva in a progressing gingivitis.

The attached gingiva appears slightly depressed between adjacent teeth, corresponding to the depression on the alveolar process between eminences of the sockets. In these depressions the attached gingiva often forms slight vertical folds.

The interdental papilla is that part of the gingiva that fills the space between two adjacent teeth and is limited at its base by a line connecting the margin of

Margin of gingiva

Free gingiva

Free gingival groove

Attached gingiva (stippled)

Mucogingival junction

Alveolar mucosa

Fig. 180B. Diagram illustrating the difference between the free gingiva, the attached gingiva, and the alveolar mucosa.

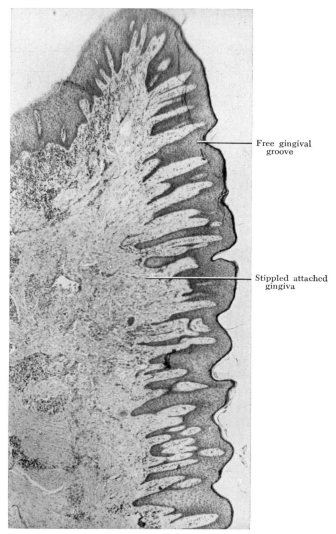

Free gingival groove

Stippled attached gingiva

Fig. 181. Biopsy specimen of the gingiva showing a free gingival groove and stippled attached gingiva.

the gingiva at the center of one tooth and the center of the next. The interdental papilla is tent shaped. Vestibular and oral corners are elevated. The ridge of the papilla is concave. From the similarity to a pass between two mountain peaks, it is called a col. Vestibular and oral parts of the papilla partly fill the embrasures between two adjacent teeth. The interdental part, in the strict sense of the term, seems to lack keratinization.

Dentogingival junction

Physiologically and clinically, the juncture of the soft oral tissues and the hard dental tissues is of great importance. This union is unique in many ways and does constitute a point of lessened resistance to mechanical and bacterial attack. The gingiva consists of two elements that, though integrated in their function, show a division of labor in protecting the underlying structures. The resistance to the mechanical forces of mastication rests mainly on the strength of the dense, unelastic but resilient connective tissue, the lamina propria. The protection against chemical and bacterial injuries is the function of the thick and mostly parakeratinized or keratinized epithelium.

Both of these layers are attached to the tooth, and the structure of each of these components contributes to the security of the dentogingival junction. Again, the firmness of this junction is the function of the connective tissue attached to the tooth through the gingival division of the periodontal ligament. This dental attachment of the lamina propria is reinforced by fibers that reach into the gingiva from the edge of the alveolar bone and by circular fiber bundles in the free gingiva.[2]

The biologic protection, the sealing off of the dentogingival junction, is the function of the epithelial attachment. The epithelium of the gingiva is continuous over the free gingival margin and then, in the real sense of the word, is attached to the surface of the tooth. This attached epithelium has the shape of a collar or cuff and can, therefore, be termed either *epithelial attachment* or *attached epithelial cuff*.

While the attachment of the epithelium to the tooth surface is a well-documented fact, the mode of attachment of the epithelial cuff is maintained by a layer of mucopolysaccharides, formerly termed the secondary enamel cuticle.[38] It seems important to analyze the development of this attachment during and after eruption of the tooth.

Development. At the conclusion of enamel matrix formation the ameloblasts produce a thin membrane on the surface of the enamel, the *primary enamel cuticle*. It is a limiting membrane, connected with the interprismatic enamel substance and the ameloblasts.[39] The ameloblasts shorten after the primary enamel cuticle has been formed, and the epithelial dental organ is reduced to a few layers of flat cuboidal cells that are then called *reduced dental epithelium*. Under normal conditions it covers the entire enamel surface, extending to the cementoenamel junction (Fig. 182), and remains attached to the primary enamel cuticle. During eruption the tip of the tooth approaches the oral mucosa, and the reduced dental epithelium fuses with the oral epithelium (Fig. 183).

The epithelium that covers the tip of the crown degenerates in its center, and the crown emerges through this perforation into the oval cavity (Fig. 184). The reduced dental epithelium remains organically attached to that part of the enamel which has not yet erupted. Once the tip of the crown has emerged, the reduced dental epithelium is termed the *epithelial attachment*[12] or, better, the *attached epithelial cuff*. At the margin of the gingiva the attached epithelium continues into the oral epithelium. (Fig. 185.) As the tooth erupts, the attached epithelium is gradually separated from its surface. The shallow groove that de-

Oral epithelium

Reduced dental epithelium

Enamel

Dentin

Reduced dental epithelium

Pulp

Cementoenamel junction

Periodental ligament

Apical area

Fig. 182. Human permanent incisor. The entire surface of the enamel is covered by reduced dental epithelium. Mature enamel is lost by decalcification. (From Gottlieb, B., and Orban, B.: Biology of the investing structures of the teeth. In Gordon, S. M., editor: Dental science and dental art, Philadelphia, 1938, Lea & Febiger.)

velops between the gingiva and the surface of the tooth and extends around its circumference is the *gingival sulcus* (Fig. 185). It is bounded by the surface of the tooth on one side and by the free gingiva on the other side. The bottom of the sulcus is found where the epithelial attachment separates from the surface of the tooth. The part of the gingiva that is coronal to the bottom of the sulcus is the free or *marginal gingiva*. The attached epithelium elaborates, while the tooth erupts, a layer of a cementing substance consisting of mucopolysaccharides, formerly termed the *secondary enamel* or *dental cuticle*.[13] It is a noncellular layer that may measure up to 10 microns in thickness.

In erupting teeth the attached epithelial cuff extends to the cementoenamel junction (Fig. 185). Occasionally, the epithelium degenerates in the cervical areas of the enamel. Then the surrounding connective tissue may deposit cemen-

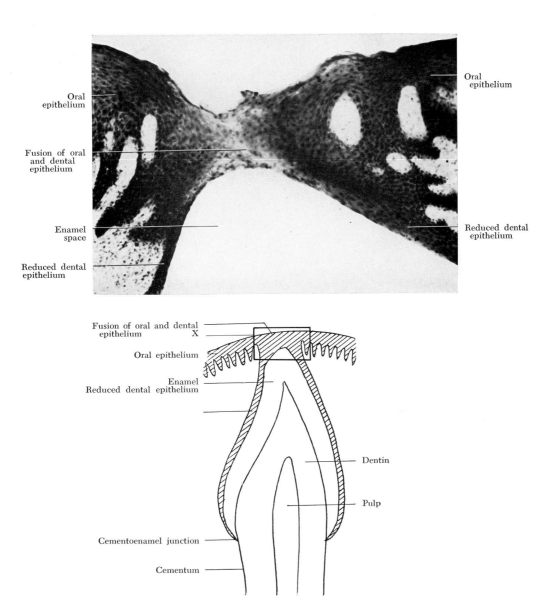

Fig. 183. Reduced dental epithelium fuses with oral epithelium. *X* in the diagram indicates the area from which the photomicrograph was taken.

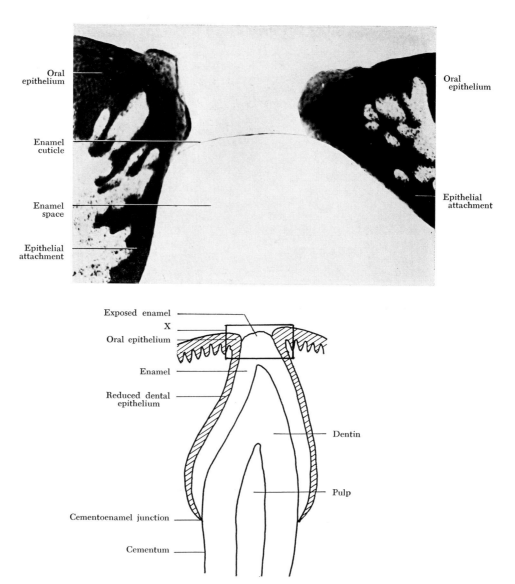

Oral epithelium

Enamel cuticle

Enamel space

Epithelial attachment

Oral epithelium

Epithelial attachment

Exposed enamel

X

Oral epithelium

Enamel

Reduced dental epithelium

Dentin

Pulp

Cementoenamel junction

Cementum

Fig. 184. Tooth emerges through a perforation in the fused epithelia. *X* in the diagram indicates the area from which the photomicrograph was taken.

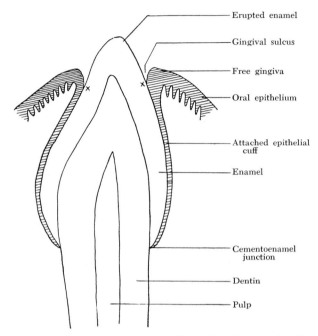

Erupted enamel

Gingival sulcus

Free gingiva

Oral epithelium

Attached epithelial cuff

Enamel

Cementoenamel junction

Dentin

Pulp

Fig. 185. Diagrammatic illustration of the attached epithelial cuff and gingival sulcus at an early stage of tooth eruption. Bottom of the sulcus at *x*.

tum upon the enamel. Different sections of the same tooth may, and frequently do, show varying relationships in the area where enamel and cementum meet (Fig. 186).

Structure of the epithelial attachment. The attached epithelium is the derivative of the reduced enamel epithelium. In some cases, ameloblasts may still function near the cementoenamel junction when the tip of the crown has already emerged through the oral mucosa. This is the rule in continuously growing teeth and high-crowned teeth of many animals. The ameloblasts flatten out rapidly and then the reduced dental epithelium is called the epithelial attachment. This is thin at first and consists of three to four layers of cells (Figs. 189 and 190), but it thickens gradually with advancing age to about ten to twenty rows of cells or more (Figs. 191 and 192).

The epithelium that forms the attachment is a stratified squamous epithelium. As a rule the basement membrane at the junction between the epithelial attachment and connective tissue is smooth. It may be considered as a sign of irritation if the epithelial attachment sends projections, epithelial ridges, into the connective tissue. The cells within the epithelial attachment are elongated and are arranged more or less parallel to the surface of the tooth (Fig. 187). There is a distinct pattern in the direction of these flattened cells that may be the result of functional influences upon the attachment.[28] The attachment of the surface cells to enamel or cementum seems to be more firm than the connection

Fig. 186. Three sections of the same tooth showing different relations of tissues at the cementoenamel junction. **A,** Epithelial attachment reaching to the cementoenamel junction. **B,** Epithelial attachment ends coronal to the cementoenamel junction. **C,** Epithelial attachment covers part of the cementum. Cementum overlaps the edge of the enamel. *EA,* Epithelial attachment. *E,* Enamel (lost in decalcification). *C,* Cementum. *x,* End of epithelial attachment. (From Orban, B.: J.A.D.A. **17:**1977, 1930.)

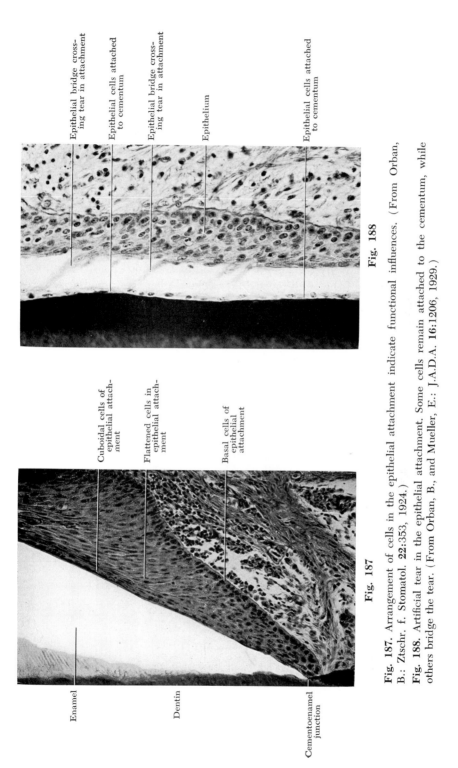

Fig. 187

Fig. 188

Fig. 187. Arrangement of cells in the epithelial attachment indicate functional influences. (From Orban, B.: Ztschr. f. Stomatol. **22**:353, 1924.)

Fig. 188. Artificial tear in the epithelial attachment. Some cells remain attached to the cementum, while others bridge the tear. (From Orban, B., and Mueller, E.: J.A.D.A. **16**:1206, 1929.)

of these cells to the deeper layers of the epithelium. For this reason tears occur frequently between the cuboidal cells attached to the tooth and the rest of the epithelial attachment. Such tears are found as artifacts in microscopic specimens (Fig. 188) but may also occur during life[26] or in experimental flap operations.[32]

Shift of the dentogingival junction. The relation between the gingiva and the surface of the tooth changes constantly. When the tip of the enamel first emerges through the mucous membrane of the oral cavity, the epithelium covers almost the entire enamel (Fig. 189). Tooth eruption is relatively fast until the tooth reaches the plane of occlusion (see Chapter XI). This causes the epithelial attachment to separate from the enamel surface, while the crown gradually emerges into the oral cavity. When the tooth reaches the plane of occlusion, one-third to one-fourth of the enamel is still covered by the gingiva (Fig. 190). The gradual exposure of the crown by separation of the epithelial attachment from the enamel and by recession of the gingiva is termed passive eruption. The actual movement of the teeth toward the occlusal plane is termed active eruption (see Chapter XI).

Fig. 189. Epithelial attachment and gingival sulcus in an erupting tooth. Erupted part of the enamel is indicated by the dotted line. Enamel lost in decalcification. (From Kronfeld, R.: J.A.D.A. **18:**382, 1936.)

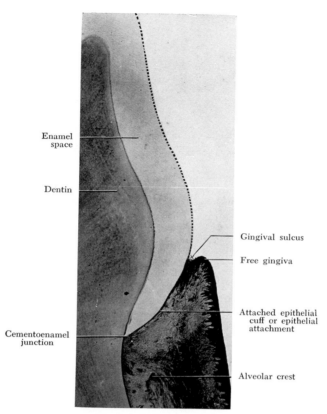

Enamel
space

Dentin

Gingival sulcus

Free gingiva

Attached epithelial
cuff or epithelial
attachment

Cementoenamel
junction

Alveolar crest

Fig. 190. Tooth in occlusion. One-fourth of the enamel is still covered by the epithelial attachment. (From Kronfeld, R.: J.A.D.A. **18:**382, 1936.)

First stage. The bottom of the gingival sulcus remains in the region of the enamel-covered crown for some time, and the apical end of the attached epithelial cuff stays at the cementoenamel junction. This relation of the epithelial attachment to the tooth characterizes the *first stage* in passive exposure. (See Fig. 191.) It persists in primary teeth almost up to one year before shedding and, in permanent teeth, usually to the age of about 20 or 30 years. However, this relation is subject to a wide range of variations.

Second stage. The epithelial attachment forms, at first, a wide band or cuff around the cervical part of the crown that is gradually narrowed as the separation of epithelium from the enamel surface proceeds. Long before the bottom of the sulcus reaches the cementoenamel junction, the epithelium proliferates along the surface of the cementum, and the apical end of the epithelial attachment is then found on the cementum in the cervical part of the root. This is the *second stage* in passive eruption. In this phase the bottom of the gingival sulcus is still on the enamel. The apical end of the epithelial attachment has shifted to the surface of the cementum. (See Fig. 192.)

The downgrowth of the epithelial attachment along the cementum is but one

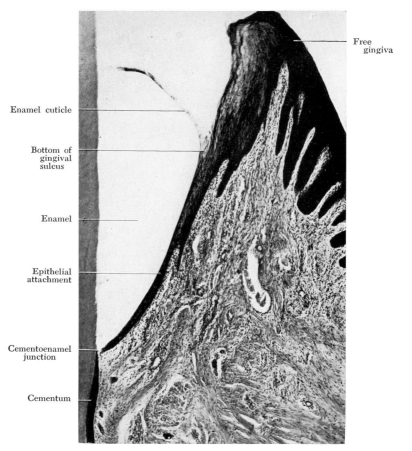

Free
gingiva

Enamel cuticle

Bottom of
gingival
sulcus

Enamel

Epithelial
attachment

Cementoenamel
junction

Cementum

Fig. 191. Epithelial attachment on the enamel. First stage in passive tooth exposure. (From Gottlieb, B., and Orban, B.: Biology and pathology of the tooth [translated by M. Diamond], New York, 1938, The Macmillan Co.)

facet of the shift of the dentogingival junction. This entails detachment of fiber bundles that were anchored in the cervical parts of the cementum, now covered by the epithelium, and an apical shift of the gingival and transseptal fibers. It is still questionable whether the degeneration of the fibers or the proliferation of the epithelium is the primary change.[41] Recent findings indicate that destruction of the fibers is caused by the proliferating epithelial cells actively dissolving the principal fibers by enzyme action, desmolysis. The second stage of passive tooth exposure may persist to the age of 40 years or later.

Third stage. For a short time the bottom of the gingival sulcus is at the cementoenamel junction, the epithelial attachment is entirely on the cementum, and the enamel-covered crown is fully exposed (Fig. 193). This is the *third stage* in passive eruption. Because of the continuous active eruption and passive exposure of the teeth, the epithelium shifts gradually along the surface of the tooth,

Free
gingiva

Bottom of
gingival
sulcus

Enamel

Epithelial
attachment
to enamel

Cementoenamel
junction

Epithelial
attachment
to cementum

Cementum

End of
epithelial
attachment

Fig. 192. Epithelial attachment partly on the enamel and partly on the cementum. Second stage in passive tooth exposure. (From Gottlieb, B., and Orban, B.: Biology and pathology of the tooth [translated by M. Diamond], New York, 1938, The Macmillan Co.)

and the attachment does not remain at the linear cementoenamel junction for any length of time. The third stage in passive eruption is often only a transitional stage in a more or less continuous, but normally slow, process.

Fourth stage. If a part of the cementum is already exposed by separation of the epithelial attachment from the tooth surface, the *fourth stage* of passive eruption is reached. The entire epithelial cuff is attached to the cementum. (See Fig. 194.)

It would appear that the epithelial attachment has to maintain a certain minimal width, 0.25 to 6 mm., to assure normal function of the tooth. Therefore, the proliferation of the epithelium along the cementum should be considered a physiologic process, if it is in correlation to active eruption and attrition. If it progresses too rapidly or precociously and therefore loses correlation to active eruption, it must be considered as a pathologic process.

An atrophy of the gingiva is correlated with the apical shift of the dentogingival junction, exposing more and more of the crown and, later, of the root

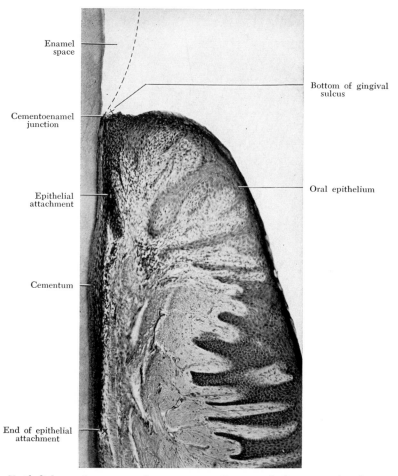

Enamel space

Cementoenamel junction

Epithelial attachment

Cementum

End of epithelial attachment

Bottom of gingival sulcus

Oral epithelium

Fig. 193. Epithelial attachment on the cementum. Bottom of the gingival sulcus at the cementoenamel junction. Third stage in passive tooth exposure. (From Gottlieb, B.: J.A.D.A. **14**:2178, 1927.)

to the oral cavity. The recession of the gingiva is therefore a physiologic process if it is correlated both to the occlusal wear and to the compensatory active eruption.

The rate of passive eruption varies in different persons and in different teeth of the same individual, as well as on different surfaces of the same tooth. In some cases the fourth stage of passive eruption is observed in persons during their twenties. In others, even at 50 years of age or older the teeth are still in the first or second stage of eruption. The rate varies also in different teeth of the same jaw and on different surfaces of the same tooth. One side may be in the first stage and the other in the second or even the fourth stage (Fig. 195). Hardly at any time are all parts of the bottom of the gingival sulcus in the same relation to the tooth.

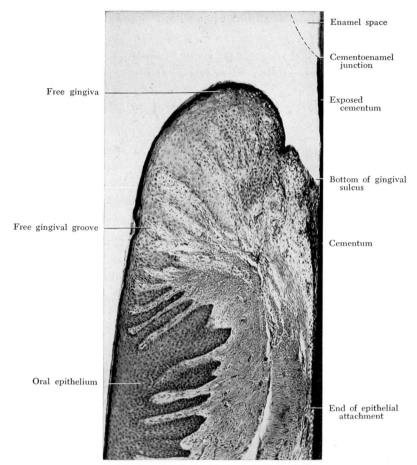

Enamel space

Cementoenamel
junction

Free gingiva

Exposed
cementum

Bottom of gingival
sulcus

Free gingival groove

Cementum

Oral epithelium

End of epithelial
attachment

Fig. 194. Epithelial attachment on the cementum. Bottom of the gingival sulcus also on the cementum. Fourth stage in passive tooth exposure. (From Gottlieb, B.: J.A.D.A. **14:**2178, 1927.)

Gradual exposure of the tooth to the oral cavity makes it possible to distinguish between the anatomic and the clinical crowns of the tooth (Fig. 196). That part of the tooth which is covered by enamel is the anatomic crown. The clinical crown is that part of the tooth exposed in the oral cavity.[14] In the first and second stages the clinical crown is smaller than the anatomic crown. In the third stage the entire enamel-covered part of the tooth is exposed, and the clinical crown is equal to the anatomic crown. However, this condition is not actually encountered because the bottom of the gingival sulcus is never at the same level all around the tooth. In the fourth stage the clinical crown is larger than the anatomic crown because parts of the root have been exposed.

Mode of attachment of epithelium. For a long time the epithelium was thought to be only in close contact with the enamel. The contact was supposed

Fig. 195. Three sections of the same tooth showing different relation of soft to hard tissues. **A,** Bottom of the sulcus on the enamel (second stage). **B,** Bottom of the sulcus at the cementoenamel junction (third stage). **C,** Bottom of the sulcus on the cementum (fourth stage). *E,* Enamel lost in decalcification, indicated by the dotted line. *EA,* Epithelial attachment. *x,* Bottom of the gingival sulcus. *xx,* End of the epithelial attachment.

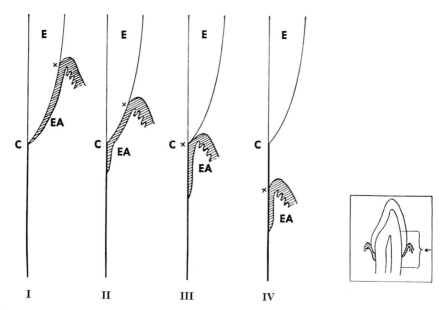

Fig. 196. Diagrammatic illustration of the four stages in passive eruption. In Stages I and II the anatomic crown is larger than the clinical. In Stage III the anatomic and clinical crowns are equal. In Stage IV the clinical crown is larger than the anatomic crown. The arrow in the small diagram indicates the area from which the drawings were made. *E,* Enamel. *EA,* Epithelial attachment. *C,* Cementoenamel junction. *x,* Bottom of the gingival sulcus.

to be maintained by the turgor of the connective tissue elements of the gingiva, and thus a capillary space was supposed to extend between the gingiva and enamel to the cementoenamel junction. Although this concept has lately been resurrected,[40] there seems hardly any doubt of the existence of an organic, true attachment of the epithelium to the enamel and later also to the cementum in the form of a rather broad cuff. It is true, however, as was mentioned before, that this epithelial attachment is but a part of the dentogingival junction.

A most important problem is that of the mode or mechanism of the epithelial attachment. So long as enamel maturation is not completed, there is every evidence for a primary organic union between ameloblasts and the enamel, mediated by the primary enamel cuticle.[39] It was thought that this primary union persists after the maturation of the enamel and calcification of the primary cuticle in the erupted and functioning tooth.

However, there is considerable doubt that this primary union could persist into the functioning period of the tooth. It seems more probable that it is replaced by a secondary attachment through the formation of a cementing substance, viz., a layer of mucopolysaccharides, formerly called secondary enamel cuticle. The replacement starts from the coronal parts of the crown, gradually progressing cervically. When the epithelium proliferates beyond the cementoenamel junction, it gains an organic attachment to the cementum. The secondary

Epithelial
attachment

Epithelial
attachment

A   B

Fig. 197. Ground section of hard and soft tissues of teeth. Epithelial attachment to the enamel. **A,** General view of the interdental papilla. **B,** Higher magnification of the gingival sulcus and epithelial attachment. *E,* Enamel. *D,* Dentin. *CP,* Contact point. *x,* Bottom of the gingival sulcus. *xx,* End of the epithelial attachment (cementoenamel junction). (From Bodecker, C. F., and Applebaum, E.: D. Cosmos **176:**1127, 1934.)

enamel cuticle extends now along the cementum (Figs. 198 and 199). Secondary enamel cuticle and the cemental cuticle are referred to as dental cuticle. The function of the dental cuticle as a cementing substance is supported by findings of extensions of the cuticle into the minute spaces of the cementum formerly occupied by Sharpey's fibers (Fig. 199).

Although the mechanical resistance of the dentogingival junction is mainly due to the connective tissue attachment and to the fiber bundles in the gingiva, the attachment of the epithelium to the enamel is by no means loose or weak. This could be demonstrated by microscopic studies of ground sections of frozen specimens where enamel and soft tissues are retained in their normal relation.[37] If, in such specimens, an attempt is made to detach the gingiva from the tooth, the epithelium tears rather than peeling off the enamel surface. Similar results were obtained when gingival flaps were pulled away from the tooth in vivo or post mortem.[32]

Enamel
space

Secondary
enamel
cuticle

Epithelial
attachment

Cemento-
enamel
junction

Cemental
cuticle

Fig. 198. "Secondary enamel cuticle" follows the epithelial attachment to the cementum forming the dental cuticle. Arrow in the diagram indicates the area from which the photomicrograph
was taken.

Cementum

Dentin

Cementing
substance

Extension of cementing substance
into space in cementum

Fig. 199. Cementing substance of the layer of mucopolysaccharides extends into the spaces of
the cementum. (From Gottlieb, B., and Orban, B.: Biology and pathology of the tooth [trans-
lated by M. Diamond], New York, 1938, The Macmillan Co.)

The firmness of the epithelial attachment may also be shown by studying ground sections prepared by a special method of investing soft and hard tissues[4] (Fig. 197).

Gingival sulcus. The gingival sulcus forms when the tip of the crown emerges through the oral mucosa. It deepens as a result of separation of the reduced dental epithelium from the actively erupting tooth. Shortly after the tip of the crown has appeared in the oral cavity, the tooth establishes occlusion with its antagonist. At first the epithelium separates rapidly from the surface of the tooth. Later, after occlusal relations are established, separation of the epithelial attachment from the surface of the tooth slows down.

The formation and relative depth of the gingival sulcus at different ages is still a controversial subject. Until the epithelial attachment was discovered, it was believed that the gingival sulcus extended to the cementoenamel junction from the time the tip of the crown had pierced the oral mucosa (Fig. 200, *I*). It was assumed that the attachment of the gingival epithelium to the tooth was linear at the cementoenamel junction. After the epithelial attachment had been discovered, it was recognized that no cleft exists between epithelium and enamel but that these tissues are organically connected. The gingival sulcus is merely a shallow groove, the bottom of which is at the point of separation of the attached epithelium from the tooth (Fig. 200, *II*).

Some investigators contend that the deepening of the gingival sulcus is due to a tear in the attached epithelium (Fig. 200, *III*). Tears may deepen the

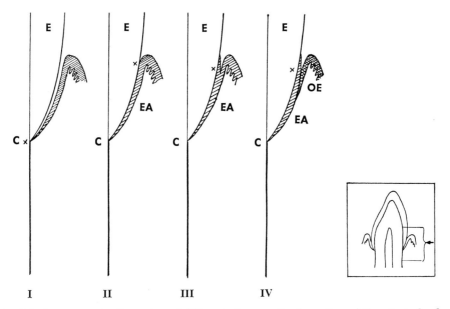

Fig. 200. Diagrammatic illustration of different views on the formation of the gingival sulcus as discussed in the text. Arrow in the small diagram indicates the area from which the drawings were made.

gingival sulcus when the free margin of the gingiva is exposed to excessive mechanical trauma.

Others claim[1,36] that the gingival sulcus forms at the line of fusion between the enamel epithelium attached to the surface of the enamel and the oral epithelium (Fig. 200, *IV*). The oral epithelium proliferates at the connective tissue side of the epithelial cuff and replaces the former enamel epithelium, which degenerates progressively.

The depth of the normal gingival sulcus has been a frequent cause of disagreement, investigations, and measurements.[25] Under normal conditions the depth of the sulcus varies from near zero to 6 mm.; 45 per cent of all measured sulci were below 0.5 mm., the average being 1.8 mm. The more shallow the sulcus, the more favorable are the conditions at the gingival margin. Every sulcus may be termed normal, regardless of its depth, if there are no signs of pathologic, mainly inflammatory, changes in the gingival tissues.

The presence of lymphocytes and plasma cells in the connective tissue at the bottom of the gingival sulcus should not, in itself, be considered a pathologic condition. It is evidence, rather, of a defense reaction in response to the constant presence of bacteria in the gingival sulcus and of a barrier against the invasion of bacteria and the penetration of their toxins.[9]

Hard palate

The mucous membrane of the hard palate is tightly fixed to the underlying periosteum and, therefore, immovable. Its color is pink, like that of the gingiva. The epithelium is uniform in character throughout the hard palate, with a rather thick keratinized layer and numerous long papillae. The lamina propria, a layer of dense connective tissue, is thicker in the anterior than in the posterior parts of the palate. Various regions in the hard palate differ because of the varying structure of the submucous layer. The following zones can be distinguished (Fig. 201):

1. The gingival region, adjacent to the teeth
2. The palatine raphe, also known as the median area, extending from the incisive or palatine papilla posteriorly
3. The anterolateral area or fatty zone between the raphe and gingiva
4. The posterolateral zone or glandular zone between the raphe and gingiva

The marginal area shows the same structure as the other regions of the gingiva. In this zone a submucous layer cannot be differentiated from the lamina propria or periosteum (Fig. 202). Similarly, the layers of the lamina propria, submucosa, and periosteum cannot be distinguished in the palatine raphe, or median area (Fig. 203). If a palatine torus is present, the mucous membrane is noticeably thin, and the otherwise narrow raphe spreads over the entire torus.

In the lateral areas of the hard palate (Fig. 204), in both fatty and glandular zones, the lamina propria is fixed to the periosteum by bands of dense fibrous

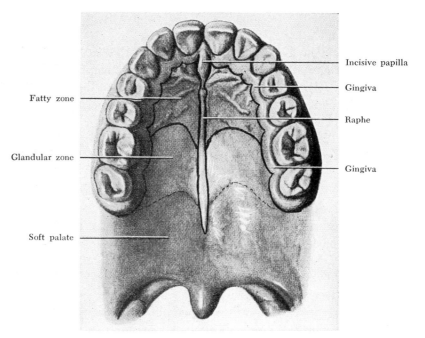

Fatty zone

Glandular zone

Soft palate

Incisive papilla

Gingiva

Raphe

Gingiva

Fig. 201. Surface view of the hard and soft palates. The different zones of palatine mucosa.

Palatine mucosa

Alveolar crest

Gingiva

Fig. 202. Structural differences between the gingiva and palatine mucosa. Region of the first molar.

Fig. 203. Transverse section through the hard palate. Palatine raphe. Fibrous bands connecting the mucosa and periosteum in the lateral areas. Palatine vessels. (From Pendleton, E. C.: J.A.D.A. **21**:488, 1934.)

connective tissue that are at right angles to the surface and divide the submucous layer into irregularly shaped spaces. The distance between lamina propria and periosteum is smaller in the anterior than in the posterior parts. In the anterior zone the connective tissue spaces contain fat (Fig. 203), whereas in the posterior part mucous glands are packed into the spaces (Fig. 204). The glandular layer of the hard palate continues posteriorly into that of the soft palate.

In the sulcus between the alveolar process and hard palate, the anterior palatine vessels and nerves are surrounded by loose connective tissue. This area, wedge shaped in cross section (Fig. 205), is relatively large in the posterior parts of the palate and gradually diminishes in size anteriorly.

Incisive papilla. The pear-shaped or oval incisive or palatine papilla is formed of dense connective tissue. It contains the oral parts of the vestigial nasopalatine ducts. These are blind epithelial ducts of varying lengths. They are lined by a simple or pseudostratified columnar epithelium, rich in goblet cells. Small mucous glands open into the lumen of the ducts. Frequently the ducts are surrounded by small, irregular islands of hyalin cartilage, vestigial extensions of the paraseptal cartilages. The nasopalatine ducts are patent in most mammals and, together with Jacobson's organ, are considered as auxiliary olfactory sense organs. The cartilage is sometimes found in the anterior parts of the papilla. It then shows no apparent relation to nasopalatine ducts (Fig. 206).

Palatine rugae (transverse palatine ridges). The palatine rugae, irregular and often asymmetric in man, are ridges of mucous membrane extending laterally

Soft palate

End of hard palate

Glandular zone

Fatty zone

Lamina propria

Musculus incisivus

Alveolar crest

Fig. 204. Longitudinal section through the hard and soft palates lateral to the midline. Fatty and glandular zones of the hard palate.

Fig. 205. Transverse section through the posterior part of the hard palate, region of the second molar. Loose connective tissue in the groove between the alveolar process and hard palate around the palatine vessels and nerves.

Fig. 206. Sagittal section through the palatine papilla and anterior palatine canal. Cartilage in the papilla.

from the incisive papilla and the anterior part of the raphe. Their core is a dense connective tissue layer with fine interwoven fibers.

Epithelial pearls. In the midline, especially in the region of the incisive papilla, epithelial pearls may be found in the lamina propria. They consist of concentrically arranged epithelial cells that are frequently keratinized. They are remnants of the epithelium in the line of fusion between the palatine processes (see Chapter I).

Lining mucosa

All the zones of the lining mucosa are characterized by a relatively thick nonkeratinized epithelium and by the thinness of the lamina propria. They differ from one another in the structure of their submucosa. Where the lining mucosa reflects from the movable lips, cheeks, and tongue to the alveolar bone, the submucosa is loosely textured. In regions where the lining mucosa covers muscles, as on the lips, cheeks, and underside of the tongue, it is immovably fixed to the epimysium or fascia of the respective muscle. In these regions the mucosa is also highly elastic. These two characteristics safeguard the relative smoothness of the mucous lining in any functional phase of the muscle and prevent a heavy folding which may lead to injuries of the lips or cheeks if such folds were caught between the teeth. The mucosa of the soft palate is a transition between this type of lining mucosa and that which is found in the fornix vestibuli and in the sublingual sulcus at the floor of the oral cavity. In the latter zones the submucosa is loose and of considerable volume. The mucous membrane is movably attached to the deep structures, which allows for the free movement of lips and cheeks and also the tongue.

Lip and cheek

The epithelium of the mucosa on the lips (Fig. 171) and on the cheek (Fig. 207) is stratified squamous nonkeratinized epithelium.

The lamina propria of the labial and buccal mucosa consists of dense connective tissue that sends short, irregular papillae into the epithelium.

The submucous layer connects the lamina propria to the thin fascia of the muscles and consists of strands of densely grouped collagenous fibers. Between these strands is found loose connective tissue containing fat and small mixed glands. The strands of dense connective tissue limit the mobility of the mucous membrane against the musculature and prevent its elevation into folds. Small wrinkles appear in the mucosa during the contraction of the muscles, thus preventing the mucous membrane of the lips and cheeks from lodging between the biting surfaces of the teeth during mastication. The mixed glands of the lips are situated in the submucosa, whereas the larger glands of the cheek are usually found between the bundles of the buccinator muscle, and sometimes on its outer surface. A horizontal middle zone on the cheek, lateral to the corner of the mouth, may contain isolated sebaceous glands, Fordyce spots (Fig. 208).

Epithelium

Lamina propria

Dense connective tissue bands

Fat

Submucosa

Buccinator muscle

Fig. 207. Section through the mucous membrane of the cheek. Note the bands of dense connective tissue attaching the lamina propria to the fascia of the buccinator muscle.

Fig. 208. Sebaceous gland in the cheek, Fordyce spot. Biopsy specimen.

Vestibular fornix and alveolar mucosa

In the vestibular fornix the mucosa of the lips and cheeks reflects into the mucosa covering the bone. The mucous membrane of the cheeks and lips is attached firmly to the buccinator muscle in the cheeks and the orbicularis oris muscle in the lips. In the fornix the mucosa is loosely connected to the underlying structures and thus permits the necessary movements of the lips and cheeks. The mucous membrane covering the outer surface of the alveolar process is attached loosely to the periosteum in the area close to the fornix. It continues into, but is sharply limited from, the gingiva which is firmly attached to the periosteum of the alveolar crest and to the teeth.

The median and lateral labial frenula are folds of the mucous membrane, containing loose connective tissue. No muscle fibers are found in these folds.

Gingiva and alveolar mucosa are separated by a scalloped line, the mucogingival junction. The attached gingiva is stippled, firm, and thick, lacks a separate submucous layer, is immovably attached to bone and teeth, and has no glands. The gingival epithelium is thick and mostly parakeratinized or keratinized. The epithelial ridges and the papillae of the lamina propria are high. The alveolar mucosa is thin and loosely attached to the periosteum by a well-defined submucous layer of loose connective tissue, and it may contain small mixed glands. The epithelium is thin, not keratinized, and the epithelial ridges and papillae are low and are often entirely missing. These differences cause the difference in color between the pale pink gingiva and the dark red lining mucosa.

Mucous membrane of the inferior surface of the tongue and of the floor of the oral cavity

The mucous membrane on the floor of the oral cavity is thin and loosely attached to the underlying structures to allow for the free mobility of the tongue. The epithelium is not keratinized and the papillae of the lamina propria are short. (See Fig. 209.) The submucosa contains adipose tissue. The sublingual glands lie close to the covering mucosa in the sublingual fold. The sublingual mucosa joins the lingual gingiva in a sharp line that corresponds to the mucogingival line on the vestibular surface of the jaws. At the inner border of the horseshoe-shaped sublingual sulcus, the sublingual mucosa reflects onto the lower surface of the tongue and continues as the ventral lingual mucosa.

The mucous membrane of the inferior surface of the tongue is smooth and relatively thin (Fig. 210). The epithelium is not keratinized. The papillae of the connective tissue are numerous but short. Here, the submucosa cannot be identified as a separate layer. It binds the mucous membrane tightly to the connective tissue surrounding the bundles of the muscles of the tongue.

Soft palate

The mucous membrane on the oral surface of the soft palate is highly vascularized and of reddish color, noticeably differing from the pale color of the hard

Epithelium

Lamina propria

Submucosa

Minor sublingual gland

Fig. 209. Mucous membrane from floor of the mouth.

Muscles

Submucosa

Lamina propria

Epithelium

Fig. 210. Mucous membrane on the inferior surface of the tongue.

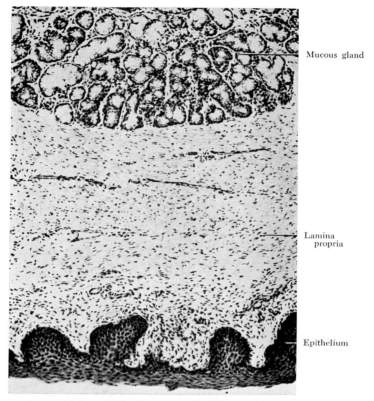

Mucous gland

Lamina propria

Epithelium

Fig. 211. Mucous membrane from the oral surface of the soft palate.

palate. The papillae of the connective tissue are few and short. The stratified squamous epithelium is not keratinized. (See Fig. 211.) The lamina propria shows a distinct layer of elastic fibers separating it from the submucosa. The latter is relatively loose and contains an almost continuous layer of mucous glands. Typical oral mucosa continues around the free border of the soft palate for a variable distance and is then replaced by nasal mucosa with its pseudo-stratified, ciliated columnar epithelium.

Specialized mucosa

Dorsal lingual mucosa. The superior surface of the tongue is rough and ir-regular (Fig. 212). A V-shaped line divides it into an anterior part, or body, and a posterior part, or base. The former comprises about two-thirds of the length of the organ, and the latter forms the posterior one-third. The fact that these two parts develop from different areas of the branchial region (see Chapter I) accounts for the different source of nerves of general sense: the anterior two-thirds are supplied by the trigeminal nerve through its lingual branch and the posterior one-third by the glossopharyngeal nerve.

The body and the base of the tongue differ widely in the structure of the

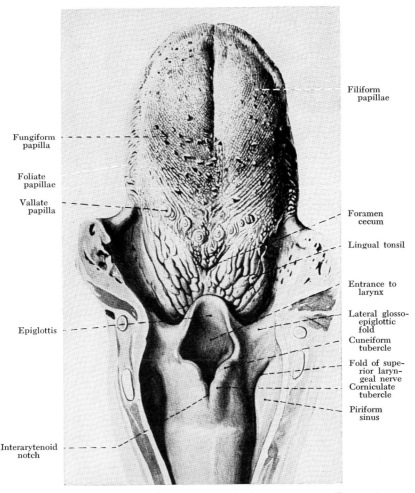

Fungiform
papilla

Foliate
papillae

Vallate
papilla

Epiglottis

Interarytenoid
notch

Filiform
papillae

Foramen
cecum

Lingual tonsil

Entrance to
larynx

Lateral glosso-
epiglottic
fold

Cuneiform
tubercle

Fold of supe-
rior laryn-
geal nerve

Corniculate
tubercle

Piriform
sinus

Fig. 212. Surface view of the human tongue. (From Sicher, H., and Tandler, J.: Anatomie für Zahnärzte [Anatomy for dentists], Vienna, 1928, Julius Springer.)

mucous membrane. The anterior part can be termed the papillary and the posterior part the lymphatic portion of the dorsal lingual mucosa. On the anterior part are found numerous fine-pointed, cone-shaped papillae that give it a velvetlike appearance. These projections, the filiform thread-shaped papillae, consist of a core of connective tissue that carries secondary papillae (Fig. 213, A). The covering epithelium is keratinized and forms at the apex of the papillae, hairlike tufts over the secondary papillae of the connective tissue.

Interspersed between the filiform papillae are the isolated mushroom-shaped or fungiform papillae (Fig. 213, B), which are round, reddish prominences. Their color is derived from a rich capillary network visible through the relatively thin epithelium. Fungiform papillae contain a few taste buds.

In front of the dividing V-shaped terminal sulcus, between the body and the

Fig. 213. Filiform, **A**, and fungiform, **B**, papillae.

base of the tongue, are the vallate, walled-in, papillae (Fig. 214), 8 to 10 in number. They do not protrude above the surface of the tongue but are bounded by a deep circular furrow that seems to cut them out of the substance of the tongue. They are slightly narrower at their base. Their free surface shows numerous secondary papillae that are covered by a thin, smooth epithelium. On the lateral surface of the vallate papillae and occasionally on the walls surrounding them, the epithelium contains numerous taste buds. Into the trough open the ducts of small serous glands, von Ebner's glands, which serve to wash out the soluble elements of food that stimulate the taste buds.

Vallate
papilla

Taste bud

Taste bud

Opening of duct
of v. Ebner's
gland

v. Ebner's
gland

Mucous gland

Fig. 214. Vallate papilla.

Lingual
lymph
follicle
with
germinal
center

Follicular
crypt

Lingual
follicle

Fig. 215. Lingual lymph follicle.

At the angle of the V-shaped terminal groove on the tongue is located the foramen cecum, the remnant of the thyroglossal duct (see Chapter I). Posterior to the terminal sulcus, the surface of the tongue is irregularly studded with round or oval prominences, the lingual follicles. Each of these shows one or more lymph nodules, sometimes containing a germinal center (Fig. 215). Most of these prominences have a small pit at the center, the lingual crypt, which is lined with stratified squamous epithelium. Innumerable lymphocytes migrate into the crypts through the epithelium. Ducts of the small posterior lingual mucous glands open into the crypts. Together the lingual follicles form the lingual tonsil.

On the lateral border of the posterior parts of the tongue sharp parallel clefts of varying length can often be observed. They bound narrow folds of the mucous membrane and are the vestige of the large foliate papillae found in many mammals. They contain taste buds.

Taste buds. Taste buds are small ovoid or barrel-shaped intraepithelial organs about 80 microns in height and 40 microns thick (Fig. 216). They touch with their broader base the basement membrane, while their narrower tip almost

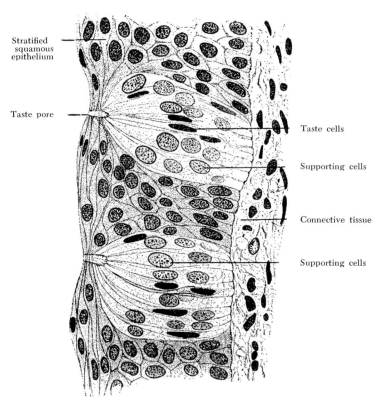

Stratified squamous epithelium

Taste pore

Taste cells

Supporting cells

Connective tissue

Supporting cells

Fig. 216. Taste buds from the slope of a vallate papilla. (From Schaffer, J.: Lehrbuch der Histologie und Histogenese [Textbook of histology and histogenesis], ed. 2, Leipzig, 1922, Wilhelm Engelmann.)

reaches the surface of the epithelium. The tip is covered by a few flat epithelial cells, which surround a small opening, the taste pore. It leads into a narrow space between the peripheral ends of the sustentacular or supporting cells of the taste bud. The outer supporting cells are arranged like the staves of a barrel. The inner and shorter ones are spindle shaped. Between the latter are arranged ten to twelve neuroepithelial cells, the receptors of taste stimuli. They are slender, dark-staining cells that carry a stiff hairlike process at their superficial end. The hairs reach into the space beneath the taste pore.

A rich plexus of nerves is found below the taste buds. Some fibers enter the taste bud from the base and end in contact with the taste cells. Others end in the epithelium between the taste buds.

Taste buds are numerous on the inner wall of the trough surrounding the vallate papillae, in the folds of the foliate papillae, on the posterior surface of the epiglottis, and on some of the fungiform papillae at the tip and the lateral borders of the tongue.

The primary taste sensations, i.e., sweet, salty, bitter, and sour, are not perceived in all regions of the tongue. Sweet is tasted at the tip and salty at the lateral border of the body of the tongue. Bitter and sour are recognized in the posterior part of the tongue, bitter in the middle, and sour in the lateral areas. The distribution of the receptors for primary taste qualities can, diagrammatically and somewhat arbitrarily, be correlated to the different types of papillae. The vallate papillae recognize bitter taste; the foliate papillae, sour taste. The taste buds on the fungiform papillae at the tip of the tongue are receptors for sweet taste and those at the borders for salty taste. Bitter and sour taste sensations are mediated by the glossopharyngeal nerve and sweet and salty taste by the intermediofacial nerve via the chorda tympani.

CLINICAL CONSIDERATIONS

To understand the pathogenesis of periodontal disease and the pathologic involvements of the different structures, it is essential to be thoroughly familiar with the structure of cementum, periodontal ligament, alveolar bone, marginal gingiva, gingival sulcus, and dentogingival junction, as well as their biologic interrelations. Periodontal disturbances frequently have their origin in the gingival sulcus and marginal gingiva, leading to the formation of a deep gingival pocket. The reduction of the depth of the gingival pocket is the primary objective of treatment. Any given method of treatment should be judged by its ability to accomplish this end, whether the method be surgical, chemical, or electrical.

In restorative dentistry the extent of the epithelial attachment plays an important role. In young persons the attachment of the epithelium to the enamel is of considerable length, and the clinical crown is smaller than the anatomic crown. The enamel cannot be removed entirely without destroying the epithelial attachment. It is, therefore, very difficult to prepare a tooth properly for an abutment or crown in young individuals. On the other hand, the preparation may be mechanically inadequate when it is extended only to the bottom of the gingival sulcus. It should be understood, therefore, that in young persons a restoration may be only temporary and may require later replacement.

When large areas of the root are exposed and a restoration is to be placed, the preparation need not cover the entire clinical crown. The first requirement is that the restoration be adapted to mechanical needs.

In extending the gingival margin of any restoration in the direction of the bottom of the gingival sulcus, the following rules should be observed. If the epithelial attachment is still on the enamel, and the gingival papilla fills the entire interdental space, the gingival margin of a cavity should be placed below the marginal gingiva. Special care should be taken to avoid injury to the gingiva and the dentogingival junction to prevent premature recession of the gingiva. When the gingiva is pathologically affected, treatment should precede the placing of a restoration. If the gingiva has receded from the enamel, if the gingival papilla does not fill the interdental space, and if the gingival sulcus is very shallow, the margin of a cavity need not necessarily be carried below the free margin of the gingiva. The gingival margin of a cavity should be placed far enough from the contact point to permit proper cleansing.

With exposure of the cervical part of the anatomic root, cemental caries or abrasion may occur. Improperly constructed clasps, overzealous scaling, and strongly abrasive dentifrices may result in marked abrasion. After loss of the cementum, the dentin may be extremely sensitive to thermal or chemical stimuli. Drugs, judiciously applied, may be used to accelerate sclerosis of the tubules and reparative dentin formation.

The difference in the structure of the submucosa in various regions of the oral cavity is of great clinical importance. Wherever the submucosa consists of a layer of loose connective tissue, edema or hemorrhage causes much swelling, and infections spread speedily and extensively. As a rule, inflammatory infiltrations in such parts are not very painful. If possible, injections should be made into loose submucous connective tissue. Such areas are the region of the fornix and the neighboring parts of the alveolar mucosa. The only place in the palate where larger amounts of fluid can be injected without damaging the tissues is the loose connective tissue in the furrow between the palate and the alveolar process (Fig. 205).

The gingiva is exposed to heavy mechanical stresses during mastication. Moreover, the epithelial attachment to the tooth is relatively weak, and injuries or infections can cause permanent damage here. Strong keratinization of the gingiva may afford relative protection. Therefore, steps taken to increase keratinization can be considered preventive measures. One of the methods of inducing keratinization is mechanical stimulation, such as massage or brushing.

Unfavorable mechanical irritations of the gingiva may ensue from sharp edges of carious cavities, overhanging fillings or crowns, and accumulation of calculus. These may cause chronic inflammation of the gingival tissue.

Many systemic diseases cause characteristic changes in the oral mucosa. For instance, metal poisoning (lead, bismuth) causes characteristic discoloration of the gingival margin. Leukemia, pernicious anemia, and other blood dyscrasias can be diagnosed by characteristic infiltrations of the oral mucosa. In the first stages of measles, small red spots with bluish white centers can be seen in the mucous membrane of the cheeks, even before the skin rash appears. They are known as Koplik's spots. Endocrine disturbances, including those of the sex hormones and of the pancreas, may be reflected in the oral mucosa.

Changes of the tongue are sometimes diagnostically significant. In scarlet fever the atrophy of the lingual mucosa causes the peculiar redness of the strawberry tongue. Systemic diseases such as pernicious anemia and vitamin deficiencies, especially vitamin B complex deficiency, lead to characteristic changes, such as magenta tongue and beefy-red tongue.[31]

In denture construction it is important to observe the firmness or looseness of attachment of the mucous membrane. Denture-bearing areas should be those where the attachment of the mucosa is firm.[33,34]

In old age the mucous membrane of the mouth may atrophy in the cheeks and lips. It is then thin and parchmentlike. The atrophy of the lingual papillae leaves the upper surface of the tongue smooth, shiny, and varnished in appearance. Atrophy of the major and minor salivary glands may lead to xerostomia, dry mouth, and sometimes to a secondary atrophy of the mucous membrane. In a large percentage of individuals the sebaceous glands of the cheek are visible as fairly large, yellowish patches, Fordyce spots. They do not represent a pathologic change (Fig. 208).

REFERENCES

1. de Aprile, E. C.: Contribucion al estudio de los elementos reticulo endoteliales de la mucosa gingival, Arch. hist. normal y pat. 3:473, 1947.
2. Arnim, S. S., and Hagerman, D. A.: The connective tissue fibers of the marginal gingiva, J.A.D.A. 47:271, 1953.
3. Becks, H.: Normal and pathological pocket formation, J.A.D.A. 16:2167, 1929.
4. Bodecker, C. F., and Applebaum, E.: The clinical importance of the gingival crevice, D. Cosmos 176:1127, 1934.
5. Cattoni, M.: Melanoblasts in the inflamed gingiva, Oral Surg., Oral Med. & Oral Path. 6: 1095, 1952.
6. Emslie, R. D., and Weinmann, J. P.: The architectural pattern of the boundary between epithelium and connective tissue of the gingiva in the rhesus monkey, Anat. Rec. 105: 35, 1949.
7. Erausquin, Jorge: Histologia dentaria humana, Buenos Aires, 1953, Progrental.
8. Fehr, C., and Mühlemann, H. R.: The surface of the free and attached gingiva, studied with the replica method, Oral Surg., Oral Med. & Oral Path. 8:649, 1955.
9. Fish, E. W.: Bone infection, J.A.D.A. 26:691, 1939.
10. Gairns, F. W., and Aitchison, J. A.: A preliminary study of the multiplicity of nerve endings in the human gum, D. Rec. 70:180, 1950.
11. Gerson, S. J., and Meyer, J.: Metaplastic keratinization in the human buccal mucosa, J. D. Res. 43:536, 1964.
12. Gottlieb, B.: Der Epithelansatz am Zähne (The epithelial attachment), Deutsche Monatschr. f. Zahnh. 39:142, 1921.

13. Gottlieb, B.: Aetiologie und Prophylaxe der Zahnkaries (Etiology and prophylaxis of caries), Ztschr. f. Stomatol. **19**:129, 1921.
14. Gottlieb, B.: Tissue changes in pyorrhea, J.A.D.A. **14**:2178, 1927.
15. Gottlieb, B., and Orban, B.: Biology of the investing structures of the teeth. In Gordon, S. M. (editor): Dental science and dental art, Philadelphia, 1938, Lea & Febiger.
16. Gottlieb, B., and Orban, B.: Biology and pathology of the tooth (Translated by M. Diamond), New York, 1938, The Macmillan Co.
17. Keller, G. J., and Cohen, D. W.: India ink profusion of the vascular plexus of oral tissues, Oral Surg., Oral Med. & Oral Path. **8**:539, 1955.
18. Kronfeld, R.: The epithelial attachment and so-called Nasmyth's membrane, J.A.D.A. **17**:1889, 1930.
19. Kronfeld, R.: Increase in size of the clinical crown of human teeth with advancing age, J.A.D.A. **18**:382, 1936.
20. Lehner, J.: Ein Beitrag zur Kenntniss vom Schmelzoberhäutchen (Contribution to the knowledge of the dental cuticle), Ztschr. f. mikr.-anat. Forsch. **27**:613, 1931.
21. Marvah, A. S., and Weinmann, J. P.: A sex difference in the epithelial cells of human gingiva, J. Periodont. **26**:11, 1955.
22. Meyer, J., Marwah, A. S., and Weinmann, J. P.: Mitotic rate of gingival epithelium in two age groups, J. Invest. Dermat. **27**:237, 1956.
23. Meyer, J., and Gerson, S. J.: A comparison of human palatal and buccal mucosa, Periodontics **2**:284, 1964.
24. Meyer, W.: Ueber strittige Fragen in der Histologie des Schmelzoberhäutchens (Controversial questions in the histology of the enamel cuticle), Vrtljsschr. f. Zahnh. **46**:42, 1930.
25. Orban, B., and Kohler, J.: Die physiologisiche Zahnfleischtasche, Epithelansatz und Epitheltiefenwucherung (The physiologic gingival sulcus), Ztschr. f. Stomatol. **22**:353, 1924.
26. Orban, B., and Mueller, E.: The gingival crevice, J.A.D.A. **16**:1206, 1929.
27. Orban, B.: Hornification of the gums, J.A.D.A. **17**:1977, 1930.
28. Orban, B.: Zahnfleischtasche und Epithelansatz (Gingival sulcus and epithelial attachment), Ztschr. f. Stomatol. **22**:353, 1924.
29. Orban, B.: Clinical and histologic study of the surface characteristics of the gingiva, Oral Surg., Oral Med. & Oral Path. **1**:827, 1948.
30. Orban, B., and Sicher, H.: The oral mucosa, J. D. Educ. **10**:94, 163, 1946.
31. Orban, B., and Wentz, F. M.: Atlas of clinical pathology of the mucous membrane, St. Louis, 1955, The C. V. Mosby Co.
32. Orban, B., Bhatia, H., Kollar, J. A., and Wentz, F. M.: The epithelial attachment, J. Periodont. **27**:167, 1956.
33. Pendleton, E. C.: The minute anatomy of the denture bearing area, J.A.D.A. **21**:488, 1934.
34. Pendleton, E. C., and Glupker, H.: Research on the reaction of tissues supporting full dentures, J.A.D.A. **22**:76, 1935.
35. Robinson, H. B. G., and Kitchin, P. C.: The effect of massage with the toothbrush on keratinization of the gingivae, Oral Surg., Oral Med. & Oral Path. **1**:1042, 1948.
36. Skillen, W. G.: The morphology of the gingivae of the rat molar, J.A.D.A. **17**:645, 1930.
37. Toller, J. R.: Studies of the epithelial attachment on young dogs, Northwestern Univ. Bull. **40**:13, 1940. (Abst.)
38. Toto, P. D., and Sicher, H.: The epithelial attachment, Periodontics **2**:154, 1964.
39. Ussing, M. J.: The development of the epithelial attachment, Acta odont. scandinav. **13**:123, 1955.
40. Waerhaug, J.: Gingival pocket: anatomy, pathology, deepening and elimination, Odont. Tskr. **60**(supp. 1): 5, 1952.
41. Wassermann, F.: Personal communication.
42. Weinmann, J. P.: Progress of gingival inflammation into the supporting structures of the teeth, J. Periodont. **12**:71, 1941.

43. Weinmann, J. P.: The keratinization of the human oral mucosa, J. D. Res. **19:**57, 1940.
44. Wentz, F. M., Maier, A. W., and Orban, B.: Age changes and sex differences in the clinically "normal" gingiva, J. Periodont. **23:**13, 1952.
45. Wermuth, J.: Beitrag zur Histologie der Gegend seitlich von der Papilla palatina (Histology of the region lateral to the incisive papilla), Deutsche Monatschr. f. Zahnh. **45:** 203, 1927.

Chapter X

Salivary glands*

INTRODUCTION

CLASSIFICATION OF THE SALIVARY GLANDS

STRUCTURAL ELEMENTS OF THE SALIVARY GLANDS

Terminal portions (acini and tubules)
    Mucous cell
    Serous cells
    Arrangement of cells in mixed glands
Ducts
    Intercalated ducts
    Striated ducts
    Myoepithelial cells
    Oncocytes
Interstitial connective tissue; blood, lymph, and nerve supply

MAJOR SALIVARY GLANDS
    Parotid gland
    Submandibular gland
    Sublingual glands

MINOR SALIVARY GLANDS
    Labial glands
    Minor buccal glands

    Glossopalatine glands
    Palatine glands
    Glands of the tongue

DEVELOPMENT AND GROWTH

CYTOLOGIC, CHEMICAL, AND PHYSIOLOGIC CORRELATIONS
    Serous cell
    Mucous cell
    Intercalated ducts
    Striated ducts
    Myoepithelial cells

FUNCTIONS OF THE SALIVARY GLANDS
    Saliva
    Iodine metabolism
    Nerve growth factor
    Endocrine interrelations

CLINICAL CONSIDERATIONS
    Dental caries
    Periodontal disease

INTRODUCTION

The human salivary glands are compound merocrine glands. Their ducts open into the oral cavity. There are three pairs of large glands, which are often classified as major salivary glands or salivary glands proper. They are the parotid, the submandibular, and the sublingual glands. (See Plate 3.) In addition, there are numerous small glands widely distributed in the mucosa and submucosa of the oral cavity. These are known as the minor salivary glands. They perform many functions, of which the most extensively studied is the production of saliva. Saliva is the secretory product of the salivary glands, and among many other functions it assists in the mastication and deglutition of food and in the digestion of certain food elements.

In this chapter the classification of the salivary glands and their structure as seen with the light microscope using ordinary staining procedures will be presented first. The low resolving power of the light microscope is inadequate for

---

*By George A. Krikos.

266

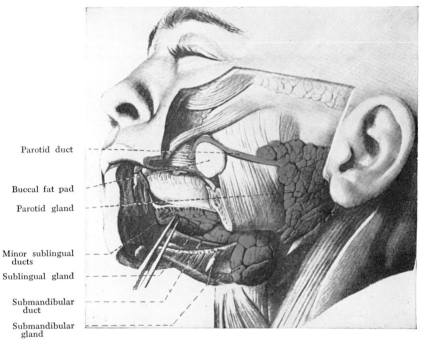

Parotid duct

Buccal fat pad

Parotid gland

Minor sublingual
ducts

Sublingual gland

Submandibular
duct

Submandibular
gland

Plate 3. Salivary glands of major secretion. Part of the mandible and mylohyoid muscle removed. (From Sicher, H., and Tandler, J.: Anatomie für Zahnärtze [Anatomy for dentists], Berlin, 1928, Julius Springer.)

the detailed study of certain tissue elements, and the ordinary staining procedures do not offer information on the chemical makeup of cellular and intercellular structures. In recent years the high resolving power of the electron microscope and the development of fine histochemical and cytochemical methods have given us the opportunity to study with greater accuracy the structure and chemistry of tissue components. It is also becoming increasingly evident that alterations in functions are frequently accompanied by changes in structure at all levels of observation. The relations of structure and function are indeed at the heart of modern histology. For these reasons an attempt will be made to correlate the cytologic, cytochemical, and biochemical observations on salivary glands. Finally, the functions of salivary glands and saliva and the contribution of the knowledge of the histology of the salivary glands to clinical practice will be discussed.

CLASSIFICATION OF THE SALIVARY GLANDS

The salivary glands of man can be classified in at least three ways: (1) according to the location of the glands, into glands of the vestibule and glands of the oral cavity proper, (2) according to size, into major and minor salivary glands, and (3) according to the nature of the substances that the secretory cells elaborate, into mucous, serous, and mixed glands. The secretory cells of the mucous glands elaborate a viscid secretion containing mucin. The secretory portions of the serous (albuminous) glands produce a watery secretion containing protein. Finally, the mixed glands consist of both mucous and serous cells. The first two classifications are helpful in designating the size and location but are of little help in the functional analysis of the salivary gland in question. The third classification, initially proposed by Heidenhain,[29] has been of the greatest service because it has attempted to classify the salivary glands on a functional basis considering the nature of the secretory product.

It is preferable to use all classifications conjointly in order to designate simultaneously location and nature of the secretory product of the salivary gland in question. It must be emphasized, however, that the classification of the secretory cells into serous and mucous does not mean that the serous cells are sources of pure protein secretion. Recent histochemical studies on serous cells of salivary glands[78] and biochemical analyses of parotid saliva[54,110] have shown the presence of sialic acid-containing mucoproteins. Approximately one-third of the protein of parotid saliva is mucoprotein.

The parotid gland of the adult is a pure serous gland. Glands with very few or no mucous cells are those of the vallate papillae. Glands in which both serous and mucous cells are present are referred to as predominantly serous or predominantly mucous depending upon the ratio of the cell types. Those with a few mucous cells include the submandibular gland and the parotid gland of the newborn infant. Those predominantly of mucous character include the labial glands, small buccal glands, anterior lingual glands, and the sublingual glands. In man pure mucous glands are those at the base and border of the tongue, the glossopalatine glands and the palatine glands. Following is a classification of the salivary glands according to location[109]:

A. Glands of the vestibule
  1. Labial glands
    (a) Superior labial glands
    (b) Inferior labial glands
  2. Buccal glands
    (a) Minor buccal glands
    (b) Parotid gland
B. Glands of the oral cavity proper (Plate 3)
  1. Glands of the floor of the mouth (alveololingual complex)
    (a) Submandibular gland
    (b) Major sublingual gland
    (c) Minor sublingual glands
    (d) Glossopalatine glands
  2. Glands of the tongue
    (a) Anterior lingual glands
    (b) Posterior lingual glands
      (1) Glands of the vallate papillae
      (2) Glands of the base of the tongue
  3. Palatine glands

STRUCTURAL ELEMENTS OF THE SALIVARY GLANDS

In general, the plan of organization of the salivary glands is similar to that of other exocrine glands. It consists of the following:

1. Connective tissue, which forms a capsule and extends as sheets or strands into the gland proper, dividing the gland into lobes and, on further subdivision, into lobules. It bears the ducts, blood vessels, lymphatics, and the nerves of the gland.
2. Ducts—in the connective tissue of the gland the larger ducts divide into ducts of progressively smaller caliber. In this way a complex duct system is formed. The smallest branches of this system are connected with the secretory or terminal portions of the gland.
3. Secretory cells—these cells are located in the terminal portions, which in turn lie in the lobules of the gland.

Detailed descriptions of the gross anatomy of salivary glands have been published by Sicher[91] and Carmalts.[11] The monographs by Stormont[100] and Zimmermann[109] describe the microscopic appearance of these glands.

Terminal portions (acini and tubules)

In general, a terminal portion consists of a layer of secretory cells lining a narrow lumen. These cells rest on a basement membrane that separates them from the underlying capillary bed. The shape of the terminal portions is not the same in all salivary glands. The pure mucous glands are compound tubular glands, the terminal portions usually being long, branching tubules. On the other hand, the serous and mixed salivary glands are compound tubuloacinous, their terminal portions being branched tubules with numerous outpocketings on the wall and on the blind ends.

Mucous and serous cells have certain structural characteristics. It must be emphasized, however, that it is not always possible to distinguish mucous from serous cells on the basis of morphology alone. The submandibular gland of the rabbit, for instance, has two types of secretory cells. One of these two types, known as "tropochrome cells," has an appearance very similar to mucous cells. However, the cells, when fixed in sublimate, do not exhibit some features be-lieved to be characteristic of mucous cells. They do not stain red with muci-carmine, they are not metachromatic, and the secretion from this gland does not contain mucin.[77,100] These cells belong to the category of "special" serous cells, and their functional significance is at present poorly understood.

Mucous cell. The appearance of mucous and serous cells varies with the state of functional activity. When examined in the fresh state, the mucous cells are seen to contain many droplets or granules of mucigen, the antecedent of mucin. The mucous cell is usually so completely filled with the droplets of mucigen that these droplets obscure the other elements. A few granules, probably mito-chondria, have been observed between the droplets, but the nuclei are not visible in fresh material.[41]

In fixed preparations stained with hematoxylin and eosin, the mucous cells have an entirely different appearance. The droplets of mucigen are destroyed by the fixatives used, and the cell body assumes its classical clear, lightly stained appearance, because it now contains a wide-meshed network. The spaces of this network are not stained, while the trabeculae are slightly basophilic and are made up of cytoplasm and precipitated mucigen. The trabeculae stain red with muci-carmine and are metachromatic. In such preparations the nucleus is angular in shape, stains deeply, and is located at the base of the cell. (Fig. 217.) There it is surrounded by a small accumulation of cytoplasm containing only small amounts of basophil material, which is so abundant in serous cells. However, when appropriate methods are used, such as freeze-drying, the droplets of muci-gen are preserved, and the cells maintain characteristics similar to those seen in the fresh state. In such preparations the mucous cells are found to contain large stainable granules that are separated from one another by thin partitions of protoplasm. Mucous cells are not associated with secretory capillaries. The lumina of mucous terminal portions are wider than those of serous terminal portions.

The previous description is that of a mucous cell in the "resting" state. The appearance changes with the state of functional activity. When the cell pours its secretion into the lumen, it becomes smaller, and only a few mucigen drop-lets remain which are confined near the free surface. The nucleus rises from the basal portion of the cell, becomes round, and one or more oxyphil nucleoli appear.

Serous cells. When examined in the fresh state, the serous cells are seen to

Demilune
(serous cells)

Lumen of
alveolus

Mucous cell

Mucous cell

Fig. 217. Mucous alveoli of a human sublingual gland.

contain a large number of highly refractile granules, known as secretion or zymogen granules. These are located primarily between the nucleus and the free
surface of the cell and are less labile than the droplets of mucigen.

The secretion granules are easily destroyed by most fixatives, particularly
those containing acetic acid. However, when appropriate fixatives are used, such
as bichromates, they are preserved and can be stained by a number of methods,
such as iron hematoxylin. These granules do not stain positively to mucicarmine
and are not metachromatic. The nuclei of serous cells are round and are located
in the basal third of the cell. The basal portion of the cytoplasm of serous cells
contains large concentrations of a substance that stains strongly with basic dyes.
This material has been known under a variety of names, such as basophil substance, chromophil substance, and ergastoplasm. In preparations fixed with acid
fixatives, this material becomes arranged in parallel rods and filaments that give
a vertical striation to the basal portion of the serous cell. This appearance is believed to be an artifact resulting from the precipitation of the basophil material
by the acid fixative. The intense staining of the cytoplasmic constituents of the
serous cells in sections stained with hematoxylin and eosin gives these cells a
dark color that contrasts to the clear appearance of the mucous cells. Rod-
shaped mitochondria are located in the cytoplasm at the basal portion of the
cell, and a Golgi apparatus is located above the nucleus. Serous cells are always
associated with secretory capillaries located between their lateral surfaces. The

Albuminous cell
Serous alveolus
Myoepithelial cell
Striated duct cell

Myoepithelial cell
Intercellular secretory capillary
Demilune
Basement membrane
Mucous cells
Intercalated duct

Fig. 218. Reconstruction of a terminal portion and its duct of a salivary gland. *a* and *b*, Cross section through a serous alveolus. *c*, Cross section through a mucous alveolus. *d*, Cross section through an intercalated duct. *e*, Cross section through a striated duct. (From Maximow, A. A., and Bloom, W.: A textbook of histology, ed. 4, Philadelphia, 1942, W. B. Saunders Co.)

serous cells are roughly pyramidal in shape and line a small lumen (Fig. 218).

This is the appearance of a serous cell in the "resting" state. When the cell is stimulated to secrete, there is a decrease in the number of secretion granules, which are now confined close to the free surface. The volume of the cell decreases, and the intensity of the staining of the basophil material undergoes significant changes. The mitochondria increase in size and number, and the Golgi apparatus becomes larger. The nucleus increases in size, stains less intensely, and moves away from the base of the cell. The nucleolus becomes more prominent. It increases in size and stains more deeply. (See Fig. 219.)

These descriptions point to certain differences between serous and mucous cells as seen in sections stained with hematoxylin and eosin. There are differences in the size, shape, location, and stainability of the nucleus, in the architecture of the cytoplasm, and in the intensity of the staining of the basophil material. It is also apparent that further differences can be observed when special methods of tissue preparation are employed. In such cases, droplets of mucigen, secretion granules, intercellular capillaries, and other structures can be observed and their chemical makeup studied. As previously mentioned, it is almost impossible in many cases to distinguish between mucous and serous cells on the basis of the morphologic characteristics alone. Furthermore, it must be emphasized that all mucous cells are not functionally identical. There are chemical differences in the

Fig. 219. Albuminous gland. Different functional stages of the cells. The secretory cycle is indicated by the letters A to G. (From Zimmermann, K. W.: Die Speicheldrüsen der Mundhöhle und die Bauchspeicheldrüse. In von Möllendorff, W. [editor]: Handbuch der mikroskopischen Anatomie des Menschen, vol. 5, pt. 1, Berlin, 1927, Julius Springer.)

products elaborated by mucous cells of different glands in the same species or by mucous cells of the same gland in different species.[74] The same holds true for serous cells.

Arrangement of cells in mixed glands. Mixed glands consist of both mucous and serous cells. In these glands can be observed not only pure serous and pure mucous terminal portions but also terminal portions lined by both types of cells. In such mixed terminal portions the mucous and serous cells occupy different positions. The serous cells are located at the blind end of the terminal portion, whereas the mucous cells lie close to the excretory duct. In mixed glands in which the mucous cells predominate, the lumen of the mixed secretory portions is lined entirely by mucous cells, whereas the serous cells are arranged in small groups that in sections appear as crescents capping the blind ends of the mucous tubules. The serous cells of the crescents are connected with the lumen of the terminal portion by secretory capillaries that lie between the mucous cells. These crescents are known as demilunes of von Ebner or Giannuzzi, and they have all the previously mentioned characteristics of serous cells. (See Figs. 218 and 227.)

Ducts

The duct system of the salivary glands is formed by the successive division within the connective tissue of the gland of larger ducts into ducts of progressively smaller caliber (Fig. 220). The ducts are named with reference to the gross architecture of the gland. Intralobular, interlobular, lobar, and primary ducts may be distinguished. The necks or intercalated ducts and the striated or secretory ducts are the two orders of intralobular ducts. The intercalated and the striated ducts are not equally developed in all salivary glands.

Intercalated ducts. The intercalated ducts are thin, branching tubes of varying lengths that connect the terminal portions with the striated ducts. They are lined by a single layer of low cuboidal epithelial cells. The cytoplasm of these

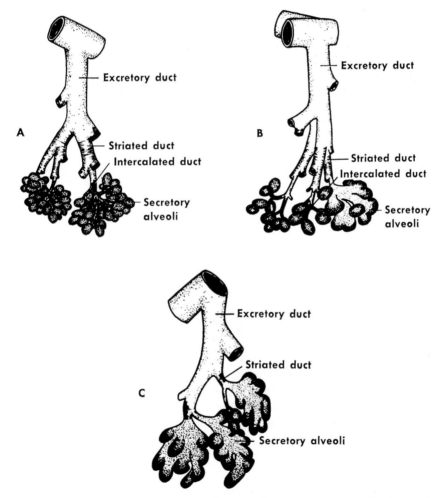

Fig. 220. Diagrams of the duct system and terminal secretory portions of salivary glands. **A,** Parotid. **B,** Submandibular. **C,** Sublingual. (Modified from Braus, H.: Anatomie des Menschen [Human anatomy], vol. 2, ed. 2, Berlin, 1934, Julius Springer.)

cells is relatively small in amount, stains faintly, and is free of granules. The nucleus is located in the center of the cell.[100] Whenever the intercalated ducts contain secretory cells, the transition between these ducts and the terminal portions is a gradual one. The proximal portion of the ducts consists of cells that resemble miniature acinous cells in having basophilic basal cytoplasm and secretory granules in their apical parts. The distal portion is lined by nonsecretory cells similar to those described previously. (See Figs. 218 and 223.)

Striated ducts. The striated ducts are lined by a single layer of tall, columnar epithelial cells. Their nuclei are large and spherical and usually lie in the center of the cell. The cytoplasm is relatively large in amount, is eosinophilic, and, when appropriately fixed and stained, shows a pronounced striation at the basal portion of the cell perpendicular to the basal surface. This vertical striation is due in part to the presence of radially arranged mitochondria (Figs. 218, 221, and 223).

The larger excretory ducts have a pseudostratified columnar epithelium that may contain a few goblet cells. The epithelium of the main ducts gradually merges into the stratified squamous epithelium of the oral cavity.

In the terminal portions and in the ducts of the salivary glands several other cell types can be found in addition to the secretory cells and the ductal epithelium. The most important of these cells are the myoepithelial cells and the oncocytes.

Myoepithelial cells. The myoepithelial cells (basal cells, basket cells) form a syncytium of branched cells and lie between the basement membrane and the

Fig. 221. Albuminous alveoli and striated duct of a submandibular gland with myoepithelial cells. (Modified from Zimmermann, K. W.: Die Speicheldrüsen der Mundhöhle und die Bauchspeicheldrüse. In von Möllendorff, W. [editor]: Handbuch der mikroskopischen Anatomie des Menschen, vol. 5, pt. 1, Berlin, 1927, Julius Springer.)

glandular or ductal epithelium. In cross section they are spindle shaped. When viewed from the surface, they exhibit a stellate body and numerous processes embracing the secretory portion or duct (Figs. 218 and 221).

The myoepithelial cells are most likely epithelial in nature. They are believed to be contractile and, by their contraction, to facilitate the movement of the secretion.

Oncocytes. The oncocytes are large cells having a small, centrally placed pyknotic nucleus and abundant, strongly eosinophilic cytoplasm. They are more frequently encountered in the parotid and submandibular glands of older individuals.

Interstitial connective tissue; blood, lymph, and nerve supply

The connective tissue may form a capsule around the gland and then extend into the gland proper, dividing it into lobes and lobules. This collagenous connective tissue is continuous with the reticular connective tissue of the lobules and the basement membrane, upon which rest the secretory cells and duct elements.

The salivary glands possess a rich blood supply. The larger arteries follow the course of the excretory ducts, giving off branches that accompany the divisions of the ducts to the lobules. The veins and the lymph vessels follow the arteries in reverse order to drain the gland.

The pattern of the vascular supply of acini and ducts within the microscopic lobule has not been adequately investigated. Kowalewsky[37] stated that in the submandibular gland of the cat there are two blood vessel systems: one system with capillaries in the walls of the ducts and another with capillaries between the alveoli. Presence of arteriovenous anastomoses has also been claimed.[75] Burgen and Seeman[9] stated that the findings of their radioisotope studies in the formation of saliva are not consistent with two separate systems of capillaries but, rather, with a series of continuous systems of capillaries that supply the ducts and acini and in which the direction of blood flow is opposite to that of the saliva (countercurrent portal system). It is obvious that there is a great need for the investigation of the intralobular blood supply of salivary glands, particularly if observations on the secretion of saliva are to be interpreted accurately.

The main branches of the nerves supplying the salivary glands also follow the course of the vessels to break up into terminal plexuses in the connective tissue adjacent to the terminal portions. Nerve fibers penetrate the basement membrane and end as fine filaments on the basal and intercellular surfaces of the acinar cells. It is not known if nerve fibers end on the surfaces of duct cells. It is generally accepted that the parasympathetic nerves supply the salivary glands with secretory fibers and that the sympathetic nerves carry vasoconstrictor fibers. It is not known with certainty if the salivary glands are supplied with secretory fibers from the sympathetic nervous system. Even if it be accepted that this is the case, and there is evidence in favor of this opinion, it is not known if a single salivary gland cell receives fibers from both divisions of the autonomic nervous system. The difficulty in investigating the different types of fibers present in salivary gland nerves is primarily due to the possibility that salivary secretion is not only effected by secretory fibers but also by motor fibers controlling blood flow and possibly the contractility of the myoepithelial cells.[8,21] The electrophysiologic studies of Lundberg on the submaxillary gland of the cat favor the concept that each acinar and duct cell has a double innervation.[49]

MAJOR SALIVARY GLANDS

The parotid, submandibular, and sublingual glands are often classified as the major salivary glands. They are located at some distance from the oral cavity, with which they communicate by variably long ducts. A comparison of the anatomic features of the three large salivary glands is presented in Table 4.

Parotid gland. The parotid gland is the largest of the salivary glands. Its superficial portion is located in front of the external ear, while its deeper part fills the retromandibular fossa. The gland is enclosed within a well-formed capsule. The main excretory duct (Stensen's duct) of the parotid gland opens into the oral cavity on the mucosa of the cheek opposite the maxillary second molar. Usually a small papilla marks the opening. (See Plate 3.)

The parotid gland is a branched tubuloacinous gland. In the adult it is a pure serous gland (Fig. 222), although occasional mucous acini can be found. In the newborn infant, however, mucous acini are encountered with greater frequency. The intercalated ducts are long and branching. The striated ducts are conspicuous (Figs. 220 and 223). In the parotid gland the connec-

X

Branching
duct

Fig. 222. Section through a human parotid gland. *X,* See Fig. 223.

Table 4. Comparison of the major salivary glands*

	Parotid	*Submandibular*	*Sublingual*
Size and shape	Largest; main and accessory parts both encapsulated; compound, branched, alveolar	Intermediate; well limited and encapsulated; compound, branched, alveolar, partly tubular	Smallest; major gland and several minor ones; no capsule; compound, branched, tubuloalveolar
Position	Filling retromandibular fossa and reaches around mandibular ramus anterior to ear	Beneath mandible	In floor of mouth
Ducts	Parotid (Stensen's) duct opens opposite second upper molar; double layer columnar cells on marked basement membrane	Submandibular (Wharton's) duct opens on either side of frenulum of tongue; structure same	Major sublingual (Bartholin's) duct opens near submandibular sometimes by common aperture, also several minor sublingual (Rivinian) ducts; structure same
Secretory ducts	Single layer very conspicuously striated columnar cells	Same but somewhat longer and may contain yellow pigment	Rare or absent
Intercalated ducts	Long, narrow, branching made of single layer of flattened cells	Much shorter but similar structure	Absent
Secretory epithelium	Serous alveoli, mucous alveoli rare (in newborn infant)	Serous alveoli predominate, some mucous alveoli have serous crescents	Major gland: mucous alveoli predominate; many serous crescents and alveoli. Minor glands all mucous
Interstitial tissue	Fat cells most abundant		Connective tissue septa most abundant
Nerve supply	Sensory: fifth nerve. Secretory: (1) sympathetic, superior cervical ganglion (vasoconstriction); (2) parasympathetic, ninth nerve, otic ganglion (vasodilation)	Sensory: fifth nerve. Secretory: (1) sympathetic, same; (2) parasympathetic, seventh nerve, chorda tympani, submandibular ganglion (vasodilation)	Sensory: fifth nerve. Secretory: same as submandibular gland

*After Finerty, J. C., and Cowdry, E. V.: A textbook of histology, ed. 5, Philadelphia, 1960, Lea & Febiger.

tive tissue septa frequently contain fat cells, which increase in number with age.

Submandibular gland. The greater part of the submandibular gland is located in the submandibular triangle behind and below the free border of the mylohyoid muscle. A tonguelike extension of the gland usually lies above the mylohyoid muscle close to the sublingual glands. (See Plate 3.) A well-formed capsule envelops the gland. The main excretory duct (Wharton's duct) opens by a narrow

Intercalated
duct

Striated duct

Striated duct

Fig. 223. Higher magnification of field *X* in Fig. 222.

Interlobular
septum

X

Fat cell

Albuminous
alveoli

Mucous
alveoli

Fig. 224. Section through a human submandibular gland. *X*, See Fig. 225.

Demilune

Mixed
alveolus

Interlobular
septum

Albuminous
alveoli

Intercalated
duct

Mucous
alveolus

Striated duct

Fig. 225. Higher magnification of field X in Fig. 224.

orifice on the summit of a small papilla, caruncula sublingualis, at the side of
the lingual frenum at the floor of the mouth.

The submandibular gland is a compound tubuloacinous gland. It is of the
mixed type, with the serous elements predominating. There are many serous
terminal portions and only a few mucous terminal portions. The latter are capped
by demilunes of serous cells. (See Figs. 224 and 225.) The intercalated ducts are
shorter but otherwise are similar in structure to those of the parotid gland. The
striated ducts are also structurally similar to those of the parotid gland but are
somewhat longer. (See Figs. 220 and 225.)

Sublingual glands. The sublingual glands are located in the floor of the mouth
in the sublingual fold (Plate 3). They are a composite of one larger and several
smaller glands. The main secretory duct of the large sublingual gland (Bartholin's
duct) opens into the oral cavity with or near, but independently from, the duct
of the submandibular gland. The ducts of the smaller sublingual glands usually
are eight to twenty in number, and most of them open independently into the
mouth on the sublingual fold.

The major sublingual gland is a compound tubuloacinous gland. It is of the
mixed type, but, in contrast to the submandibular gland, the mucous elements
predominate. (See Fig. 226.) There are numerous mucous terminal portions. The
blind ends of some of them are capped by demilunes of serous cells. The majority of the mucous secretory portions do not possess demilunes. Pure serous
alveoli are rare. (See Fig. 227.) Striated and intercalated ducts, particularly the
latter, are scarce or entirely absent (Fig. 220). The connective tissue septa
separating the lobes and lobules are more pronounced in the sublingual than in

Mixed
alveoli

Mucous
alveoli

Interlobular
septum

X

Fig. 226. Section through a human major sublingual gland. *X*, See Fig. 227.

Septum

Mucous
alveoli

Demilune

Mucous
alveoli

Fig. 227. Higher magnification of field *X* in Fig. 226.

either the parotid or the submandibular gland. However, the sublingual gland is practically devoid of an investing capsule. The smaller sublingual glands are mucous in character.

MINOR SALIVARY GLANDS

Labial glands. The labial glands, which are located near the inner surface of the lips, are of the mixed type. They are variable in size and are closely packed in the submucosa, where they may be easily palpated. They are not encapsulated. The terminal portions may contain both serous and mucous cells lining the same lumen, but more often typical demilunes are formed. A considerable number of the terminal portions may contain only mucous cells (Fig. 228). The cells have a distinct mucoalbuminous character. The intercalated ducts are short.

Minor buccal glands. The buccal glands, which are a continuation of the labial glands in the cheek, bear a marked resemblance to those of the lips. Those glands that lie in the immediate vicinity of the opening of the parotid duct and drain into the third molar region often are designated the molar glands. Buccal glands are found frequently on the outer surface of the buccinator muscle.

Glossopalatine glands. The glossopalatine glands are pure mucous glands. They are located in the isthmus region and are a continuation, posteriorly, of the lesser sublingual glands. They ascend in the mucosa of the glossopalatine fold. They may be confined to the anterior faucial pillar or may extend into the soft palate to fuse with the palatine glands proper. They may also be seen on the lingual side of the retromolar area of the mandible.

Palatine glands. The palatine glands, which occupy the roof of the oral cav-

Fig. 228. Section through a human labial gland.

ity, can be topographically divided into glands of the hard palate and glands of the soft palate and uvula. They are composed of independent glandular aggregates numbering approximately 250 in the hard palate, 100 in the soft palate, and 12 in the uvula. In the posterior area of the hard palate the glands lie between the mucous membrane and the periosteum, supported by a dense framework of connective tissue characteristic of this region. Continuing backward, the lateral groups become arranged into compact rows and take on considerable size. They merge with those of the soft palate, the latter forming a thick layer between the mucous membrane and the palatal musculature (see Chapter IX).

The palatine glands are of the pure mucous type. The intercalated ducts are short. Many undergo mucous transformation, in which case they function as part of the mucous terminal portion.

Glands of the tongue. The glands of the tongue are divided into anterior and posterior lingual glands. The anterior lingual gland (gland of Blandin-Nuhn) is embedded within the musculature of the inferior aspect of the tongue close to the midline near the apex. Approximately five small ducts open on the inferior surface of the tongue near the lingual frenum. The anterior part of this gland is chiefly mucous in character. The posterior part consists of branching tubules lined with mucous cells and capped with demilunes of serous cells.

The posterior lingual glands are located at the base (root) of the tongue and in the vicinity of the vallate papillae. The glands of the base of the tongue are of the pure mucous variety. The glands of the vallate papillae (von Ebner) are pure serous and open into the trough of the vallate papillae. Their secretion probably serves to wash out the furrows of the vallate papillae (see Chapter IX).

DEVELOPMENT AND GROWTH

During fetal life, each salivary gland is formed at a specific location in the oral cavity through the growth of a bud of oral epithelium into the underlying connective tissue. The primordia of the parotid and submandibular glands, appear during the sixth week, while the primordium of the sublingual gland appears during the seventh week of fetal life. The primordia of the minor salivary glands appear later.[69] The epithelial bud grows into an extensively branched system of cords of cells which are at first solid, but gradually the older portions develop a lumen and become ducts. The secretory portions develop later than the duct system and arise from the terminations of the finer ducts. For instance, in the human parotid gland acini do not appear until the fourth month in utero,[76] while in the rat submandibular gland acini are not present at birth. Their formation is complete at six weeks, and the gland is fully developed approximately four months after birth.[33,98]

The connective tissue component of the salivary gland plays an important role in the morphogenesis of the glandular epithelium. The tissue culture studies of Grobstein[26] have shown that the isolated epithelial component of the mouse submandibular rudiment can undergo branching and form an extensive system of ducts and terminal buds only if recombined with fragments of submandibular capsular mesenchyme. All other sources of mesenchyme were not effective in inducing submandibular epithelial morphogenesis.

The nervous system plays an important role in the regulation of the growth of the salivary glands. Deprivation of the submandibular gland of the rat of its sympathetic nervous stimulation by extirpation of the superior cervical ganglion or the administration of dibenamine, an adrenergic blocking agent, results in a significant reduction in gland weight.[106] On the other hand, the repeated amputation of the incisor teeth[106] or the administration of isoproterenol,[88] a sympathomimetic drug, significantly increases the weight of the rat submaxillary gland. The effect of incisor amputation is mediated through the sympathetic nervous system, while isoproterenol appears to act directly on the gland itself. The increase in gland weight is a true increase in nonaqueous cellular material and is due to an increase in size (hypertrophy) of the acinar cells.[106] While the nervous system plays a role in the growth of the salivary glands, there is good evidence to suggest that, in turn, the salivary glands are the sites of concentration of a factor that affects the growth and differentiation of sympathetic ganglia[47] (see discussion of functions of the salivary glands).

CYTOLOGIC, CHEMICAL, AND PHYSIOLOGIC CORRELATIONS

Knowledge about the ultrastructure, chemistry, and biochemical activity of the cell components and the secretory products of salivary glands and about the role the cell components play in the production of the secretory products is most valuable for the understanding of the general economy of the gland and the secretory cells. The development of fine histochemical and cytochemical methods, the development of cell fractionation procedures, and the use of the electron microscope have been of great help in this respect. Significant studies have been made on various exocrine glands,[65] particularly the pancreas.[63] However, studies of this type on salivary glands are not numerous. The number of such studies on *human* salivary glands is exceedingly small. In the majority of cases different procedures have been employed on different salivary glands of different animal species. We have already emphasized that there are significant differences from one salivary gland to another and from one species to another. This state of affairs makes correlation a difficult task.

The process of secretion consists of at least the following three steps[35]:

1. Ingestion of raw material into the cell
2. Synthesis of complex molecules, which may then be stored in the form of granules, crystals, vacuoles, etc.
3. Extrusion of the secretory product from the cell.

In the salivary glands we are particularly concerned with the synthesis of proteins or proteins combined with a variable amount of polysaccharides.

Serous cell. In a recent electron microscopic study, Parks[66] observed that the acinous cell of the mouse parotid gland is very similar in structure to the exocrine cell of the pancreas.[94,95] In the mouse parotid gland the endoplasmic reticulum appears as an extensive system of flattened membranous vesicles that are commonly known as cisternae.[64] These membranous structures reach their highest intracellular concentration in the basal region of the acinous cell and are characteristically arranged parallel to one another. Numerous dense particles are attached to their outer surface. Many particles of similar structure lie also free in the cytoplasm. (See Fig. 229.) It has been demonstrated that these particles in the pancreatic acinous cell of the guinea pig are ribonucleoprotein (RNP) particles. Caspersson and associates,[13] using ultraviolet microspectrophotometric methods, demonstrated high concentrations of RNA in the basal cytoplasm of serous cells of dog parotid and submandibular glands, and Noback and Montagna[59] showed that the intense basophilia of the basal cytoplasm of the serous cells of mouse parotid and submandibular glands is removable with the enzyme ribonuclease. It is thus apparent that the endoplasmic reticulum and RNP particles are identical with the basophil substance or ergastoplasm of the histologists.

Fig. 229. Endoplasmic reticulum in a parotid acinous cell of a mouse. The endoplasmic reticulum consists mainly of flattened membranous vesicles or cisternae that present long, thin profiles when sectioned in a plane perpendicular to their broad surfaces. The cisternae appear in sections to begin and end blindly (arrows), but they are generally considered to be dilated parts of a continuous netlike membranous formation. The external surfaces of the cisternae have numerous tiny, dense ribonucleoprotein granules attached to them. These granules are believed to be importantly concerned in protein synthesis. Three small mitochondria are seen in the top of the field. (Courtesy Dr. Harold F. Parks.)

There is a considerable body of evidence to suggest that the cytoplasmic RNA is associated with protein synthesis,[12,13] and recent radioisotope studies have implicated the RNA particles as the probable site of this process.[93] It is, therefore, not surprising that in protein-producing cells, such as the serous cells of salivary glands, significant changes have been observed in the endoplasmic reticulum during the various stages of their secretory activity. In the charged state the endoplasmic reticulum is sparse, while shortly after discharge of the secretory products it increases significantly in amount.[87]

Although protein synthesis is connected with the endoplasmic reticulum, the zymogen granule, which is the morphologically recognizable form of a secretory product (Figs. 230 and 231), makes its first appearance in the Golgi bodies (with the possible exception of the acinous cell of the guinea pig pancreas).[62] From the observation that the Golgi apparatus undergoes significant morphologic changes during the secretory activity of the cell, many microscopists[3,58] hypothesized

Fig. 230. Golgi apparatus in a parotid acinous cell of a mouse. This organelle consists of two membranous components: tiny spherical vesicles, *V*, and larger flattened vesicles or lamellae, *L*. The lamellae tend to be stacked in parallel groups. Four immature secretion granules, *G*, may be seen in the space enclosed by the Golgi body. The impression is gained from examining lamellae that they swell up to form the secretion granules: that L_2 is thicker than L_1, and the contents of L_3 have taken on a texture like that of the secretion granules. The arrow at the right shows a nongranular diverticulum of a cisterna of the endoplasmic reticulum. This frequently seen configuration suggests that the small Golgi vesicles may arise by pinching off from the endoplasmic reticulum or that they coalesce with the endoplasmic reticulum and thus contribute to its substance. (Courtesy Dr. Harold F. Parks.)

Fig. 231. Secretory activity in a parotid acinus of a mouse. The lumen, *L*, of an intercellular secretion canal is seen to be bordered by four cells. At its lower left, a secretion granule, *G*, has extruded its contents into the lumen, and the membrane that once surrounded the granule is now part of the cell membrane. Examples of secretion granules, *G*, Golgi apparatus, *GA*, and mitochondria, *M*, are labeled. (From Parks, Harold F.: J. Ultrastructure Res. 6:449, 1962.)

that this apparatus is in some way connected with the production of secretory granules. Recent electron microscopic studies[95] have substantiated this hypothesis. In the acinous cell of the mouse parotid gland,[60,68] the Golgi bodies consist of small spherical membranous structures, known as vesicles, and of lamellae, which are larger, flattened membranous vesicles arranged parallel to one another (Fig. 230). In this cell the zymogen granules appear to arise by a swelling and enspherulation of the Golgi lamellae (Fig. 230). The granules enlarge and mature and move toward the luminal surface of the cell. However, in electron microscopic studies of the rat parotid gland, Scott and Pease did not observe a relation between zymogen granules and any of the elements of the Golgi apparatus, suggesting that elements of the Golgi apparatus are transformed to zymogen granules.[87]

Studies on the living gland[40] and of microscopic sections[100] have suggested that the secretory granules are extruded into the lumen. The details of this extrusion process have recently been investigated by the use of the electron microscope. In the acinous cell of the mouse parotid gland the membrane enclosing the granule fuses with the cell membrane. This fusion is followed by a perforation at the site of the fusion, which allows the contents of the secretion granule to flow into the lumen.[67] (See Fig. 231.) It is most interesting that the secretory granules are always separated from the cytoplasm by a membrane and that during extrusion the cell membrane does not lose its continuity. Similarly, in their study of the rat parotid gland, Scott and Pease found that the plasma membrane was not disrupted during the discharge of the secretory products. However, they did not observe the previously described fusion of the membrane of the zymogen granule with the plasma membrane and the perforation at the site of fusion. They found that, prior to discharge, the membranes of the zymogen granules became fragmented and finally disappeared, resulting in a merging of the contents of the granules with the cytoplasmic matrix, but offered no mechanism for the extrusion of the secretory products into the lumen of the acini.[87]

Recently the zymogen granules of the rat parotid gland were isolated and were found to contain large amounts of amylase and DNAse, smaller amounts of RNAse, and other unidentified proteins.[84] Approximately 50 per cent of the amylase of the gland was located in the zymogen granule fraction, while the remainder was largely found in the postmicrosomal supernatant. The radioisotope studies of Gromet-Elhanan and Winnick[27] have shown that amylase is synthesized in the microsomes of the rat parotid gland. The zymogen granules are, as a rule, periodic acid–Schiff (PAS) positive,[35, 66] which suggests that they may contain polysaccharides.

Although much has been learned, much is still unknown. The process of protein synthesis, the transfer of the product from the site of synthesis (presumably the RNP particles) to the Golgi bodies, the aggregation of the zymogen molecules into granules, the mechanism of the movement of these granules from the Golgi region to the luminal surface of the cell, and the nature of the forces that eject the zymogen material into the lumen are all questions that need intensive investigation. There is evidence[68] to suggest that the Golgi vesicles may transfer the secretion antecedents from their site of synthesis to the Golgi lamellae.

The changes in the number and form of the mitochondria during the secretory cycle caused many histologists to suggest that these organelles participate in the process of secretion. In the rat parotid gland, for instance, the mitochondria in the charged state are sparse and are confined to the perinuclear cytoplasm. However, shortly after discharge of the secretory products the mitochondria increase in number, are found throughout the whole extent of the cytoplasm, and exhibit a variety of shapes.[87] (See Figs. 229 and 231.) The mitochondria contain the enzymes for the citric acid cycle, electron transport, and oxidative phosphorylation.[24] They are, therefore, the centers of biologic oxidation and act as energy suppliers for the cell. Since there is evidence to suggest that aerobic oxidation is an important source of energy for the secretory process in salivary glands, it is not surprising that the mitochondria undergo significant changes during the secretory cycle. Several enzymes of the citric acid cycle and the cytochrome system have been found in salivary glands.[34,81,83] Secretion of saliva results in an increased oxygen utilization by the gland.[83] Furthermore, the secretion of amylase and DNAse by gland slices is dependent on oxygen and is inhibited by cyanide and 2,4 dinitrophenol.[2] These findings indicate that aerobic processes are involved in the supply of energy for secretion.

Mucous cell. In an electron microscope study of the salivary glands of the rat, Scott and Pease[86] observed that in the mucous cell of the sublingual gland the cytoplasm is located basally and is richly endowed with mitochondria and endoplasmic reticulum, while the mucoid mass occupies the center and apical portion of the cell. They also observed that the mucous granules arise directly from the Golgi vacuoles. These granules lose their limiting membranes and finally coalesce into a secretory mass that is located between the nucleus and the luminal cell surface, As with the zymogen granules, the mucous granules are not extruded as distinct bodies, and during discharge the plasma membrane remains intact.[87]

Mucins are an important secretory product of the mucous cells. As a group the mucins are principally glycoproteins, i.e., large molecules consisting of a carbohydrate moiety firmly bound to protein. Recently, a number of salivary gland mucins from various mammals have been isolated and characterized and have been found to contain sialic acid.[1,25,28,74] There are, however, important chemical differences among these mucins. For instance, the bovine sublingual and canine submandibular mucins contain significantly larger amounts of galactose and fucose than do the bovine and ovine submandibular mucins. Neuraminidase removes sialic acid from the mucin of the sublingual gland of the mouse but does not affect the sialic acid of the mucin of the sublingual gland of the rat.[97] These differences among mucins from different species and different glands point to the fact that mucous cells, although morphologically similar, may not be functionally identical.

Intercalated ducts. Electron microscopic studies of intercalated ducts draining serous terminal portions have shown that secretory cells, when present, are similar to the serous cells in that they have large amounts of endoplasmic reticulum and contain secretion granules. The nonsecreting cells of these ducts are free of secretion granules and are practically devoid of granular endoplasmic reticulum.[66]

Striated ducts. The most characteristic electron microscopic features of the epithelium of striated ducts are the presence of large numbers of radially arranged mitochondria and particularly the presence of extensive infoldings of the basal cell membrane. The basal cytoplasm of these cells is divided into a series of processes, which are lamellar to cylindical in form, and which extend radially beyond the lateral boundaries of the cells. These processes closely fit into appropriately shaped indentations or furrows present in adjacent cells[66,101] (Fig. 232). Similar but not identical complex folding of the cell membrane has

Fig. 232. Basal part of a striated duct cell from a mouse parotid gland. The nucleus is in the upper right. The basal surface of the cell is at the left. It can be seen that the basal striations of these cells are due in part to the presence of radially arranged mitochondria and in part to numerous infoldings of the plasma membrane. (From Parks, Harold F.: Am. J. Anat. **108:** 303, 1961.)

been observed also in cells noted for their water transport, such as epithelial cells of the kidney, choroid plexus, and ciliary body.[72] This folding increases to a significant extent the area of basal cell membrane available for the transfer of water and electrolytes and brings the cell membrane into close proximity with larger numbers of mitochondria.

There is good evidence to suggest that the ducts do not play a passive role but instead modify the secretion elaborated by the acinous cells. For instance, striated ducts are present in parotid and submandibular glands which elaborate hypotonic secretions, and they are absent in sublingual glands and pancreas which produce isotonic secretions independent of rate of flow. During the early postnatal period, the salivary glands of certain species contain few or no acini and are composed mainly of ducts. These glands are nevertheless capable of secreting fluid, and sodium and potassium, and in some instances flow rate and electrolyte concentration are within normal range.[82] It is interesting to note that from the earliest stage of their development, the ductal cells of such glands exhibit infoldings of their basal cell membrane.[43] The degree and complexity of the infoldings of the basal cell membrane correlate well with the degree of secretory activity of the ductal cells. In the hypoactive state the infoldings are almost absent, while shortly after stimulation with pilocarpine they reach their maximal state of development.[87] Finally, in the submandibular glands the cytochrome oxidase activity of the ducts is higher than that of the acini, indicating that the ducts have a high metabolic activity.[81]

The foregoing findings suggest that the ducts contribute to the production of saliva. However, our knowledge of the specific physiologic actions of the ducts is inadequate. It has been shown that water and several electrolytes can be secreted and reabsorbed by the duct epithelium,[6,8,82,103] and the studies of Burgen[7] suggest that all substances do not cross the ducts in the same place, but different ions are transferred at different sites. For instance, Cl^- and HCO_3^- appear to enter the saliva at a more distal portion of the duct than Na^+ and K^+. However, for a given ion very little is known about the contribution by the acinar cell, the ratio of secretion and reabsorption by the duct cell, and the controlling factors. Perhaps the only well-established physiologic action of the ducts is the demonstration by radioautographic methods that in certain animals the duct epithelium concentrates and exclusively secretes iodide and thiocyanate into the saliva.[48] It is obvious that studies on the functions of the acinus and the character of its secretion and on the development of methods for the analysis of secretion in various segments of the duct system are needed in order to get a better understanding of the mechanisms involved in the production of saliva.

In addition to the participation of the ducts in water and electrolyte transport, several other functions have been attributed to the ducts. In the submandibular gland of the rat the proteolytic enzymes are located almost exclusively in the convoluted portion of the intralobular duct system.[99] The work of Junqueira and associates suggests that amylase is not synthesized by the submandibular gland of the rat but is transferred from serum to saliva. The duct system appears to be the site of this transfer.[36] Finally, the nerve growth factor is localized in the duct epithelium.[47]

Myoepithelial cells. Study of myoepithelial cells with the electron microscope[60] has shown that these cells resemble smooth muscle cells. Their cytoplasm shows faint longitudinal striations resembling myofibrils, and their cell membrane has "pinocytotic vesicles." These observations are consistent with the assumed contractile nature of the myoepithelial cells.

FUNCTIONS OF SALIVARY GLANDS

The production of saliva is the most extensively studied function of the salivary glands. Experimental studies conducted during the past fifteen years indicate that the salivary glands, in addition to producing saliva, play a significant role in iodine metabolism, store a factor that affects the growth and differentiation of the sympathetic nervous system, contain a substance that affects calcium metabolism, and are functionally related with various endocrine organs. Observations of this sort suggest that the salivary glands not only affect the oral cavity through the saliva but also have far-reaching effects on the whole organism.

Saliva. The secretion of proteins, electrolytes, and water by the salivary glands has been discussed in the previous section. For the average "resting" secretion in man, approximately 69 per cent seems to be derived from the submandibular glands, 26 per cent from the parotid glands, and 5 per cent from the sublingual glands. The minor salivary glands do not contribute significantly. Since the composition of saliva varies greatly from individual to individual and from one gland to another and depends upon the nature and intensity of the stimuli causing its secretion, the designation of the percentages of its various constituents is meaningless unless the exact conditions under which the saliva was collected are also described. It may suffice to say that saliva contains 0.3 to 0.7 per cent of solid matter. The latter consists of inorganic salts, such as bicarbonates, chlorides, and phosphates of calcium, sodium and potassium, and of organic substances, such as proteins, mucins, enzymes, blood group substances, antibodies, blood-clotting factors, lipids, vitamins, amino acids, and urea. In addition, dissolved gases, mostly carbon dioxide and oxygen, are also present.[18,38,73,75]

The proteins are the principal organic constituents of saliva. Various electrophoretic methods have been employed for the separation of proteins and other charged macromolecules of human parotid and submandibular saliva.[71,105] Each type of secretion contained six to twelve electrophoretically separable components at pH 6, 7, and 8.5, and considerable differences between samples from different individuals were apparent. Amylase was the first electrophoretic component to be identified.[70] Mandel and Ellison eluted the electrophoretic components of parotid and submandibular saliva and examined them chemically and immunochemically. Submandibular saliva was found to be more complex than parotid saliva. Both salivas contained distinctive glycoproteins, serum proteins such as albumin and alpha, beta and gamma globulins, and intrinsic salivary proteins.[51,52] The concentration of protein and carbohydrate was higher in parotid saliva, but when calculated per 100 mg. of protein, submandibular saliva had a higher carbohydrate value, indicating either a higher proportion of mucoprotein or mucoprotein richer in carbohydrate. The carbohydrate of parotid and submandibular saliva consisted of hexosamines, galactose, mannose, fucose, glucose, and sialic acid.[52,54,55]

It must be emphasized that the saliva in the oral cavity is different from the saliva collected from the ducts. The latter is significantly modified in the oral cavity by the activities of microbes and of the oral tissues and by such other substances as may be taken into the mouth from time to time. For instance, in whole saliva, ammonia, urease, and hyaluronidase are believed to be entirely of microbial origin, whereas lysozyme appears to be entirely of salivary gland origin. A host of other constituents of whole saliva, such as amino acids, vitamins, lipase, acid phosphatase, etc., are both of salivary and extrasalivary gland origin.[14,73,75] A number of enzymes found in saliva collected directly from the

Fig. 233. Smear of human saliva (Wright's stain). (From Orban, B., and Weinmann, J. P.: J.A.D.A. **26**:2008, 1939.)

main excretory ducts[14,30] have also been demonstrated histochemically in salivary glands.[10,15] For this reason, in studies on the secretion of saliva and on the contribution of the salivary glands to oral health and disease, the pure secretions from the individual salivary glands must be used. The collection of these pure secretions is accomplished by the use of special devices.

Saliva also contains desquamated epithelial cells and cells known as salivary corpuscles. The latter resemble blood leukocytes morphologically, physically, and biochemically.[80] The epithelial cells are large and flat and have oval nuclei[61] (Fig. 233). The gingival sulci appear to be the major source of salivary corpuscles. Saliva obtained directly from the ducts of healthy salivary glands is practically free of salivary corpuscles.[108] Salivary corpuscles obtained from fresh saliva have been found to contain bacteria, and under certain in vitro conditions they exhibit ameboid movement, chemotaxis, phagocytosis, and intracellular digestion. Salivary corpuscles may contribute actively as well as passively to the state of the oral environment. The active contribution would be the result of their phagocytic ability and their enzymatic activity. The passive contribution would result from the breakdown products of the cell constituents as well as from the enzymes liberated from degenerating cells.[80] In this respect it is interesting to note that recent studies showed that the largest part of the aerobic and anaerobic metabolic activity of whole human saliva is predominantly associated with its content of oral leukocyte protoplasm, the contribution of the oral microorganisms being of a low order of magnitude.[19]

The digestive function of saliva has mechanical and chemical aspects. From the mechanical standpoint, saliva brings food components into solution, thus facilitating chemical reactivity and the stimulation of the taste organs. Mucin aids in the lubrication of the bolus of food for deglutition. From the chemical standpoint, salivary amylase hydrolyzes starch components into monosaccharides, disaccharides, and trisaccharides. The role of salivary amylase in the breakdown of the starch of foodstuffs is not great since the foodstuffs remain in the oral cavity for only a short period of time, and amylase reactivity is destroyed shortly after the entrance of the bolus into the stomach. Most likely this enzyme acts as a cleansing agent by liquefying starchy foodstuffs that cling to the oral tissues.

Additional functions of saliva will be discussed under clinical considerations.

Iodine metabolism. The salivary glands play an important role in iodine metabolism.[57] In human beings and in certain animals they possess a powerful mechanism for concentrating iodide.[20] The iodide concentration of human mixed saliva is usually over twenty times higher than in the blood plasma. Autoradiographic methods have shown that the iodide-concentrating mechanism is located in the cells of the striated ducts.[48] The accumulation of iodide in the salivary glands is not affected by thyrotrophic hormone,[102] which is known to produce hyperplasia and to stimulate the iodide-concentrating mechanism in the thyroid gland. In this connection it is interesting to note that the salivary glands may control the level of thyroxin in the blood. Fawcett and Kirkwood[23] proposed that the salivary glands deiodinate thyroxin and recycle the iodide ion to the thyroid gland via the saliva and the gastrointestinal tract.

Nerve growth factor. The growth and maintenance of sympathetic nerve cells throughout their life and of some sensory nerve cells before they are fully differentiated is under the control of a specific protein factor known as nerve growth factor (NGF). This factor is highly specific, and when injected in minute amounts into newborn mice causes a pronounced hypertrophy and hyperplasia of the sympathetic nerve cells. In contrast, the injection of a specific antiserum to new growth factor in newborn mice results in total destruction of the sympathetic nerve cells. This factor is localized in the tubular portion of the submandibular glands of mice but most likely is not produced by the gland because extirpation of this gland has no effect on the sympathetic ganglia. Nerve growth factor has also been found in rapidly proliferating cells of mesenchymal origin, in snake venom, and in the serum and sympathetic ganglia of a variety of mammals, including man.[47]

Endocrine interrelations. In 1940 Lacassagne[39] observed that there is a sexual dimorphism in the tubular portion of the mouse submandibular glands, this portion being more highly developed in male than in female mice. This observation suggested a relation between the salivary glands and the sex organs and stimulated a large number of studies that have shown that the salivary glands, at least in the experimental animal, are intimately associated with the endocrine organs. These studies have been reviewed recently by Shafer and Muhler.[89] It has been observed, for instance, that thyroidectomy causes a decrease in the size and number of the so-called granular tubules of the submandibular glands, a decrease in salivary flow, and an increase in the viscosity of saliva. It is most interesting that these structural and functional changes are accompanied by significant changes in the incidence of dental caries. In thyroidectomized animals, the incidence of dental caries is increased. In these animals thyroxin replacement therapy causes a return of the structure of the salivary gland and of the salivary flow and viscosity back to control levels, and this is associated with a return of the caries scores to those of the control level. The interrelations between endocrine glands, salivary glands, saliva, and caries are still obscure, but here we have a well-controlled experimental model that may help solve some of the unexplained aspects of the problem of dental caries.

The sex organs and the hypophysis and other endocrine glands have been shown to influence the morphology of the salivary glands and their secretion.[8,89,99]

In 1935 Ogata[60] presented a hypothesis that the salivary glands secrete a hormone acting on the mesenchymal tissues. Subsequently, an active principle was isolated from bovine parotid and submandibular glands and was named parotin. This substance lowers the serum calcium level and enhances the calcification of incisor dentin in rabbits and rats.[32] Although the Japanese workers claim that the salivary glands are endocrine organs, their studies are not convincing, and certainly more research is necessary before their endocrine role is established firmly.

CLINICAL CONSIDERATIONS

The salivary glands are the site of numerous pathologic conditions. On the other hand, the fact that the oral mucous membrane and the teeth are in continuous contact with the saliva would suggest that saliva could exert a profound influence on oral health and disease.

Dental caries. In a simplified form the process of dental caries appears to depend on an interplay between tooth composition, diet, and oral microbial flora. In turn, each of these factors is influenced by a large number of other agents, saliva being only one of these. Salivary factors, such as the viscosity, pH, and buffering capacity of saliva and its content in various electrolytes and organic substances, such as enzymes and antibacterial factors, have been investigated as to their significance in dental caries. With few exceptions, none of the physical and chemical characteristics of saliva has been related consistently to human dental caries. This state of affairs is understood easily if we consider that experiments on human beings subsisting under different environmental conditions and eating different diets cannot be easily controlled. The variable under study is affected to different degrees in different individuals by factors having similar or opposite effects. The need to study the role of the various salivary factors on dental caries under well-controlled experimental conditions is obvious. Since all carious lesions are initiated under a dental plaque, well-controlled studies on the role of salivary factors on the formation, composition, and permeability of the dental plaque are of even greater significance.

In a few instances the role of salivary factors on dental caries is reasonably well documented. A significant decrease in the rate of salivary flow, such as occurs in salivary gland extirpation, congenital aplasia, Mikulicz's disease, etc., is always associated with an increase in the incidence of dental caries.[16,104] This is attributed to the absence of the cleansing action of saliva, resulting in protein and amino acid retention and in an increase in the number of microorganisms.[85] After eruption and throughout the life span of the teeth, fluoride from saliva is taken up by the enamel surface, as shown by the observation that the fluoride content of the enamel surface of erupted teeth increases with age in individuals drinking water containing fluoride.[4] This is associated with a decrease in the incidence of dental caries. In experimental animals, diets high in phosphate cause a reduction in the incidence of dental caries.[56] This reduction has been attributed primarily to a decrease in the carbonate content of surface enamel brought about by the action of the high levels of salivary phosphate on the enamel surface.[5,56] However, dietary additions of phosphate have failed to influence the incidence of dental caries in man.[90] Finally, Fanning and associates[22] observed that desalivation of rats at 21 days of age resulted in a much higher incidence of dental caries than desalivation at 61 days of age. These observations suggest that there is a decrease in caries susceptibility with advancing posteruptive age of teeth and that the normal flow of saliva has a critical effect on this increasing resistance of the teeth to dental caries. The nature of the salivary factor that contributes to this effect remains unknown.

Periodontal disease. Saliva may affect calculus formation and the oral microorganisms contributing to periodontal disease. However, there is no specific, well-documented information on the role of salivary factors on the microbes contributing to periodontal disease. There is a need for well-controlled experiments in this area.

Dental calculus is an important local factor in the etiology of periodontal disease. All elements found in calculus are also contained in saliva. Calculus formation begins with the formation of a bacterial mucinous plaque that later becomes calcified. Our knowledge on the conditions controlling the formation of this plaque is limited. Whether acid precipitation of salivary proteins is a factor in plaque formation remains a matter of controversy.[17,107] The studies of Leach suggest that the release of sialic acid from salivary mucin, leading to its precipitation under mildly acid or neutral conditions, plays an important part in the formation of dental plaque.[42] The calcification of this plaque is in part controlled by changes in the physiochemical properties of saliva. Changes in the salivary proteins and protein-carbohydrate complexes, which help maintain the supersaturated state of saliva with respect to calcium,[77] or an increase in salivary pH, which usually results from the loss of carbon dioxide from saliva,[31,44] will cause precipitation of calcium salts. There is also evidence to suggest that the nature of the carbohydrate-protein components of the bacterial plaque may play an important role in the calcification process, since it was observed that with the onset of calcification there were changes in the histochemical reactivity of these components of the plaque similar to those associated with calcification in other areas of the body.[50,53] It is possible that the protein carbohydrate components of the plaque may chelate calcium and that this compound may act as a nucleus for the crystallization of hydroxyapatite. This possibility is strengthened by the observation that bovine submandibular mucoid has a specific action in binding calcium.[45,46] It is thus obvious that further studies on the nature of the salivary proteins and protein carbohydrate complexes and on the regulation of the carbon dioxide tension in saliva will help to a better understanding of calculus formation and possibly in finding methods for its prevention.

REFERENCES

1. Apostolopoulos, A. X.: Studies on the mucoproteins of human saliva, University of Rochester, Rochester, N. Y., 1964, doctoral dissertation.
2. Bdolah, A., and Schramm, M.: Factors controlling the process of enzyme secretion by the rat parotid slice, Biochem. & Biophys. Res. Com. 8:266, 1962.
3. Bowen, R. H.: On a possible relation between the Golgi apparatus and secretory products, Am. J. Anat. 33:197, 1924.
4. Brudevold, F.: Inorganic and organic components of tooth structure, Ann. New York Acad. Sc. 85:110, 1960.
5. Brudevold, F., et al.: Effect of ingested supplementary phosphate on the tooth surface, J. D. Res. 43:1168, 1964.
6. Burgen, A. S. V.: The salivary glands—some contemporary problems, J. Canad. D. A. 26:258, 1960.
7. Burgen, A. S. V.: Kinetic methods for the study of salivary secretions: their scope and limitations. In Sreebny, L. M., and Meyer, J. (editors): Salivary glands and their secretions, New York, 1964, Pergamon Press, p. 197-215.
8. Burgen, A. S. V., and Emmelin, N. G.: Physiology of the salivary glands, Baltimore, 1961, Williams & Wilkins Co.
9. Burgen, A. S. V., and Seeman, P.: The role of the salivary duct system in the formation of the saliva, Canad. J. Biochem. Physiol. 36:119, 1958.
10. Burstone, M. S.: Esterase in the salivary glands, J. Histochem. & Cytochem. 4:130, 1956.
11. Carmalts, C.: Contribution to the anatomy of the adult human salivary glands. In Studies in cancer and allied subjects, vol. 4, New York, 1913, Columbia University Press.
12. Caspersson, T.: Cell growth and cell function, New York, 1950, W. W. Norton Co., Inc.
13. Caspersson, T., Landstrom-Hyden, H., and Aquilonius, L.: Cytoplasma-nucleotide in Eiweissproduzierenden Drusenzellen, Chromosoma 2:111, 1941.
14. Chauncey, H. H., Lionetti, F., Winer, R. A., and Lisanti, V. F.: Enzymes of human saliva. I. The determination, distribution and origin of whole saliva enzymes, J. D. Res. 33:321, 1954.

15. Chauncey, H. H., and Quintarelli, G.: Histochemical localization of hydrolytic enzymes in human salivary glands, J. D. Res. **38**:961, 1959.
16. Cheyne, V. D.: Effect of salivary gland extirpation upon experimental dental caries in the rat, Proc. Soc. Exper. Biol. & Med. **18**:587, 1939.
17. Dawes, C.: Is acid-precipitation of salivary proteins a factor in plaque formation? Arch. Oral Biol. **9**:375, 1964.
18. Docu, H. C., and Taylor, R. G.: Thromboplastin generation by saliva, Oral Surg., Oral Med. & Oral Path. **15**:1295, 1962.
19. Eichel, B., and Lisanti, V. F.: Leucocyte metabolism in human saliva, Arch. Oral Biol. **9**:229, 1964.
20. Elmer, A. W.: Iodine metabolism and thyroid function, London, 1938, Oxford University Press.
21. Emmelin, N.: Secretory nerves of the salivary glands. In Sreebny, L. M., and Meyer, J., (editors): Salivary glands and their secretions, New York, 1964, Pergamon Press, pp. 161-173.
22. Fanning, R. J., et al.: Salivary contribution to enamel maturation and caries resistance, J.A.D.A. **49**:668, 1954.
23. Fawcett, D. M., and Kirkwood, S.: Role of the salivary glands in extrathyroidal iodine metabolism, Science **120**:547, 1954.
24. Green, D. E.: Mitochondrial structure and function. In Hayashi, T. (editor): Subcellular particles, New York, 1959, The Ronald Press Co., p. 84.
25. Gottschalk, A.: The basic structure of glycoproteins and problems of their chemical and physicochemical analysis, Ann. New York Acad. Sc. **106**:168, 1963.
26. Grobstein, C.: Epithelio-mesenchymal specificity in the morphogenesis of mouse submandibular rudiments in vitro, J. Exper. Zool. **124**:383, 1953.
27. Gromet-Elhanan, L., and Winnick, T.: Microsomes as site of alpha-amylase synthesis in the rat parotid gland, Biochim. & Biophys. Acta **69**:89, 1963.
28. Hashimoto, Y., and Pigman, W.: A comparison of the composition of mucins and blood-group substances, Ann. New York Acad. Sc. **93**:541, 1962.
29. Heidenhain, R.: Beiträge zur Lehre von der Speichelsecretion, Studien Physiol. Inst. Breslau **4**:1, 1868.
30. Henriques, B. L., and Chauncey, H. H.: Comparative enzyme concentrations of submaxillary and parotid salivas, J. D. Res. **38**:733, 1959 (Abst.)
31. Hodge, H. C., and Leung, S. W.: Calculus formation, J. Periodont. **21**:211, 1950.
32. Ito, Y.: Parotin: A salivary gland hormone, Ann. New York Acad. Sc. **85**:228, 1960.
33. Jacoby, F., and Leeson, C. R.: The post-natal development of the rat submaxillary gland, J. Anat. **93**:201, 1959.
34. Junqueira, L. C. U.: Cytological, cytochemical and biochemical observations on secreting and resting salivary glands, Exper. Cell Res. **2**:327, 1951.
35. Junqueira, L. C. U., and Hirsch, G. C.: Cell secretion: A study of pancreas and salivary glands, Internat. Rev. Cytol. **5**:323, 1956.
36. Junqueira, L. C. U., et al.: Studies on the physiology of rat and mouse submaxillary glands. I. Amylase and protease activities in serum, submaxillary gland, and submaxillary saliva of rat and mouse. In Sreebny, L. M., and Meyer, J. (editors): Salivary glands and their secretions, New York, 1964, Pergamon Press, pp. 105-118.
37. Kowalewsky, N.: Ueber das Blutgefäss-system der Speicheldrusen, Arch. Anat. & Physiol., p. 385, 1885.
38. Kraus, F. W., and Kono, J.: Antibodies in saliva, Ann. New York Acad. Sc. **106**:311, 1963.
39. Lacassagne, A.: Dimorphism sexuel de la glande sous-maxillaire chez la souris, Compt. rend. Soc. de biol. **133**:180, 1940.
40. Langley, J. N.: On the changes of serous cells during secretion, J. Physiol. **2**:261, 1879-1880.
41. Langley, J. N.: On the histology of the mucous salivary glands and on the behavior of their mucous constituents, J. Physiol. **10**:433, 1889.

42. Leach, S. A.: Release and breakdown of sialic acid from human salivary mucin and its role in the formation of the dental plaque. Nature **199**:486, 1963.
43. Leeson, C. R., and Jacoby, F.: An electron microscopic study of the rat submaxillary gland during its post-natal development and in the adult, J. Anat. **93**:287, 1959.
44. Leung, S. W.: Calculus formation; salivary factors, Dental Clinics of North America, Philadelphia, November, 1960, W. B. Saunders Co.
45. Leung, S. W., and Draus, F. J.: Effect of bovine submaxillary mucoid on ultrafiltration of calcium, preprinted abstracts, Thirty-Ninth General Meeting of the International Association for Dental Research, March, 1961.
46. Leung, S. W., and Draus, F. J.: The calcium binding characteristics of a salivary gland mucoid, Arch. Oral Biol. **7**:327, 1962.
47. Levi-Montalcini, R., et al.: Symposium on the nerve growth factor, Ann. New York Acad. Sc. **118**:147, 1964.
48. Logothetopoulos, J. H., and Myant, N. B.: Concentration of radio-iodide and ^{35}S-thiocyanate by the salivary glands, J. Physiol. **134**:189, 1956.
49. Lundberg, A.: The electrophysiology of the submaxillary gland of the cat, Acta physiol. scandinav. **35**:1, 1955.
50. Mandel, I. D.: Calculus formation; the role of bacteria and mucoprotein, Dental Clinics of North America, Philadelphia, November, 1960, W. B. Saunders Co.
51. Mandel, I. D., and Ellison, S. A.: Characterization of salivary components separated by paper electrophoresis, Arch. Oral Biol. **3**:77, 1961.
52. Mandel, I. D., and Ellison, S.: The proteins of human parotid and submaxillary saliva, Ann. New York Acad. Sc. **106**:271, 1963.
53. Mandel, I. D., et al.: Histochemistry of calculus formation, J. Periodont. **28**:132, 1957.
54. Mandel, I. D., et al.: The carbohydrates of human parotid saliva, Arch. Oral Biol. **3**: 278, 1961.
55. Mandel, I. D., et al.: The carbohydrate components of human submaxillary saliva, Arch. Oral Biol. **9**:601, 1964.
56. McClure, F. J., and Muller, A.: Further observations on the cariostatic effect of phosphates, J. D. Res. **38**:776, 1959.
57. Myant, N. B.: Iodine metabolism of salivary glands, Ann. New York Acad. Sc. **85**:208, 1960.
58. Nassonov, D.: Das Golgische Binnennetz und seine Beziehungen zu der Sekretion, Arch. f. mikr. Anat. **100**:433, 1924.
59. Noback, C. R., and Montagna, W.: Histochemical studies of the basophilia, lipase and phosphatases in the mammalian pancreas and salivary glands, Am. J. Anat. **81**:343, 1947.
60. Ogata, T.: Internal secretions of the salivary glands, Transactions Ninth Congress of Far East, Association of Tropical Medicine **2**:709, 1935.
61. Orban, B., and Weinmann, J. P.: Cellular elements of saliva and their possible role in caries, J.A.D.A. **26**:2008, 1939.
62. Palade, G. E.: Intracisternal granules in the exocrine cells of the pancreas, J. Biophys. & Biochem. Cytol. **2**:417, 1956.
63. Palade, G. E.: Functional changes in the structure of cell components. In Hayashi, T. (editor): Subcellular particles, New York, 1959, The Ronald Press Co., p. 64.
64. Palade, G. E., and Porter, K. R.: Studies on the endoplasmic reticulum. I. Its identification in situ, J. Exper. Med. **100**:641, 1954.
65. Palay, S. L.: The morphology of secretion. Frontiers of cytology, New Haven, 1958, Yale University Press, pp. 305-336.
66. Parks, H. F.: On the fine structure of the parotid gland of the mouse and rat, Am. J. Anat. **108**:303, 1961.
67. Parks, H. F.: Morphological study of the extrusion of secretory materials by the parotid glands of mouse and rat, J. Ultrastructure Res. **6**:449, 1962.
68. Parks, H. F., and Johansen, E.: The Golgi apparatus of parotid acinous cells of the mouse, preprinted abstracts, International Association for Dental Research, Thirty-Ninth General Meeting, March, 1961, p. 8.

69. Patten, B. M.: Human embryology, Philadelphia, 1946, The Blakiston Co.
70. Patton, J. R., and Pigman, W.: Amylase in electrophoretic and ultracentrifugal patterns of human parotid saliva, Science **125**:1292, 1957.
71. Patton, J. R., and Pigman, W.: Electrophoretic and ultracentrifugal components of human salivary secretions, J. Am. Chem. Soc. **81**:3035, 1959.
72. Pease, D. C.: Infolded basal plasma membranes found in epithelia noted for their water transport, J. Biophys. & Biochem. Cytol. **2**(supp.):203, 1956.
73. Pigman, W.: Some recent developments in the composition and physiology of human saliva, J.A.D.A. **54**:469, 1957.
74. Pigman, W., and Hashimoto, Y.: Recent studies of mucins and blood-group substances. In Staple, P. H. (editor): Advances in oral biology, vol. 1, New York, 1964, Academic Press, pp. 11-129.
75. Pigman, W., and Reid, A. J.: The organic compounds and enzymes of human saliva, J.A.D.A. **45**:325, 1952.
76. du Plessis, D. J.: Some important features in the development, structure and function of the parotid salivary glands, South African M. J. **31**:773, 1957.
77. Prinz, H.: The origin of salivary calculus, D. Cosmos **63**:231, 269, 503, 619, 1921.
78. Quintarelli, G.: Histochemical identification of salivary mucins, Ann. New York Acad. Sc. **106**:339, 1963.
79. Quintarelli, G., and Chauncey, H. H.: Metachromatic reactivity of mammalian salivary glands, Arch. Oral Biol. **2**:162, 1960.
80. Rovelstad, G. H.: Salivary corpuscle activity, J.A.D.A. **68**:364, 1964.
81. Schneider, R. M., and Person, P.: Aerobic oxidative metabolism of salivary glands, Ann. New York Acad. Sc. **85**:201, 1960.
82. Schneyer, C. A., and Schneyer, L. H.: Secretion by salivary glands deficient in acini, Am. J. Physiol. **201**:939, 1961.
83. Schneyer, L. H., and Schneyer, C. A.: Secretion of saliva. In Staple, P. H. (editor): Advances in oral biology, vol. 1, New York, 1964, Academic Press, pp. 1-31.
84. Schramm, M., and Dannon, D.: The mechanism of enzyme secretion by the cell. I. Storage of amylase in the zymogen granules of the rat parotid gland, Biochim. & Biophys. Acta **50**:102, 1961.
85. Schwartz, A., and Weisberger, D.: Salivary factors in experimental animal caries. In Sognnaes, R. F. (editor): Advances in experimental caries research, Washington, D. C., 1955, American Association for the Advancement of Science.
86. Scott, B. L., and Pease, D. C.: Electronmicroscopy of the salivary and lacrimal glands of the rat, Am. J. Anat. **104**:115, 1959.
87. Scott, B. L., and Pease, D. C.: Electron microscopy of induced changes in the salivary gland of the rat. In Sreebny, L. M., and Meyer, L. (editors): Salivary glands and their secretions, New York, 1964, Pergamon Press, pp. 13-44.
88. Selye, H., et al.: Excessive stimulation of salivary gland growth by isoproterenol, Science **133**:44, 1961.
89. Shafer, W. G., and Muhler, J. C.: Endocrine influences upon the salivary glands, Ann. New York Acad. Sc. **85**:215, 1960.
90. Ship, I. I., and Mickelsen, O.: The effects of calcium acid phosphate on dental caries in children: a controlled clinical trial, J. D. Res. **43**:1144, 1964.
91. Sicher, H.: Oral anatomy, ed. 4, St. Louis, 1965, The C. V. Mosby Co.
92. Sicher, H., and Tandler, J.: Anatomie für Zahnärzte, Berlin, 1928, Julius Springer.
93. Siekevitz, P., and Palade, G. E.: A cytochemical study of the pancreas of the guinea pig. III. In vitro incorporation of leucine-l-C^{14} into the proteins of cell fractions, J. Biophys. & Biochem. Cytol. **4**:557, 1958.
94. Sjostrand, F. S., and Hanzon, V.: Membrane structures of cytoplasm and mitochondria in exocrine cells of mouse pancreas as revealed by high resolution electron microscopy, Exper. Cell Res. **7**:393, 1954.
95. Sjostrand, F. S., and Hanzon, V.: Ultrastructure of Golgi apparatus of exocrine cells of mouse pancreas, Exper. Cell Res. **7**:415, 1954.

96. Spanner, R.: Der Abkurzungskreislauf der Glandula submaxillaris, Ztsch. f. Anat. u. Entwcklngsgesch. **107**:124, 1937.
97. Spicer, S. S., and Warren, L.: The histochemistry of sialic acid containing mucoproteins, J. Histochem. & Cytochem. **8**:135, 1960.
98. Sreebny, L. M., Meyer, J., Bachem, E., and Weinmann, J. P.: Post-natal changes in proteolytic activity and in the morphology of the submaxillary gland in male and female albino rats, Growth **19**:57, 1955.
99. Sreebny, L. M., and Meyer, J.: Hormones, inanition and salivary glands. In Sreebny, L. M., and Meyer, J. (editors): Salivary glands and their secretions, New York, 1964, Pergamon Press, pp. 83-103.
100. Stormont, D. L.: The salivary glands. In Cowdry, E. V. (editor): Special cytology, vol. 1, New York, 1932, Paul B. Hoeber, Inc., pp. 153-196.
101. Tandler, B.: Ultrastructure of the human submaxillary gland. II. The base of the striated duct cells, J. Ultrastructure Res. **9**:65, 1963.
102. Taurog, A., et al.: The effect of hypophysectomy and of TSH on the mouse submaxillary iodine pump, Endocrinology **64**:1038, 1959.
103. Thaysen, J. H., et al.: Excretion of sodium, potassium, chloride and carbon dioxide in human parotid saliva, Am. J. Physiol. **178**:155, 1954.
104. Trimble, H. C., et al.: Rate of secretion and incidence of dental caries, J. D. Res. **17**:299, 1938.
105. Weinstein, E., et al.: An improved technique for the paper electrophoresis of parotid saliva, J. D. Res. **39**:110, 1960.
106. Wells, H.: The neural regulation of salivary gland growth, Ann. New York Acad. Sc. **106**:654, 1963.
107. Winkler, K. C., and Backer-Dirks, O.: The mechanism of dental plaque, Internat. D. J. **8**:561, 1958.
108. Wright, D. E.: The source and rate of entry of leucocytes in the human mouth, Arch. Oral Biol. **9**:321, 1964.
109. Zimmermann, K. W.: Die Speicheldrüsen der Mundhöhle und die Bauchspeicheldrüse. In von Möllendorff, W. (editor): Handbuch der mikroskopischen Anatomie des Menschen, vol. 5, pt. 1, Berlin, 1927, Julius Springer.
110. Zipkin, I., et al.: Sialic acid content of human saliva, Biochem. & Biophys. Res. Com. **4**:76, 1961.

Chapter XI

Eruption of the teeth*

INTRODUCTION

HISTOLOGY OF ERUPTION

    Preeruptive phase
    Prefunctional eruptive phase
    Functional eruptive phase

MECHANISM OF ERUPTION

CLINICAL CONSIDERATIONS

INTRODUCTION

The human teeth develop in the jaws and do not enter the oral cavity until the crown has matured. In the past the term eruption was generally applied only to the appearance of the teeth in the oral cavity. It is, however, known that the movements of the teeth do not cease when the teeth meet their antagonists.[6,7] Movements of eruption begin at the time of root formation and continue throughout the life span of a tooth. The emergence through the gingiva is merely an incident in the process of eruption. The eruption of deciduous as well as of permanent teeth can be divided into prefunctional and functional phases. At the end of the prefunctional phase the teeth come into occlusion. In the functional phase the teeth continue to move to maintain a proper relation to the jaw and to each other.

Eruption is preceded by a period in which the developing and growing teeth move to adjust their position in the growing jaw.[3] A knowledge of the movements of the teeth during this preeruptive phase is necessary for a complete understanding of eruption. Thus, the movements of the teeth can be divided into the following phases: (1) preeruptive phase, (2) prefunctional eruptive phase, and (3) functional eruptive phase.

During these phases the teeth move in different directions.[20] These movements can be termed:

1. Axial—occlusal movement in the direction of the long axis of the tooth
2. Drifting—bodily movement in a distal, mesial, lingual, or buccal direction
3. Tilting or tipping—movement around a transverse axis
4. Rotating—movement around a longitudinal axis.

HISTOLOGY OF ERUPTION

Preeruptive phase. During the preeruptive phase, the dental organ develops to its full size, and formation of the hard substances of the crown takes place.

---

*First draft submitted by Joseph P. Weinmann; revised by the editor.

301

At this time the tooth germs are surrounded by the loose connective tissue of the dental sac and by the bone of the dental crypt.

The development of the teeth and the growth of the jaw are simultaneous and interdependent processes. The microscopic picture of the growing jaw indicates that extensive growth takes place in that area of the jaws in which the alveolar process will develop (Fig. 234). The tooth germs maintain their relation to the growing alveolar margin by moving occlusally and buccally.[1]

Two processes are responsible for the developing teeth attaining and maintaining their position in the growing jaw: bodily movement and excentric growth. *Bodily movement* is characterized by a shift of the entire tooth germ. It is recognized by apposition of bone behind the moving tooth and by resorption of bone in front of it. In *excentric growth* one part of the tooth germ remains stationary. Excentric growth leads to a shift of the center of the tooth germ. It is characterized by resorption of the bone at the surface toward which the tooth germ grows. No apposition takes place on the bony surfaces from which the tooth germ seems to move.

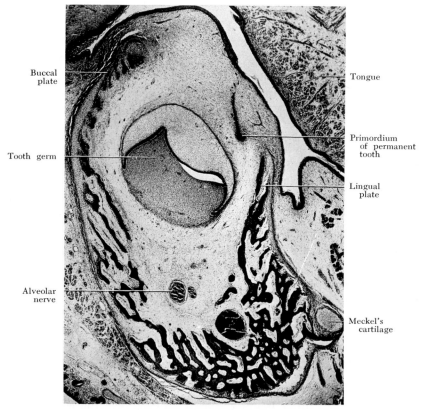

Fig. 234. Cross section through the lower jaw and a deciduous molar of a human fetus (fourth month). Tooth germ moves buccally by excentric growth indicated by resorption at the inner surface of the buccal plate and lack of apposition at the inner surface of the lingual plate.

When the deciduous teeth develop and grow, upper and lower jaws grow in length in the midline and at their posterior ends. Accordingly, the growing germs of the deciduous teeth shift in vestibular direction. At the same time the anterior teeth move mesially and the posterior teeth move distally, into the expanding alveolar arches.[19] These movements of the deciduous teeth are partly bodily movements and partly shifts by excentric growth. The deciduous tooth germ grows in length at about the same rate as the jaws grow in height. The deciduous teeth maintain, therefore, their superficial position throughout the preeruptive phase.

The permanent teeth that have temporary predecessors undergo an intricate movement before they reach the position from which they emerge. The permanent incisor (Fig. 235) and the canine develop at first lingual to the deciduous tooth germ at the level of its occlusal surface.[14] At the close of the preeruptive phase they are found lingual to the apical region of their deciduous predecessors. The permanent premolars (Fig. 236) begin their development lingual to, and at the level of, the occlusal plane of the deciduous molars.[13] Later, they are found between the divergent roots and, at the end of the preeruptive phase, below the roots of the deciduous molars (see Chapter XII). The changes in axial relationship between deciduous and permanent teeth are due to the occlusal movement of the deciduous teeth and to the growth of the jaw in height. The germs of the premolars move by their buccally directed excentric growth into the interradicular space of the deciduous molars.

Prefunctional eruptive phase. The prefunctional phase of eruption begins with the formation of the root (Chapter II) and is completed when the teeth reach the occlusal plane. Until the tooth emerges into the oral cavity, its crown is covered by the reduced dental epithelium. While the crown moves toward the surface, the connective tissue between the dental epithelium and the oral epithelium disappears, probably by a desmolytic action of the cells of the dental epithelium. The proliferating cells of the outer epithelium, invading the dense connective tissue between the enamel epithelium and the oral epithelium, produce enzymes (hyaluronidase?). This leads to a disappearance of the ground substance, acid mucopolysaccharides, between the fibers and within the collagenous fibers. The consequence is a change of the dense connective tissue and the heavy collagenous fibers into a loose fluid-rich connective tissue with fine argyrophil fibers. When the edge or the cusps of the crown approach the oral mucosa, oral epithelium and reduced dental epithelium fuse. In the center of the area of fusion the epithelium degenerates, and the incisal edge or the tip of a cusp emerges into the oral cavity. The gradual emergence of the crown is due to the occlusal movement of the tooth, active eruption, and also to the separation of the epithelium from the enamel, passive eruption. The reduced dental epithelium remains attached to that part of the crown which has not yet emerged (see discussion of dentogingival junction in Chapter IX). The growth of the root or roots of a tooth is initiated by simultaneous and correlated proliferation of Hertwig's epithelial root sheath and the connective tissue of the dental papilla. The proliferation of the epithelium takes place by mitotic division of the cells of the epithelial diaphragm. The proliferation of the connective tissue cells of the pulp is concentrated in the area above the diaphragm.

During the prefunctional phase of eruption, the primitive periodontal ligament, derived from the dental sac, is adapted to the relatively rapid movement of the teeth. Three layers of the periodontal ligament can be distinguished around the surface of the developing root: (1) adjacent to the surface of the root, dental fibers, (2) attached to the primitive alveolus, alveolar fibers, and (3) the intermediate plexus (Fig. 143). The intermediate plexus consists mainly of argyrophil fibers, whereas the alveolar and the dental fibers are mainly mature collagenous fibers. They can be traced into the intermediate plexus for a short distance. The intermediate plexus permits continuous readjustment of the periodontal ligament during the phase of rapid eruption.[16,20]

In the region of the fundus the dental sac differentiates into two layers. One, close to the bone, consists of loose connective tissue. The other, adjacent to the growing end of the tooth, consists of a network of rather thick fibers. These fibers are attached to the bone, curve as a strong ligament around the edge of the root, and then divide into a network whose spaces are filled with fluid. This structure is designated as the hammock or cushioned hammock ligament[21] (Fig. 237).

NB 3 mo. 9 mo. 2 yr.

Fig. 235. Buccolingual sections through deciduous and permanent lower central incisors of seven consecutive stages, from birth to 9 years of age.

In the prefunctional phase of eruption the alveolar ridge of the jaws grows rapidly. To emerge from the growing jaws, the primary teeth must move more rapidly than the ridge increases in height. Growth of the root is not always sufficient to meet these requirements. A rapid growth of bone begins at the alveolar fundus, where it is laid down as trabeculae parallel to the surface of the alveolar fundus[12] (Fig. 238). The number of trabeculae increases markedly during the prefunctional phase and varies in different teeth. The smallest number of trabeculae is found at the fundus of the molars. This variance in the number of trabeculae seems to depend upon the distance that the teeth have to travel during this phase of tooth eruption.

The germs of most permanent teeth develop in a crowded position. They occupy, therefore, a position that differs markedly from their ultimate position after emergence. The molars are tilted. The occlusal surfaces of the upper molars, which develop in the maxillary tuberosity, are directed distally and downward. The occlusal surfaces of the lower molars, which develop in the base of the

4½ yr.   6 yr.   9 yr.

Fig. 235, cont'd. For legend see opposite page.

NB 9 mo. 1½ yr. 2 yr.

3 yr. 4½ yr. 11 yr. 14 yr.

Fig. 236. Buccolingual sections through a lower deciduous first molar and a first permanent premolar of eight consecutive stages, from birth to 14 years.

Dentin — Pulp

Proliferation zone of pulp

Epithelial diaphragm

Cushioned hammock ligament

Fig. 237. Cushioned hammock ligament. Root end of an erupting permanent lower canine. Proliferation zone of the pulp above the epithelial diaphragm. Note the numerous tissue spaces in the ligament. (From Sicher, H.: J. D. Res. **21**:201, 1942.)

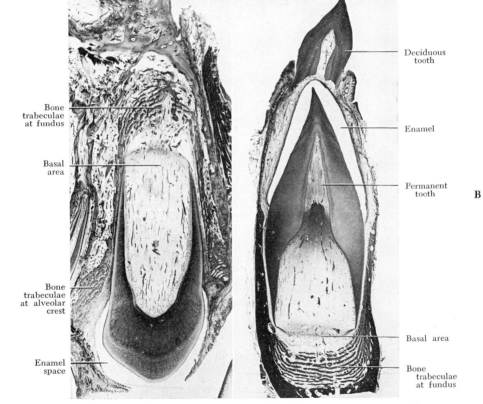

Bone trabeculae at fundus

Basal area

A

Bone trabeculae at alveolar crest

Enamel space

Deciduous tooth

Enamel

Permanent tooth

B

Basal area

Bone trabeculae at fundus

Fig. 238. Erupting upper deciduous canine, **A**, and lower permanent canine, **B**. Note formation of numerous parallel bone trabeculae at the alveolar fundus. Formation of bone trabeculae at the alveolar crest of the deciduous canine, **A**, is a sign of rapid growth of the maxilla in height. (From Kronfeld, R.: D. Cosmos **74**:103, 1932.)

mandibular ramus, are directed mesially and upward. The long axis of the upper canines deviates mesially. The lower incisors are frequently rotated around their long axes. In the later stages of the prefunctional phase of eruption, these teeth undergo intricate movements to rectify their primary position. During these tilting or tipping and rotating movements, bone growth takes place in those areas of the dental crypt from which the tooth moves. Resorption occurs in the areas toward which the tooth moves. In all other details the histologic changes correlated to eruption are identical in permanent and in deciduous teeth.

The histologic findings in erupting multirooted teeth present in later stages a characteristic picture. Bone growth occurs not only at the fundus of the socket but is also evident at the crest of the interradicular septum. The cementum in the bifurcation also shows signs of intensified growth.

Functional eruptive phase. For a long time it was believed that functioning

Fig. 239. Mesial and vertical components of eruptive movement. Mesiodisal section through the upper first and second premolars. Arrow indicates direction of drifting movement. Apposition of bundle bone at the distal surfaces, resorption of bone on the mesial surfaces of the alveoli. Apposition of bundle bone at the fundus and alveolar crest. (From Weinmann, J. P.: Angle Orthodontist 11:83, 1941.)

teeth do not continue to erupt. However, clinical observations and histologic findings show unequivocally that the teeth continue to move throughout their life. The movements are in an occlusomesial direction.

Clinically, the continued active movement of teeth can be proved by an analysis of the so-called shortened and submerged teeth (see Chapter XII). Histologically, the changes in the alveolar bone furnish the evidence for the movements of the teeth during the functional period (Fig. 241) (see Chapter VIII).

During the period of growth, the occlusal movement of the teeth is fairly rapid. The bodies of the jaws grow in height almost exclusively at the alveolar crests, and the teeth have to move occlusally as fast as the jaws grow, in order to maintain their functional position. The eruptive movement in this period is masked by the simultaneous growth of the jaws.

The continued vertical component of eruption also compensates for occlusal or incisal attrition. Only in this way can the occlusal plane and the distance between the jaws during mastication be maintained and a closing of the bite be prevented—conditions that are essential for the normal function of the masticatory muscles.

The masticatory or functional movements of the individual teeth lead at the same time to increasing wear at the contact areas. Sharp contact of the teeth is maintained despite the loss of substance at the contact surfaces by a horizontal

Fig. 240. Higher magnification of crest of interdental septum between the first and second upper premolars shown in Fig. 239. Arrows indicate the horizontal (mesial) component of movement. Apposition of bundle bone on the surface of the septum facing the first premolar and at the alveolar crest, resorption of bone on the surface of the septum facing the second premolar. (From Weinmann, J. P.: Angle Orthodontist **11**:83, 1941.)

Apical foramina

Bundle bone

Bundle bone

Canal in bone

Epithelial rests

Epithelial rest

Epithelial rest

Epithelial rest

Epithelial rest

A   B

Fig. 241. A, Bundle bone at the fundus of the alveolus and in the wall of the canal leading blood vessels and nerves to apical foramina. Epithelial rests some distance from the apex along the blood vessels and nerves. **B,** High magnification of epithelial rests shown in **A.**

component of eruptive movement of the teeth toward the midline. This movement is termed physiologic mesial drift (Fig. 239). It has to be understood that attrition occurs simultaneously at incisal or occlusal *and* contact surfaces. In compensation for this loss of tooth substance and in order to maintain the proper relation of teeth in each arch and of the two arches, the teeth in man continue their eruptive movement in an occlusomesial direction. "Vertical eruption" and "mesial drift" are but components of one coordinated movement of the teeth.

Appositional growth of cementum continues along the entire surface of the root, but growth of bone is restricted principally to the fundus, alveolar crest, and distal wall of the socket (Fig. 240). The mesial wall of the socket shows resorption in wide areas. However, zones of reparative bone apposition can always be found on the mesial wall of the alveolus.

MECHANISM OF ERUPTION

"It is a truism that laws of chemistry and physics are as valid in living organisms as they are in the inorganic world. But it is a grave mistake to describe and interpret physical processes in the living organisms, using gross, one is almost tempted to say, crude mechanical ideas.

"A tree grows on a mountain side. One tiny root has found a narrow crack in a rock and continues growing in this confined space. Sooner or later, the growing root splits the rock. A seed is planted in a flower pot. The pot is securely covered by a layer of strong aluminum foil. The seemingly weak sprout soon will perforate the foil.

"A tooth germ grows in the confined space of its bony crypt and, after due time, erupts into the oral cavity, cutting through the dense tissue of the gingival ridge. For a long time anatomists have sought—and 'found'—a force of eruption. They described the final emergence of the tooth through the soft tissues by using the colloquial expression of the tooth 'cutting' the gingiva. Such gross mechanical interpretations have, by no means, disappeared from the scientific literature.

"In describing the influence of the growing brain on the growth of its bony capsule, again the brain is seen as 'spreading' the cranial bones apart.

"In describing the rapid growth of the intestinal tube, it has been said that the narrow mesentery is pulled into the fan-shaped mesentery of jejunum and ileum.

"Examples of such mechanistic descriptions and interpretations could easily be multiplied.

"It is, of course, true that the growing tooth germ or the growing brain do exert pressure upon the surrounding and confining tissues. What, then, is the difference between the root growing in the cleft of a rock or the bean sprout piercing the aluminum foil and the action of the growing tooth germ or the growing brain?

"The answer to this question is superbly simple. The forces generated by the growing plant are exerted against inert material; they increase and, finally, the rock splits, the foil is perforated. The forces generated by the growing tooth or brain are directed against living tissues that can and do react. And their reaction is always the same in principle, namely, to reduce the developing pressure—or pull—and to eliminate it.

"This is accomplished in different ways. When the tooth grows, the slight rise in pressure within the crypt leads to the differentiation of osteoclasts and bone resorption, but also to proliferation of connective tissue and enlargement of the dental sac. In the 'cutting' of the tooth through the oral tissues the pressure of the crown against the overlying connective tissue leads to the elaboration—or activation—of desmolytic enzymes most probably by the [proliferating] cells of the united enamel or dental epithelium that covers the crown to the moment of the emergence of the tooth. That this epithelial covering remains intact while the tooth 'cuts' or 'pierces' the soft tissues is absolute evidence against crude mechanical interpretations.

"When the brain grows in its bony capsule the attending pressure is but the stimulus for the growth of the derivatives of the brain capsule: cartilage at the cranial base and fibrous tissue elsewhere. Thus the capsule grows between the bony parts of the cranium or, to use a more [traditional] term, between the cranial bones. And, again, this growth immediately eliminates intracranial pressure.

"The growing small intestine certainly exerts some traction on its mesentery. But the latter responds immediately by its surface growth and the mechanical force is eliminated.

"Briefly summarized, the forces in living organisms are acting as stimuli to set in motion changes that will recover balance of forces. Forces of pressure or traction do indeed play a role in development and growth. But they are, in truth, self-eliminating. And this is the basis of biomechanics."*

The eruptive movements of a tooth are the effect of differential growth. One speaks of differential growth if two topographically related organs, or parts of an organ, grow at different rates of speed. Changes in the spatial relations of such organs, or of the parts of an organ, are the inevitable consequence of differential growth. The ontogenesis of almost any organ and of the whole embryo proves that differential growth is one of the most important factors of morphogenesis. In the jaws it is the differential growth between tooth and bone that leads to the movement of a tooth.

The most obvious eruptive force is generated by the longitudinal growth of the dental pulp in the growing root. However, the different movements of an erupting tooth cannot be explained by the growth of its root alone. Some teeth, even while their roots develop, travel a distance that is longer than the fully developed root. An additional factor must account for the increased distance. Most teeth move during eruption also by tilting, rotating, drifting movements. The growth of the root can account only for the axial or vertical movement. Other movements are caused by the growth of bone in the neighborhood of the tooth germ.

It is also a fact that the teeth move extensively after dentinal length of their roots has been fully established. The continued growth of the cementum covering the root and growth of the surrounding bone cause the movements of the tooth in this period.

Before the development of the root starts, the outer and the inner dental epithelia continue from the region of the future cementoenamel junction as a double epithelial layer, the epithelial diaphragm, which is bent into the roughly horizontal plane of the dental base. It forms a definite boundary between the coronal pulp of the tooth germ and the connective tissue between tooth germ and bony crypt. Thus, growth of the root is possible only by active proliferation of the pulpal tissue.

The growth of the pulpal tissue causes a slight increase of pressure in the

---

*Reprinted from Sicher, Harry: Biomechanics, The Bur, March, 1962.

confined space of the dental crypt. Resorption of bone at the fundus of the crypt is prevented by the suspension of the tooth germ by the hammock ligament, much in the same way as resorption of bone under masticatory forces is prevented by suspension of the functioning tooth by the periodontal ligament. It is important to realize that the rise in pressure within the crypt is the stimulus for the initiation of tissue changes that will reduce the pressure. Thus, pressure does not build up but acts in a wavelike fashion, rhythmically rising and falling. Because of its suspensory function, the hammock ligament is the fixed base or plane from which the tooth moves toward the oral surface.

Since the growth of the root alone cannot move a crown as far as is necessary to reach the occlusal plane, its vertical erupting movement is aided by growth of bone at the bottom of the crypt, lifting the growing tooth, with the hammock ligament, toward the surface. The growth of bone, preceded by a proliferation of the odontogenic connective tissue at the bottom of the crypt, occurs in different teeth at a different rate of speed. Where growth of bone is slow, new layers of bone are laid down upon the old bone, and a more or less compact bone results. Where growth of bone is rapid, spongy bone is formed in the shape of a framework of trabeculae (Fig. 238).

While the hammock ligament and the tooth are lifted toward the surface, the anchoring fibers of the hammock ligament have to be continually reconstructed. In other words, the hammock ligament has to shift its anchoring plane toward the surface of the jaws. Details of the mechanism of this shift are as yet not known, but they are, in all probability, comparable to the adjustment of the periodontal ligament during the functional phase of tooth eruption.

Enlargement of the root does not cease when its dentinal part is fully formed. By continuous apposition of cementum the root grows slightly in its transverse diameters and more rapidly in length. Cementum growth is increased not only in the apical area of roots but also at the furcation of multirooted teeth. Simultaneously, there is continuous growth of bone at the fundus of the socket and at the crests of the alveolar process. The bone apposition at the fundus and at the free border of the alveolar process is very rapid in youth and slows down in the thirties but normally never ceases. Apposition at the alveolar crest, however, is found only when the tissues at the dentogingival junction are entirely normal. The frequency of inflammatory changes in this area accounts for the fact that this site of bone growth has been overlooked for a long time. There is also constant growth of bone on the distal wall of each socket, whereas the mesial wall shows resorption of bone alternating with reparative apposition.

Although the correlation of bone changes and movement of the teeth is self-evident, the question still must be raised whether the bone changes are primary and are thus the cause of the movement of the teeth.

All available evidence points to the differential growth as the cause of the occlusomesial movements of the functioning teeth. Growth of cementum on the entire surface of the root, but intensified in apical and furcation areas, and growth of bone at the fundus and at the distal walls of the socket, as well as at the alveolar crests, are responsible for the movements of the tooth. Resorption at the mesial wall is secondary to the mesial component of the movement. The occlusal or vertical eruption and the mesial drift compensate for occlusal and contact wear and thus maintain the total integrity of the dentition.

During the occlusomesial movement of the functioning teeth, a continual rearrangement of the principal fibers of the periodontal ligament occurs in the intermediate plexus.

On the mesial surface some principal fibers lose their attachment during the period of bone resorption and are then reattached or replaced by new fibers, which are anchored in the bone apposed during the periods of repair. Bone resorption does not occur at the same time on the entire extent of the mesial alveolar surface. Instead, at any given moment, areas of resorption alternate with areas of reparative apposition. Resorption occurs in restricted areas in one period and reconstruction occurs in the same areas, while the tooth, minutely tilting or rotating, causes resorption in another area. Only this can account for the fact that the functional integrity of the tooth is maintained in spite of its continued movements.

CLINICAL CONSIDERATIONS

The eruption of teeth is a part of general development and growth, and therefore the progress of tooth eruption may serve as an indicator of the physical condition of a growing individual. The time of emergence of a tooth is readily observed by clinical examination. Considerable work has been done in compiling data regarding this particular stage of eruption. Table 5 illustrates that the time of emergence of all teeth varies widely.[2,5,13] Only those cases that are not within the range of variation may be considered abnormal. Retarded eruption is by far more frequent than accelerated eruption, and it may have a local or a systemic cause.

Local causes, such as premature loss of deciduous teeth and closure of the space by a shift of the neighboring teeth, may retard the eruption of a permanent tooth. Severe acute trauma may result in an arrest of active tooth eruption during the functional phase if the periodontal ligament of the tooth has been injured. Resorption of the root may ensue, in which event deposition of bone in the spaces opened by resorption may lead to an ankylosis by fusion of alveolar bone and root.[6,30] The movement of such a tooth is then arrested, while the other teeth continue to erupt. If this disturbance takes place in the permanent dentition, a so-called shortened tooth results. An ankylosed deciduous tooth may eventually be covered by the rapidly growing alveolar bone. Such teeth are called submerged teeth (see Chapter XII).

Generalized retardation of eruption can be caused by nutritional deficiencies, e.g., vitamin D deficiency, or by endocrine disturbances, e.g., hypopituitarism or hypothyroidism. In the latter cases one deals with a retardation of somatic

Table 5. Chronology of the human dentition*

Tooth		Formation of enamel matrix and dentine begins	Amount of enamel matrix formed at birth	Enamel completed	Emergence into oral cavity	Root completed
Primary dentition						
Maxillary	Central incisor	4 mo. in utero	Five-sixths	1½ mo.	7½ mo.	1½ yr.
	Lateral incisor	4½ mo. in utero	Two-thirds	2½ mo.	9 mo.	2 yr.
	Canine	5 mo. in utero	One-third	9 mo.	18 mo.	3¼ yr.
	First molar	5 mo. in utero	Cusps united	6 mo.	14 mo.	2½ yr.
	Second molar	6 mo. in utero	Cusp tips still isolated	11 mo.	24 mo.	3 yr.
Mandibular	Central incisor	4½ mo. in utero	Three-fifths	2½ mo.	6 mo.	1½ yr.
	Lateral incisor	4½ mo. in utero	Three-fifths	3 mo.	7 mo.	1½ yr.
	Canine	5 mo. in utero	One-third	9 mo.	16 mo.	3¼ yr.
	First molar	5 mo. in utero	Cusps united	5½ mo.	12 mo.	2¼ yr.
	Second molar	6 mo. in utero	Cusp tips still isolated	10 mo.	20 mo.	3 yr.
Permanent dentition						
Maxillary	Central incisor	3 - 4 mo.	-------	4 - 5 yr.	7 - 8 yr.	10 yr.
	Lateral incisor	10 -12 mo.	-------	4 - 5 yr.	8 - 9 yr.	11 yr.
	Canine	4 - 5 mo.	-------	6 - 7 yr.	11-12 yr.	13-15 yr.
	First premolar	1½- 1¾ yr.	-------	5 - 6 yr.	10-11 yr.	12-13 yr.
	Second premolar	2 - 2¼ yr.	-------	6 - 7 yr.	10-12 yr.	12-14 yr.
	First molar	At birth	Sometimes a trace	2½- 3 yr.	6 - 7 yr.	9-10 yr.
	Second molar	2½- 3 yr.	-------	7 - 8 yr.	12-13 yr.	14-16 yr.
	Third molar	7 - 9 yr.	-------	12 -16 yr.	17-21 yr.	18-25 yr.
Mandibular	Central incisor	3 - 4 mo.	-------	4 - 5 yr.	6 - 7 yr.	9 yr.
	Lateral incisor	3 - 4 mo.	-------	4 - 5 yr.	7 - 8 yr.	10 yr.
	Canine	4 - 5 mo.	-------	6 - 7 yr.	9-10 yr.	12-14 yr.
	First premolar	1¾- 2 yr.	-------	5 - 6 yr.	10-12 yr.	12-13 yr.
	Second premolar	2¼- 2½ yr.	-------	6 - 7 yr.	11-12 yr.	13-14 yr.
	First molar	At birth	Sometimes a trace	2½- 3 yr.	6 - 7 yr.	9-10 yr.
	Second molar	2½- 3 yr.	-------	7 - 8 yr.	11-13 yr.	14-15 yr.
	Third molar	8 -10 yr.	-------	12 -16 yr.	17-21 yr.	18-25 yr.

*From Logan, W. H. G., and Kronfeld, R.: Development of the human jaws and surrounding structures from birth to the age of fifteen years, J.A.D.A. **20**:379, 1933; slightly modified by McCall and Schour.

growth. Since tooth eruption is but one facet of growth, delayed eruption under these conditions is to be expected.

The eruption of deciduous teeth is often preceded and accompanied by pain, slight fever, and general malaise. These symptoms cannot be considered as the consequence of a physiologic process but rather as accidents during this process. When a tooth is about to emerge into the oral cavity, pressure upon the covering tissue against sharp edges or cusps may cause slight injuries. If part of the crown is already exposed, a secondary infection may occur. Since the movement of the tooth into the oral cavity is quite rapid, these symptoms soon disappear. This is in contrast to pericoronal infections around an erupting lower third molar. Although the latter are caused by similar injuries, they lead to long-lasting discomfort because of the slow or even arrested eruption of this tooth.

The movements of the teeth during eruption are intricate and are accomplished by minute coordination of growth of the tooth, growth of the alveolar bone, and growth of the jaws. Any break in this correlation may affect the direction of the movements. This in turn may lead to an impaction or embedding of a tooth. At the time the third molars develop, the jaw has not reached its full length. Normally, the occlusal surface of a lower third molar turns anteriorly and upward. It is frequently prevented from straightening out because of a lack of correlation between growth in length of the lower jaw and tooth development. In such cases the eruption of the lower third molar is arrested because its crown comes in contact with the roots of the second molar. If, at this time, the roots of the third molar are not as yet fully developed, they will grow into the bone and may become deformed. Canines, sometimes found in an oblique or horizontal position because of crowding of the teeth, may also fail to correct this position and remain embedded.

Erupting teeth may cause resorption on the roots of neighboring teeth.[16] This has been observed frequently on the lower second molars, due to the oblique position of the erupting third molar. (See Fig. 242.) This tooth turns its occlusal surface mesially and upward and attains its upright position only in the later stages of eruption. Therefore, its crown comes into close relation to the distal surface of the distal root of the second molar and exerts pressure leading to resorption of cementum and dentin to a varying depth. It can be so extensive that the pulp may be exposed. When the pressure is relieved during the normal movement of the third molar, repair by apposition of cementum may follow. Such resorption was observed in about two-thirds of investigated jaws. A horizontal position of the lower third molar might lead to impaction. In such cases the destruction on the root of the second molar may be severe.

Impacted or embedded upper third molars may cause similar resorption of the root of the second molar. Embedded upper canines may exert pressure on the root of the lateral incisor. During the time of eruption of teeth, the reduced or united dental epithelium may undergo changes which result in cyst formation. Such a cyst forms around the crown of the developing tooth and is known as a

Fig. 242. Root resorption and repair on the distal surface of the lower second molar caused by pressure of an erupting third molar. **A,** Relation of the tooth germ of the third molar to the second molar at the beginning of the prefunctional phase of eruption. Note oblique position of the crown of the third molar. **B,** Area of contact between the tooth germ of the third molar and root of the second molar in high magnification. Resorption reaching into dentin. **C,** Relation of lower second and third molars after the third molar has attained its upright position. **D,** High magnification of the alveolar crest. Resorption on the distal root surface is partly repaired by apposition of cementum. (From Orban, B.: Arch. Clin. Path. 4:187, 1940.)

dentigerous cyst. Those which arise late may cause a noticeable swelling on the surface and are sometimes known as eruptive cysts, although they are simply a variation of dentigerous cysts.

REFERENCES

1. Brash, J. C.: The growth of the alveolar bone and its relation to the movements of the teeth, including eruption, Internat. J. Orthodont., Oral Surg. & Radiog. **14:**196, 283, 398, 487, 1928.
2. Brauer, J. C., and Bahador, M. A.: Variations in calcification and eruption of the deciduous and permanent teeth, J.A.D.A. **29:**1373, 1942.
3. Brodie, A. G.: Present status of our knowledge concerning movement of the tooth germ through the jaw, J.A.D.A. **24:**1830, 1934.
4. Brodie, A. G.: The growth of alveolar bone and the eruption of the teeth, Oral Surg., Oral Med. & Oral Path. **1:**342, 1948.
5. Cattell, P.: The eruption and growth of the permanent teeth, J. D. Res. **8:**279, 1928.
6. Gottlieb, B.: Scheinbare Verkürzung eines oberen Schneidezahnes (So-called shortening of an upper lateral incisor), Ztschr. f. Stomatol. **22:**501, 1924.
7. Gottlieb, B., Orban, B., and Diamond, M.: Biology and pathology of the tooth and its supporting mechanism, New York, 1938, The Macmillan Co.
8. Gross, H.: Histologische Untersuchungen über das Wachstum der Kieferknochen beim Menschen (Histologic investigations of the growth of the human jaw bone), Deutsche Zahnheilk. **89:**1934.
9. Herzberg, F., and Schour, I.: Effects of the removal of pulp and Hertwig's sheath on the eruption of incisors in the albino rat, J. D. Res. **20:**264, 1941.
10. Hoffman, M. M.: Experimental alterations in the rate of eruption of the rat incisor, University of Illinois Graduate School, 1939, master's thesis.
11. Hoffman, M. M., and Schour, I.: Quantitative studies in the development of the rat molar. II. Alveolar bone, cementum, and eruption (from birth to 500 days), Am. J. Orthodont. & Oral Surg. **26:**856, 1940.
12. Kronfeld, R.: The resorption of the roots of deciduous teeth, D. Cosmos **74:**103, 1932.
13. Logan, W. H. G., and Kronfeld, R.: Development of the human jaws and surrounding structures from birth to the age of fifteen years, J.A.D.A. **20:**379, 1933.
14. Logan, W. H. G.: A histologic study of the anatomic structures forming the oral cavity, J.A.D.A. **22:**3, 1935.
15. Massler, M., and Schour, I.: Studies in tooth development: theories of eruption, Am. J. Orthodont. & Oral Surg. **27:**552, 1941.
16. Orban, B.: Growth and movement of the tooth germs and teeth, J.A.D.A. **15:**1004, 1928.
17. Orban, B.: Resorption of roots due to pressure from erupting and impacted teeth, Arch. Clin. Path. **4:**187, 1940.
18. Orban, B.: Epithelial rests in the teeth and their supporting structures, Proc. Am. Assoc. D. Schools, p. 121, 1928.
19. Reichborn-Kjennerud: Ueber die Mechanik des Durchbruches der bleibenden Zähne beim Menschen (Mechanism of the eruption of the permanent teeth in man), Berlin, 1934, Hermann Meusser.
20. Sicher, H.: Tooth eruption: the axial movement of continuously growing teeth, J. D. Res. **21:**201, 1942.
21. Sicher, H.: Tooth eruption: the axial movement of teeth with limited growth, J. D. Res. **21:**395, 1942.
22. Sicher, H.: Oral anatomy, ed. 4, St. Louis, 1965, The C. V. Mosby Co.
23. Sicher, H., and Weinmann, J. P.: Bone growth and physiologic tooth movement, Am. J. Orthodont. & Oral Surg. **30:**109, 1944.
24. Stein, G., and Weinmann, J. P.: Die physiologische Wanderung der Zähne (The physiologic drift of the teeth), Ztschr. f. Stomatol. **23:**733, 1925.

25. Wasserfallen, P.: Movements of dental follicles in human fetal mandible, Schweiz. Msch. f. Zahnhk. **64:**551, 1954.
26. Wassermann, F.: Personal communication.
27. Weinmann, J. P.: Das Knochenbild bei Störungen der physiologischen Wanderung der Zähne (The bone picture in cases of disturbances of the physiologic movement of teeth), Ztschr. f. Stomatol. **24:**397, 1926.
28. Weinmann, J. P.: Bone changes related to eruption of the teeth, Angle Orthodontist **11:** 83, 1941.
29. Weinmann, J. P., and Sicher, H.: Correlation of active and passive eruption, Bur **46:**3, 1946.
30. Willman, W.: An apparent shortening of an upper incisor, J.A.D.A. **17:**444, 1930.

Chapter XII

Shedding of the deciduous teeth*

INTRODUCTION AND DEFINITION

PROCESS OF SHEDDING

CLINICAL CONSIDERATIONS
    Remnants of deciduous teeth
    Retained deciduous teeth
    Submerged deciduous teeth

INTRODUCTION AND DEFINITION

Human teeth, as those of most mammals, develop in two generations known as the deciduous and the permanent dentitions. The deciduous teeth are adapted in their number, size, and pattern to the small jaw of the early years of life. The size of their roots and, therefore, the strength of the periodontal ligament are in accordance with the developmental stage of the masticatory muscles. They are replaced by the permanent teeth, which are larger and more numerous and possess a stronger suspensory ligament. The physiologic elimination of deciduous teeth, prior to the replacement by their permanent successors, is called shedding.

PROCESS OF SHEDDING

The elimination of deciduous teeth is the result of the progressive resorption of their roots by osteoclasts. In this process both cementum and dentin are attacked. (See Fig. 243.) The osteoclasts differentiate from the cells of the loose connective tissue in response to the pressure exerted by the growing and erupting permanent tooth germ. Resorption of a deciduous tooth can, however, occur in the absence of its successor. At first, pressure is directed against the bone separating the alveolus of the deciduous tooth and the crypt of its permanent successor. Later it is directed against the root surface of the deciduous tooth itself. (See Fig. 244.)   Because of the position of the permanent tooth germ, the resorption of the roots of the deciduous incisors and canines starts at the lingual surface in the apical third (Fig. 245). The movement of the permanent germ at this time proceeds in an occlusal and vestibular direction. In later stages the germ of the permanent tooth is frequently found directly apical to the deciduous tooth (Fig. 243, A). In such cases the resorption of the deciduous root proceeds in transverse

---

*First draft submitted by Myron S. Aisenberg.

Deciduous
canine

Resorption
area

Permanent
canine

Resorption
of root

Resorption
of bone

A

Dentin

Resorption
(osteoclasts)

Cementum

Periodontal
ligament

Resorption
of bone

B

Fig. 243. Resorption of the root of a deciduous canine during eruption of the permanent successor. **A**, General view. **B**, Lingual resorption area in higher magnification. (From Kronfeld, R.: D. Cosmos **74**:103, 1932.)

Deciduous incisor

Bone between
deciduous
tooth and
successor

Enamel of perma-
nent incisor

Dentin

Fig. 244. A thin lamella of bone separates a permanent tooth germ from its predecessor.

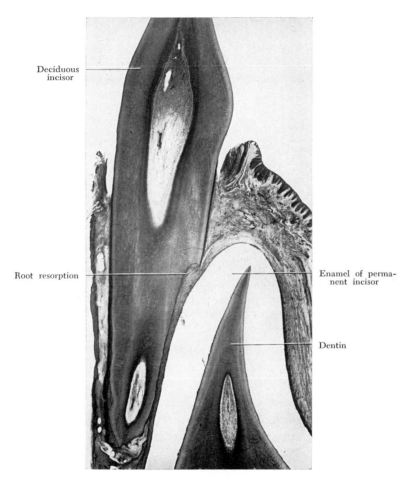

Deciduous
incisor

Root resorption

Enamel of perma-
nent incisor

Dentin

Fig. 245. Resorption of the root of a deciduous incisor due to pressure of the erupting successor.

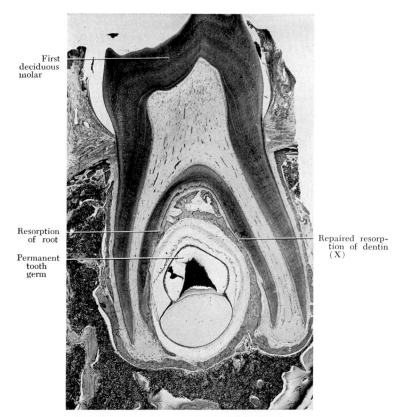

First
deciduous
molar

Resorption
of root

Permanent
tooth
germ

Repaired resorp-
tion of dentin
(X)

Fig. 246. Germ of a lower first permanent premolar between the roots of a lower first deciduous molar. Repaired resorption on the roots of the deciduous tooth (see Fig. 248).

planes, thus allowing the permanent tooth to erupt into the position of the deciduous tooth. However, movement in a vestibular direction is frequently not complete when the crown of the permanent tooth emerges through the gingiva. In such cases the permanent tooth appears lingual to its deciduous predecessor (Fig. 245). In the first-described alternative the deciduous tooth is lost before the permanent tooth erupts, whereas in the latter the permanent tooth may erupt while the deciduous tooth is still in its place.

Usually, resorption of the roots of the deciduous molars begins on the surfaces of the root facing the interradicular septum. This is due to the fact that the germs of the premolars are at first found between the roots of the deciduous molars (Fig. 246). Resorption of the roots can then be observed long before actual shedding. However, during their continued active eruption, the deciduous teeth move away from the growing permanent tooth germs, which, for the most part, then come to lie apical to the deciduous molars (Fig. 247). This change in position allows the growing premolar adequate space for its development. The areas of early resorption on the deciduous molar are then repaired by the apposition of new cementum, and the alveolar bone regenerates[7] (Fig. 248). In later

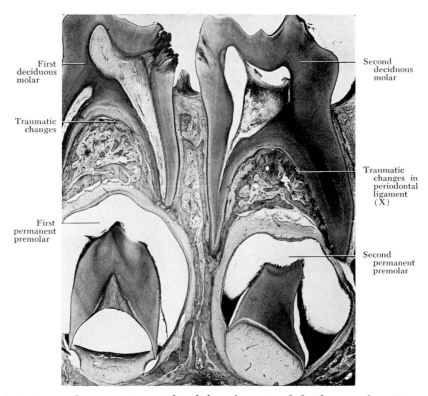

First
deciduous
molar

Traumatic
changes

First
permanent
premolar

Second
deciduous
molar

Traumatic
changes in
periodontal
ligament
(X)

Second
permanent
premolar

Fig. 247. Germs of permanent premolars below the roots of deciduous molars. Traumatic changes in the periodontal ligament of the deciduous teeth. *X,* See Fig. 250.

stages, however, the erupting premolars again overtake the deciduous molars, and in most cases their roots are entirely resorbed (Fig. 249). The resorption may even proceed far up into the coronal dentin. Occasionally some areas of the enamel may be destroyed. The premolars appear with the tips of their crowns in the place of the deciduous teeth.

Under normal conditions osteoclastic resorption is initiated by the pressure of the permanent tooth and leads to the elimination of the deciduous tooth. Two auxiliary factors have to be taken into consideration. They are as follows:

1. The weakening of the supporting tissues of the deciduous tooth because of resorption of parts of its roots and its continued active and passive eruption, which seems to be accelerated during the period of shedding. The epithelial attachment of the deciduous tooth grows down along the cementum at this time, causing the clinical crown of the tooth to be enlarged and the clinical root, to which the fibers of the periodontal ligament are anchored, to be shortened.

2. The masticatory forces increase during this period as a result of the growth of the masticatory muscles, but they act upon a tooth, weakened by resorption of its root and by its progressive axial eruption, as a traumatic

Cementum of
deciduous
tooth

Repaired
resorption

Bone

Resorption of
dentin

Loose connec-
tive tissue sur-
rounding per-
manent germ

Fig. 248. High magnification of a repaired resorption from area X of Fig. 246. New bone formed during the rest period.

force.[5,7,10] Because of the loss of large parts of the suspensory apparatus, the masticatory forces are transmitted to the alveolar bone not as tension but as pressure. This leads to compression and injury of the periodontal ligament, with subsequent bleeding, thrombosis, and necrosis. (See Fig. 250.) These changes are most frequently found in the furcation and on interradicular surfaces of deciduous molars. Resorption of bone and tooth substance, therefore, occurs most rapidly in such areas, thus relieving pressure. Repair of resorbed areas may be excessive and may even lead to ankylosis between bone and tooth. (See Fig. 251.)

The process of shedding is not continuous. Periods of great resorptive activity alternate with periods of relative rest.[7] During the rest periods, resorption not only ceases but repair may occur by apposition of cementum or bone upon the resorbed surface of cementum or dentin. Even repair of resorbed alveolar bone may take place during rest periods (Fig. 248). The periods of rest and repair are probably lengthened by the continued axial eruption of the deciduous tooth.

The pulp of the deciduous teeth plays a passive role during shedding. Even in late stages the occlusal parts of the pulp may appear almost normal, with functioning odontoblasts (Fig. 252). However, since the cellular elements of the pulp are identical with those of loose connective tissue, resorption of the dentin may occur at the pulpal surface by the differentiation of osteoclasts from

Fig. 249. Roots of a primary molar completely resorbed. Dentin of the primary tooth in contact with the enamel of the premolar. Resorption of bone on one side and formation of new bone on the opposite side of the premolar due to transmitted excentric pressure to the premolar. (From Grimmer, E. A.: J. D. Res. **18:**267, 1939.)

the cells of the pulp. The persistence of the pulpal tissue and its organic connection with the underlying connective tissue explain the fact that deciduous teeth show, to the last, a fairly strong attachment even after total loss of their roots (Fig 249). In such cases shedding may be unduly retarded, and the erupting permanent tooth may actually come into contact with the deciduous tooth. The masticatory forces are then transmitted to the permanent tooth[2] before its suspensory ligament is fully developed and may cause traumatic injuries in the periodontal ligament of the permanent tooth (Fig. 249).

CLINICAL CONSIDERATIONS

Remnants of deciduous teeth. Parts of the roots of deciduous teeth that are not in the path of erupting permanent teeth may escape resorption. Such rem-

Necrotic tissue remnants

Alveolar bone

Necrotic tissue remnants

Deciduous tooth

Traumatic destruction of periodontal ligament

Repaired resorption

Fig. 250. Traumatic changes of periodontal tissues. High magnification from area X in Fig. 247.

nants of roots, consisting of dentin and cementum, may remain in the jaw for a considerable time.[3,8] Most frequently, such remnants are found along the permanent premolars, especially in the region of the lower second premolars. (See Fig. 253). This is explained by the fact that the roots of the lower second deciduous molar are strongly curved or divergent. The mesiodistal diameter of the second premolars is much smaller than the greatest distance between the roots of the deciduous molar. Root remnants may later be found deep in the bone, completely surrounded by and ankylosed to the bone (Fig. 254). Frequently they are encased in heavy layers of cellular cementum. In cases in which the remnants are close to the surface of the jaw (Fig. 255), they may ultimately be exfoliated. Progressive resorption of the root remnants and replacement by bone may cause the disappearance of these remnants.

Retained deciduous teeth. Deciduous teeth may be retained for a long time

A

Deciduous molar

Bone

Permanent tooth

Dentin

Cementum

Bone

Resorption

Resorption of cementum

Ankylosis

Resorption of bone

B

Fig. 251. Ankylosis of a deciduous tooth as a sequence of trauma. **A,** General view of the furcation of a deciduous molar sectioned buccolingually. **B,** High magnification of area X in **A.**

Odontoblasts

Pulp

Dentin

Fig. 252. High magnification of the pulp of the resorbed deciduous molar shown in Fig. 249. Pulp of normal structure with odontoblasts.

Root remnant of
deciduous
tooth

Root remnant of
deciduous tooth

Fig. 253. Remnants of roots of a deciduous molar embedded in the interdental septa. (Courtesy Dr. G. M. Fitzgerald, University of California.)

First premolar

Second premolar

Remnant of
deciduous root

Ankylosis

Fig. 254. Remnant of deciduous tooth embedded in, and ankylosed to, the bone. (From Schoenbauer, F.: Ztschr. f. Stomatol. 29:892, 1931.)

if the permanent tooth is congenitally missing.[1] This involves most frequently the upper lateral incisor (Fig. 256, *A*), less frequently the second permanent premolar, especially in the mandible (Fig. 256, *B*), and rarely, the lower central incisor (Fig. 256, *C*). If a permanent tooth is embedded, its deciduous predecessor may also be retained (Fig. 256, *D*). This involves most often the deciduous upper canine in an impaction of the permanent canine.

The fate of retained deciduous teeth varies. In some cases they persist for many years in good functional condition (Fig. 256, *A*). More often, however, resorption of the roots and continued active eruption and passive exposure cause their loosening and final loss (Fig. 256, *B*). The loss of retained deciduous teeth has been explained erroneously by the assumption that such teeth may undergo regressive age changes in their pulp, dentin, cementum, and periodontal ligament, thus losing those faculties that are necessary for the maintenance of functional integrity.[2] The real cause, however, is the fact that such teeth, because of their smaller size, are not adapted to the strength of the masticatory forces in adult life. The roots are narrow and short, thus rendering the area available for attach-

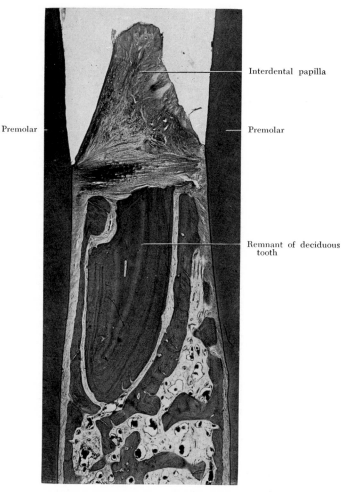

Interdental papilla

Premolar

Premolar

Remnant of deciduous
tooth

Fig. 255. Remnant of deciduous tooth at the alveolar crest.

ment of principal fibers inadequate. Their loss is then due to occlusal trauma.

If the permanent lateral incisor is missing, the deciduous tooth is often resorbed under the pressure of the erupting permanent canine. This resorption may be simultaneous with that of the deciduous canine. (See Fig. 257.) Sometimes the permanent canine causes resorption of the deciduous lateral incisor only and erupts in its place. In such cases the deciduous canine may be retained distally to the permanent canine. A supernumerary tooth or an odontogenic tumor may occasionally prevent the eruption of a permanent tooth or teeth. In such cases an ankylosis of the deciduous tooth may develop after traumatic injury.

Submerged deciduous teeth. Traumatic lesions, on the other hand, may lead to ankylosis of a deciduous tooth rather than its loss. The active eruption of an ankylosed tooth ceases, and therefore the tooth later appears "shortened" (Fig. 258) because of continued eruption of its neighbors. While the alveolar bone

Fig. 256. Roentgenograms of retained deciduous teeth. **A,** Upper permanent lateral incisor missing, and deciduous tooth retained (age 56). **B,** Lower second premolar missing and deciduous molar retained. Roots partly resorbed. **C,** Permanent lower central incisors missing and deciduous teeth retained. **D,** Upper permanent canine embedded and deciduous canine retained. (**A** and **B** courtesy Dr. M. K. Hine, University of Indiana; **C** and **D** courtesy Dr. Rowe Smith, Texarkana, Ark.)

Fig. 257. Upper permanent lateral incisor missing. Deciduous lateral incisor and deciduous canine are resorbed due to pressure of the erupting permanent canine. **A,** At the age of 11 years. **B,** At the age of 13 years.

Fig. 258. Submerging deciduous lower second molar. Second premolar missing. (Courtesy Dr. M. K. Hine, University of Indiana.)

continues to grow, the tooth may become submerged in the alveolar bone.[6] The roots and crowns of such teeth show extensive resorption and formation of bone in the tortuous cavities of the dentin. Submerged deciduous teeth prevent the eruption of their permanent successors or force them from their position. Submerged deciduous teeth should, therefore, be removed as soon as possible.

REFERENCES

1. Aisenberg, M. S.: Studies of retained deciduous teeth, Am. J. Orthodont. & Oral Surg. **27**:179, 1941.
2. Grimmer, E. A.: Trauma in an erupting premolar, J. D. Res. **18**:267, 1939.
3. Kotanyi, E.: Histologische Befunde au Milchzahnreste (Histologic findings on deciduous tooth remnants), Ztschr. f. Stomatol. **23**:516, 1925.
4. Kronfeld, R.: The resorption of the roots of deciduous teeth, D. Cosmos **74**:103, 1932.
5. Kronfeld, R., and Weinmann, J. P.: Traumatic changes in the periodontal tissues of deciduous teeth, J. D. Res. **19**:441, 1940.
6. Noyes, F. B.: Submerging deciduous molars, Angle Orthodontist **2**:77, 1932.
7. Oppenheim, A.: Histologische Befunde beim Zahnwechsel (Histologic findings in the shedding of teeth), Ztschr. f. Stomatol. **20**:543, 1922.
8. Schoenbauer, F.: Knöchern eingeheilte Milchzahnreste bei älteren Individuen (Ankylosed deciduous teeth remnants in adults), Ztschr. f. Stomatol. **29**:892, 1931.
9. Stafne, E. C.: Possible role of retained deciduous roots in the etiology of cysts of the jaw, J.A.D.A. **24**:1489, 1937.
10. Weinmann, J. P., and Kronfeld, R.: Traumatic injuries in the jaws of infants, J. D. Res. **19**:357, 1940.

Chapter XIII

Temporo-
mandibular
joint*

ANATOMIC REMARKS
HISTOLOGY
    Bony structures
    Articular fibrous covering
    Articular disc
    Articular capsule
CLINICAL CONSIDERATIONS

ANATOMIC REMARKS

The mandibular articulation, temporomandibular or craniomandibular joint, is a bilateral diarthrosis between the articular tubercle eminences of the temporal bone and the condyles, capitula, of the mandible. A fibrous plate, the articular disc, is interposed on either side between the articular surfaces of the two bones. The temporomandibular joint is a joint which permits the mandible to move as a unit with two functional patterns. The anatomy and histology of the joint are related to its functional activity.

The articular surface of the temporal bone is concave in its posterior part and convex in its anterior part. The articular fossa extends from the squamotympanic and petrotympanic fissures posteriorly to the convex articular tubercle anteriorly. The latter is strongly convex in a sagittal plane and slightly concave in a frontal plane. The convexity varies considerably, the radius ranging from 5 to 15 mm. The long axes of the articular tubercles are directed medially and slightly posteriorly. The articular surfaces of the mandibular condyles are arcuate, with their axes placed in the same direction as those of the articular tubercles on the temporal bone. The articulating parts of the temporomandibular joint are covered by a fibrous or fibrocartilaginous tissue and not by hyalin cartilage, as in most other articulations of the human body. The absence of hyalin cartilage on the articulating surface was wrongly interpreted as indicating that the joint is not a stress-bearing joint. The hyalin cartilage present in the head of the condyle is the growth center of the mandible. It is comparable to the epiphyseal cartilage in a long bone but does not disappear entirely with maturity and cessation of growth.

The articular disc is an oval fibrous plate that fuses at its anterior margin

---

*First draft submitted by Donald A. Kerr.

335

Mandibular fossa

Articular tubercle

Articular disc

Mandibular head

External auditory meatus

Fig. 259. Sagittal section through the temporomandibular joint. (From Bauer, W.: Ztschr. f. Stomatol. **30:**1136, 1932.)

with the fibrous capsule. Its posterior border is connected to the capsule by loose connective tissue, which allows its anterior movement (Fig. 259). Its medial and lateral corners are directly attached to the poles of the condyle. The articular space is divided into two compartments: a lower, between the condyle and the disc (condylodiscal), and an upper, between the disc and temporal bone (temporodiscal). The disc is biconcave in sagittal section, with the central part thin and the anterior and posterior borders thickened (Fig. 260). Some fibers of the lateral pterygoid muscle attach to the anterior border of the disc. The disc produces a movable articulation for the condyles. In the inferior portion of the joint, rotational movement about an axis through the heads of the condyles permits opening of the jaws. This is designated as a hinge movement. The superior portion of the joint permits a translatory movement as the discs and the condyles traverse anteriorly along the inclines of the articular tubercles to provide an anterior and inferior movement of the mandible.

The articular capsule is a fibrous sac strengthened laterally by the temporomandibular ligament. The inner aspect of the capsule is lined by a synovial membrane. The synovial membrane lines the joint capsule, being especially well developed behind the disc, but does not extend over the surfaces of the disc, the articular tubercle, or the condyle.

HISTOLOGY

Bony structures. The condyle of the mandible is composed of cancellous bone covered by a thin layer of compact bone (Fig. 260, A). The trabeculae are grouped in such a way that they radiate from the neck of the mandible and reach the cortex at right angles, thus giving maximal strength to the condyle. The large marrow spaces decrease in size with progressing age by a marked thickening of the trabeculae. The red marrow in the condyle is of the myeloid or cellular type. In older individuals it is sometimes replaced by fatty marrow.

During the period of growth, a layer of hyalin cartilage lies underneath the

Mandibular
fossa

Articular
disc

Fibrous
covering

Mandibular
condyle

Fibrous
covering

Articular
tubercle

Lateral
pterygoid
muscle

A

B

Fig. 260. A, Sagittal section through the temporomandibular joint of a man 28 years of age. **B,** Radiograph demonstrates the fossa, articular tubercle, and condyle in closed relation. (**A** courtesy Dr. S. W. Chase, Western Reserve University.)

fibrous covering of the condyle. This cartilaginous plate grows by apposition from the deepest layers of the covering connective tissue. At the same time its deep surface is replaced by bone (Fig. 261). Remnants of this cartilage may persist into old age (Fig. 262).

The roof of the mandibular fossa (Fig. 260) consists of a thin compact

Fig. 261. Sections through the mandibular head. **A,** Newborn infant. **B,** Young adult. Note the transitional zone between the fibrous covering and the hyalin cartilage, characteristic for appositional growth of cartilage.

layer of bone. The articular tubercle is composed of spongy bone covered with a thin layer of compact bone. In rare cases islands of hyalin cartilage are found in the articular tubercle.

Articular fibrous covering. The condyle, as well as the articular tubercle, is covered by a rather thick layer of fibrous tissue containing a variable number of chondrocytes. The fibrous covering of the mandibular condyle is of fairly even thickness (Fig. 262). Its superficial layers consist of a network of strong collag-

Articular
disc

Articular
space

Fibrous
covering

Hyalin
cartilage

Calcification
zone

Bone

Fig. 262. Higher magnification of part of the mandibular condyle shown in Fig. 260, A.

Bone

Calcification
zone

Inner fibrous
layer

Outer fibrous
layer

Articular
space

Articular
disc

Fig. 263. Higher magnification of articular tubercle shown in Fig. 260, A.

enous fibers. Chondrocytes may be present, and they have a tendency to increase in number with age. They can be recognized by their thin capsule, which stains heavily with basic dyes. The deepest layer of the fibrocartilage is rich in chondroid cells as long as growing hyalin cartilage is present in the condyle. It contains only a few thin collagenous fibers. In this zone the appositional growth of the hyalin cartilage of the condyle takes place during the period of growth.

The fibrous layer covering the articulating surface of the temporal bone (Fig. 263) is thin in the articular fossa and thickens rapidly on the posterior slope of the articular tubercle (Fig. 260, A). In this region the fibrous tissue shows a definite arrangement in two layers, with a small transitional zone between them. The two layers are characterized by the different course of the constituent fibrous bundles. In the inner zone the fibers are at right angles to the bony surface. In the outer zone they run parallel to that surface. As in the fibrous covering of the mandibular condyle, a variable number of chondrocytes are found in the tissue on the temporal surface. In adults the deepest layer shows a thin zone of calcification.

Articular tubercle

Superior articular space

Articular disc

Inferior articular space

Mandibular head

Fig. 264. Higher magnification of articular disc shown in Fig. 260, A.

There is no continuous cellular lining on the free surface of the fibrocartilage. Only isolated fibroblasts are situated on the surface itself. They are characterized by the formation of long, flat cytoplasmic processes.

Articular disc. In young individuals the articular disc is composed of dense fibrous tissue. The interlacing fibers are straight and tightly packed (Fig. 264). Elastic fibers are found only in relatively small numbers. The fibroblasts in the disc are elongated and send flat cytoplasmic winglike processes into the interstices between the adjacent bundles.

With advancing age some of the fibroblasts develop into chondroid cells. which later may differentiate into true chondrocytes. Even small islands of hyalin cartilage may be found in the discs of older persons. Chondroid cells, true cartilage cells, and hyalin ground substance develop in situ by differentiation of the fibroblasts. In the discs, as well as in the fibrous tissue covering the articular surfaces, this cellular change seems to be dependent upon mechanical influences. The presence of chondrocytes may increase the resistance and resilience of the fibrous tissue.

The fibrous tissue covering the articular eminence and mandibular condyle, as well as the large central area of the disc, is devoid of blood vessels[7] and nerves and have limited reparative ability.

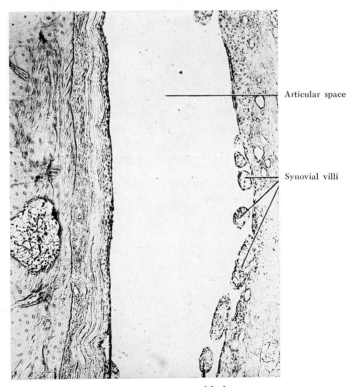

Fig. 265. Villi on the synovial capsule of the temporomandibular joint.

Articular capsule. As in all other joints, the articular capsule consists of an outer fibrous layer that is strengthened on the lateral surface to form the temporomandibular ligament. The inner or synovial layer is a thin layer of connective tissue. It contains numerous blood vessels that form a capillary network close to its surface. From its surface, folds or fingerlike processes, synovial folds and villi, protrude into the articular cavity (Fig. 265). A few fibroblasts of the synovial membrane reach the surface and, with some histiocytes and lymphatic wandering cells, form an incomplete lining of the synovial membrane.

A small amount of a clear, straw-covered viscous fluid, synovial fluid, is found in the articular spaces. It is a lubricant and also a nutrient fluid for the avascular tissues covering the condyle and the articular tubercle and for the disc. It is elaborated by diffusion from the rich capillary network of the synovial membrane, augmented by mucin possibly secreted by the synovial cells.

CLINICAL CONSIDERATIONS

The thinness of the bone in the articular fossa is responsible for fractures if the mandibular head is driven into the fossa by a heavy blow. In such cases injuries of the dura mater and the brain have been reported.

The finer structure of the bone and its fibrocartilaginous covering depends upon mechanical influences. A change in force or direction of stress, occurring especially after loss of posterior teeth, may cause structural changes. These are characterized by degeneration of the fibrous covering of the articulating surfaces and of the disc.[23] Abnormal functional activity produces injury to the fibrous covering and the articular bones. Compensation and partial repair may be accomplished by the development of hyalin cartilage on the condylar surface and in the disc. In severe trauma the articular bone is destroyed, and cartilage and new bone develop in the marrow spaces and at the periphery of the condyle. Then the function of the joint is severely impaired.

There is considerable literature on the disturbances which occur in the articulation as the result of disharmony in the relation of the teeth and the temporomandibular joint. Disharmony of the factors which govern occlusion may produce extensive degenerative changes in the mandibular articulation. The clinical symptoms are pain in the region of the joint and pain radiating to the temporal, infraorbital, supraorbital, and postauricular areas which may be of such severity as to produce trismus. A variety of noises can be observed during function depending upon the type and severity of the alterations produced.[10,13]

Many explanations have been advanced for these variable symptoms: pressure on the external auditory meatus exerted by the mandibular condyle, which is driven deeply into the articular fossa; compression of the auriculotemporal nerve; compression of the chorda tympani; compression of the auditory tube; impaired function of the tensor palati muscle. Anatomic findings do not substantiate any one of these explanations. Hypersensitivity and spasm of the muscles of mastication account for many of the symptoms.

REFERENCES

1. Bauer, W.: Anatomische und mikroskopische Untersuchungen über das Kiefergelenk (Anatomical and microscopic investigations on the temporo-mandibular joint), Ztschr. f. Stomatol. **30**:1136, 1932.

2. Bauer, W. H.: Osteo-arthritis deformans of the temporo-mandibular joint, Am. J. Path. **17**:129, 1941.

3. Baecker, R.: Zur Histologie des Kiefergelenkmeniskus des Menschen und der Säuger (Histology of the temporo-mandibular disc in man and mammals), Ztschr. f. mikr.-anat. Forsch. **26**:223, 1931.

4. Breitner, C.: Bone changes resulting from experimental orthodontic treatment, Am. J. Orthodontics **26**:521, 1940.

5. Cabrini, R., and Erausquin, J.: La articulacion temporomaxilar de la rata (Temporomandibular joint of the rat), Rev. Odont. de Buenos Aires, 1941.

6. Choukas, N. C., and Sicher, H.: The structure of the temporo-mandibular joint, Oral Surg., Oral Med. & Oral Path. **13**:1263, 1960.

7. Cohen, D. W.: The vascularity of the articular disc of the temporo-mandibular joint, Alpha Omegan, September, 1955.

8. Cowdry, E. V.: Special cytology, ed. 2, New York, 1932, Paul B. Hoeber, Inc., pp. 981-989, 1055-1075.

9. Hammar, J. Aug.: Ueber den feineren Bau der Gelenke (The microscopic architecture of the joints), Arch. f. mikr. Anat. **43**:266, 1894.

10. Kerr, D. A.: The pathology of traumatic temporomandibular joint arthritis produced by traumatic occlusion, J. D. Res. **36**:717, 1957.

11. Marquart, W.: Zur Histologie der Synovialmembran (Histology of the synovial membrane), Ztschr. f. Zellforsch. u. mikr. Anat. **12**:34, 1931.

12. Peterson, H.: Die Organe des Skeletsystems (Organs of the skeletal system) In von Möllendorff, W. (editor): Handbuch der mikroskopischen Anatomie des Menschen, vol. 2, pt. 2, Berlin, 1930, Julius Springer.

13. Ramfjord, S. P., and Ash, M. M.: Occlusion, Philadelphia, 1966, W. B. Saunders Co.

14. Sarnat, B. G.: The temporomandibular joint, ed. 2, Springfield, Ill., 1964, Charles C Thomas, Publisher.

15. Schaeffer, J. P.: Morris' human anatomy, ed. 10, Philadelphia, 1942, The Blakiston Co.

16. Schaffer, J.: Ueber den feineren Bau und die Entwicklung des Knorpelgewebes und über verwandte Formen der Stützsubstanz (On the microscopic structure and development of cartilage and related forms of supporting tissue), Ztschr. f. wissensch. Zool. **80**:155, 1905.

17. Schaffer, J.: Die Stützgewebe (Supporting tissues) In von Möllendorff, W. (editor): Handbuch der mikroskopischen Anatomie des Menschen, vol. 2, pt. 2, Berlin, 1930, Julius Springer.

18. Shapiro, H. H., and Truex, R. C.: The temporo-mandibular joint and the auditory function, J.A.D.A. **30**:1147, 1943.

19. Sicher, Harry: Temporomandibular articulation in mandibular overclosure, J.A.D.A. **36**:131, 1948.

20. Sicher, Harry: Some aspects of the anatomy and pathology of the temporomandibular articulation, New York State D. J. **14**:451, 1948.

21. Sicher, H.: Positions and movements of the mandible, J.A.D.A. **48**:620, 1954.

22. Sicker, H.: Structural and functional basis for disorders of the temporomandibular articulation, J. Oral Surg. **13**:275, 1955.

23. Steinhardt, G.: Die Beanspruchung der Gelenkflächen bei verschiedenen Bissarten (Investigations on the stresses in the mandibular articulation and their structural consequences), Deutsche Zahnh. in Vortr. **91**:1, 1934.

Chapter XIV

Maxillary sinus*

INTRODUCTION
DEVELOPMENT
ANATOMIC REMARKS
HISTOLOGY
FUNCTION
CLINICAL CONSIDERATIONS

INTRODUCTION

The maxillary sinus was described in 1489 by Leonardo da Vinci.[8] Its relationship to the dentition was first recognized by Nathaniel Highmore. In his work entitled *Corporis Humani Disquisitio Anatomica* (1651) Highmore described the adult state of the maxillary sinus in detail and stated that his attention had been called to it because a patient had an abscess there which was drained by the extraction of a canine tooth. This proved to be one of those misleading first observations. Actually, the canine root seldom is related to this space in such a way that its simple extraction would drain it. The molar roots most often, and the premolar roots less frequently, are the dental structures that lie closest to the sinus (Fig. 267, *B*). Individual variations are great and can be determined only by careful interpretation of good roentgenograms.[4]

DEVELOPMENT

The maxillary sinus, or antrum of Highmore, begins its development in the third month of fetal life, arising by a lateral evagination of the mucous membrane of the middle nasal meatus, and forming a slitlike space. In the newborn infant its measurements are about 8 by 4 by 6 mm. (Fig. 266). Thereafter, it gradually expands by pneumatization of the body of the maxilla. The sinus is well developed when the permanent dentition has erupted, but it may continue to expand, probably throughout life.[12]

ANATOMIC REMARKS

The maxillary sinus is situated in the body of the maxilla. It is pyramidal in shape. The base of the pyramid is formed by the lateral wall of the nasal cavity. The apex extends into the zygomatic process, the anterior wall corresponds to the facial surface of the body of the maxilla, the roof corresponds to its orbital surface, the posterior wall is formed by the infratemporal surface of the maxilla, and the floor often reaches into the alveolar process.

---

*First draft submitted by Paul C. Kitchin in collaboration with L. F. Edwards, Department of Anatomy, Ohio State University. Revised by Dorothy Permar.

344

The maxillary sinus communicates with a recess of the middle meatus of the nasal cavity (semilunar hiatus) by means of an aperture, the ostium maxillare, that is located high on the nasal or medial wall of the sinus. Because of its high position, this ostium is unfavorably situated for drainage (Fig. 267, A). An accessory ostium may occur that is lower and slightly more advantageously placed for drainage than the normal ostium.

There is a wide variation in size, shape and position of the maxillary sinus[15] not only in different individuals but also on the two sides of the same individual. Its average capacity in the adult is about 15 ml., and the average dimensions are as follows: anteroposteriorly, 3.4 cm.; transversely, 2.3 cm.; and vertically, 3.35 cm.

Variations in the size of the maxillary sinus are partially accounted for by

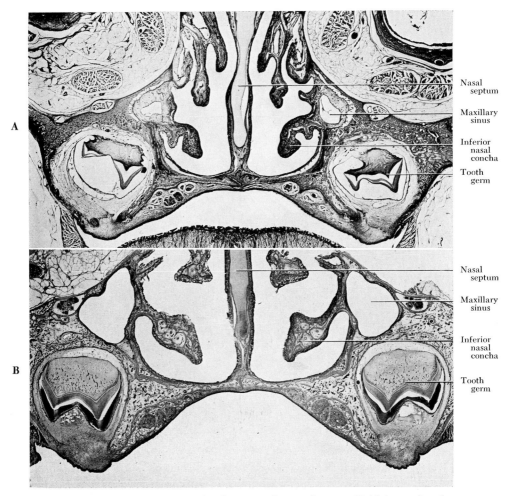

Fig. 266. Frontal sections through the head. **A,** Newborn infant. **B,** Child 9 months of age. Compare the size of the maxillary sinus.

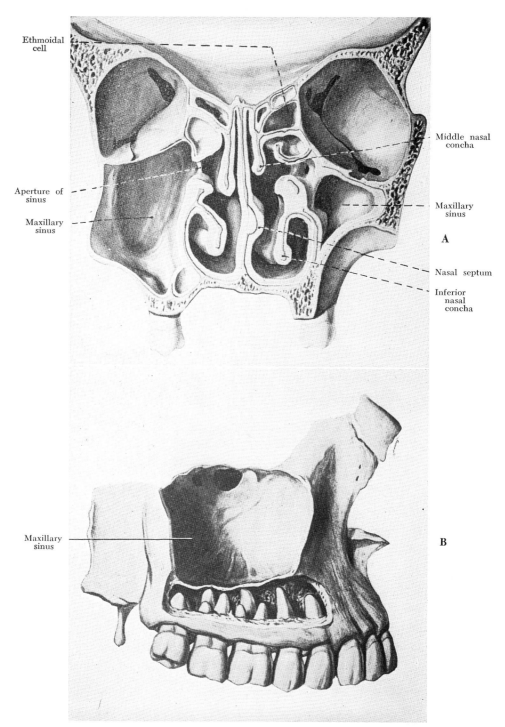

Fig. 267. Relation of the maxillary sinus and its opening into the nasal cavity. A, Frontal section showing marked asymmetry between the right and left sinuses. B, Relation of the sinus to the root apices.

differences in the extent of pneumatization of the body of the maxilla, i.e., the hollowing out by an air-filled pouch of the nasal cavity. In general, the greater the pneumatization, the thinner the walls of the sinus, since pneumatization occurs at the expense of bone tissue. The sinus walls may vary from thick walls of 5 to 8 mm. to walls that are nearly paper thin.

Enlargement of the maxillary sinus may also result from its extension into the frontal process, extension into the zygomatic process and even into the zygomatic bone, extension into the maxillary tuberosity, and extension into the alveolar process. The extension of the floor of the maxillary sinus into the alveolar process may place the sinus floor not only between the roots of adjacent teeth but also between the roots of an individual tooth, so that the root apices protrude into the sinus cavity. Usually the bone of the sinus floor is elevated in spots to accommodate the protruding roots, so that bone completely covers the roots (Fig. 268). Sometimes, however, there are defects in the bone of the sinus floor (Fig. 269, A), and the roots protrude through the openings into the sinus cavity. Here

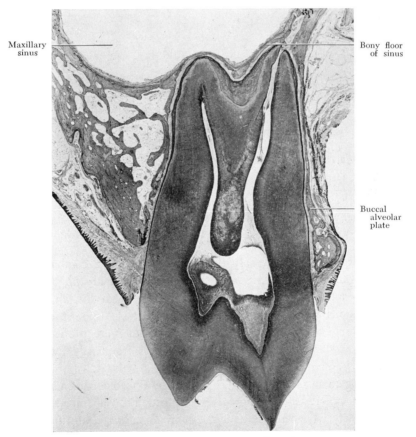

Fig. 268. Buccolingual section through a first upper premolar. The apex is separated from the sinus by a thin plate of bone.

Fig. 269. Mucous membrane and epithelium of the maxillary sinus. **A,** Apical region of a second premolar. The lining of the sinus is continuous with the periapical tissue through openings in the bony floor of the sinus. **B,** High magnification of the epithelium of the maxillary sinus. (From Bauer, W. H.: Am. J. Orthodont. & Oral Surg. **29:**133, 1943.)

they are covered only by a soft tissue composed of a combination of the periodontal ligament that surrounds the tooth root and the mucous membrane that lines the sinus cavity. The number of teeth the apices of which produce elevations in the floor of the sinus depends upon the degree and shape of pneumatization. Elevations of the sinus floor are produced most frequently by roots of the maxillary molars and less frequently by those of the premolars.

When enlargement of the sinus has placed the sinus floor deep in the alveolar process, the floor of the sinus may occupy a position lower than that of the floor of the nasal cavity. When the sinus is not so much enlarged and the bone apical to the tooth roots is comparatively thick, the floor of the sinus may be in a position that is higher than the floor of the nasal cavity. Sometimes the two floors are on the same level. The hard palate does not enter into the formation of the floor of the sinus. The hard palate forms the floor of the nasal fossae. The sinus floor is lateral to the hard palate.

The walls of the maxillary sinus may have septa that partially divide the sinus into compartments, and the placement of such septa may at times interfere with sinus drainage. Again, there may be present a septum that produces a complete division of the sinus into two separate cavities, each cavity having an independent opening into the nasal fossa. Such a septum usually is placed in such a way as to form a ventral and a dorsal compartment, but it may be placed in such a way as to form an inferior and a superior compartment.[12]

Unilateral supplemental maxillary sinuses have been observed.[12] They usually occur dorsal to the sinus proper and are, from the standpoint of origin, overdeveloped posterior ethmoid cells. Clinically they must be considered as maxillary sinuses.

HISTOLOGY

The maxillary sinus is lined by a mucous membrane that is thinner and more delicate than that of the nasal cavity.

The lamina propria of the sinus mucosa is fused with the periosteum of the underlying bone and consists of loose bundles of collagenous fibers with very few elastic fibers. It is only moderately vascular (Fig. 269, *A*). Glands of the mucous and serous types are present and are confined largely to that part of the lamina propria that is located around the opening or openings into the nasal cavity.

The epithelium of the sinus mucosa is typical of the epithelium of the respiratory passage. It is pseudostratified ciliated columnar, rich in goblet cells (Fig. 269, *B*). The goblet cells secrete mucus that moistens the surface of the sinus mucosa. The cilia beat in such a way as to convey any surface material toward the opening that communicates with the nasal cavity, and hence they act to clear the sinus cavity of inhaled substances and of mucus. A study of the ciliary movement has been made by Kohsaka.[7]

FUNCTION

Various functions have been ascribed to the maxillary sinus and to the other accessory nasal sinuses. It has been claimed by some, for instance, that the maxillary sinuses aid in warming and moistening inhaled air or that they play an important role in vocalization.

The most probable explanation for the development of all nasal sinuses is that the maintenance of bone tissue depends largely on its mechanical function. Bone tissue that has lost its mechanical function is resorbed. An example of such bone resorption in response to loss of function is seen in the formation of the marrow cavities in long bones where fatty tissue develops in place of the disappearing bone tissue. The disappearance of nonfunctioning bone tissue in the neighborhood of the air-filled nasal cavity leads to the development of air-filled pouches in the bone. The supporting function of bone is maintained with a minimum of material.

CLINICAL CONSIDERATIONS

Periapical infection in teeth the root apices of which are in close approximation to the floor of the maxillary sinus can be a cause of sinus infection.[2,5,9]

Disease of the maxillary sinus can produce dental pain. The superior alveolar nerves run in narrow canals in the thin wall of the sinus. Sometimes these canals are partly open toward the sinus, and the nerves which supply the teeth are in contact with the sinus mucosa, where they may become involved in any inflammation of the mucoperiosteum. The resulting pain resembles pulpal pain, but it involves a group of teeth or even all of the teeth in one maxilla.

Because of its proximity to the roots of the maxillary posterior teeth, the maxillary sinus may easily become involved during oral surgical procedures, if the bone of the floor of the maxillary sinus is thin, a root may accidentally be forced into the maxillary sinus in the course of a tooth extraction. Also, following the loss of a single maxillary molar or, more rarely, a premolar, modification of the floor of the sinus frequently results in an extension of the floor down between the roots of the remaining adjacent teeth (Fig. 270). Consequently, at a later time there is a risk of accidentally opening the sinus during the extraction of one of these remaining teeth. If a single molar remains in the maxilla for a long time after the loss of the neighboring teeth, downward extensions of the maxillary sinus may occur mesial and distal to this tooth. If force is applied in extracting such a tooth, the tooth and the base of the alveolus (the floor of the sinus) may be removed together rather than the tooth being removed from its alveolus.

Among possible sequelae of the accidental removal of the floor of the maxillary sinus in the process of tooth removal is the persistence of an unhealed

Fig. 270. Roentgenogram of the upper jaw. The maxillary sinus extends toward the alveolar crest after loss of the first molar.

antraoral fistula.[1] With this persistent communication between the oral cavity and the antrum, the fistulous canal becomes lined with epithelium.[3]

Another circumstance that may contribute to accidental communication between the oral cavity and the maxillary sinus is the presence of hypercementoses on the roots of maxillary molars.[1] Surgical removal of these teeth may result in the removal of the sinus floor along with the teeth.

REFERENCES

1. Archer, W. Harry: Oral Surgery, Philadelphia, 1956, W. B. Saunders Co.
2. Bauer, W. H.: Maxillary sinusitis of dental origin, Am. J. Orthodont. & Oral Surg. **29**: 133, 1943.
3. Christiansen, G. W.: The mouth as a factor in maxillary sinus disease, J.A.D.A. **22**:1926, 1935.
4. Ennis, L. M., and Batson, O.: Variations of the maxillary sinus as seen in the roentgenogram, J.A.D.A. **23**:201, 1936.
5. Hofer, O.: Dental diseases and their relation to maxillary antrum, J. D. Res. **17**:321, 1938. (Abst.)
6. Kim, M. K.: Development of the maxillary sinus, Korea J. Med. **7**:985, 1962. (In Korean.)
7. Kohsaka, T.: Studies of the ciliated epithelial cells of the mucous membrane of the maxillary sinus by phase contrast microscopy, J. Otorhino-laryngo. Soc. Japan **61**:1, 1959.
8. Libersa, C., Laude, M., and Christiaens, L.: Etude sur le development du sinus maxillaire chez l'enfant, Arch. Franc. Pediat. **20**:488, 1963.
9. MacMillan, H. W.: The relationship of the teeth to the maxillary sinus; anatomic factors underlying the diagnosis and surgery of this region, J.A.D.A. **14**:1635, 1927.
10. Matsumoto, R.: Studies on ciliated epithelium of nasal cavities and paranasal sinuses. I. Physiological function of the ciliated epithelium, Laryng. Soc. Japan **61**:1856, 1958. (In Japanese.)
11. Royer, R. Q., and Stafne, E. C.: Cyst of jaw lined with ciliated epithelium, Oral Surg., Oral Med. and Oral Path. **18**:14, 1964.
12. Schaeffer, J. P.: The sinus maxillaris and its relations in the embryo, child and adult man, Am. J. Anat. **10**:313, 1910.
13. Schaeffer, J. P.: The nose, paranasal sinuses, nasolacrymal passageways and olfactory organ in man, Philadelphia, 1920, P. Blakiston's Son & Co.
14. Schmid, F., and Voelckel, E. W.: Biological data about the development of the paranasal sinuses in childhood, Monatschr. f. Kinderh. **105**:367, 1957.
15. Sedwick, H. J.: Form, size and position of the maxillary sinus at various ages studied by means of roentgenograms of the skull, Am. J. Roentgenol. **32**:154, 1934.
16. Terracol, J., and Arduoin, P.: Les liaisons des sinus frontal et maxillaire, Pract. Otorhino-laryng. (Basel) **19**:93, 1957.
17. Zuckerkandl, E.: Normale und pathologische Anatomie der Nasenhöhle und ihrer pneumatischen Anhange (Anatomy of the nasal cavity), Leipzig, 1893, W. Braumuller.

INTRODUCTION
Structure and chemical composition of
connective tissue
Epithelial tissues and derivatives
Ground substance in normal and abnormal
conditions
Enzymes

HISTOCHEMICAL TECHNIQUES
Fixation procedures
Specific histochemical methods
Protein and lipid histochemistry of oral hard
tissues
Polysaccharide, protein, and mucin
histochemistry of oral soft tissues
Polysaccharides
Proteins and protein groups
Mucins
Enzyme histochemistry of oral tissues
Alkaline phosphatase
Acid phosphatase
Esterase
Aminopeptidase
Cytochrome oxidase
Succinic dehydrogenase
Citric acid cycle in osteoblasts and
osteoclasts
Summary
Enzyme histochemistry of oral soft tissues
Alkaline phosphatase
Acid phosphatase
Esterase
Aminopeptidase
β-glucuronidases
Cytochrome oxidase and succinic
dehydrogenase
Phosphorylases

Chapter XV

Histochemistry
of
the oral tissues*

INTRODUCTION

Since the last edition a number of new, as well as applied, histochemical techniques have been introduced which may have application in the study of the fine structure of oral tissues. Some[42,43] of these special techniques include electron microscopy, x-ray microscopy, electron beam microanalysis, x-ray diffraction, and x-ray spectrography. The reviews by Palen[95] and by Clark[40] cover some of the general principles involved in the aforementioned approaches. Polarized light and x-ray analysis have been applied in the study of human enamel.[72,123] The phosphorescence of calcified tissues (which is the induced luminescence that persists after the cessation of the irradiation that caused it) has been demonstrated in bone, dentin, and enamel at liquid nitrogen temperature ($-195°$ C. or $78°$ K.).[75,140] The application of laser spectroscopy for the qualitative and quantitative analysis of the inorganic components of calcified tissues has also been reported.[60]

Microscopic histochemical techniques may be considered as extensions of

---

*By Marvin S. Burstone.

352

routine staining procedures. True histochemical procedures, however, have a known chemical basis. Use of these techniques, most of which have been evolved during the past ten years, enables direct microscopic visualization of sites at which chemical reactions occur. Although such reactions are not quantitative from a strict numerical standpoint, nevertheless they enable the histologist to detect with precision, for example, sites of high or low enzyme activity in individual cells. Thus, the great advantage of microscopic histochemistry lies in identification of chemical constituents and accuracy of localization even at the cytologic and electron microscopic levels.[10,25,28,29,34,47,63,73]

Several newer publications and reviews have appeared which deal with mucopolysaccharides, glycogen, and enzyme histochemical aspects of oral structures, including salivary glands.[9,90,104,111,112,115,118,120,121,122] New information has also been obtained relating to the histochemistry of sialic acid containing mucoproteins.[122] The fluorescent antibody technique and the fluorescence of tetracycline has also applied to the study of oral tissues (Fig. 271).[52,67,116,128] Several studies have been made on the enzyme and protein histochemistry of the so-called salivary corpuscles or salivary gland leukocytes.[106,110] The technique of oral exfoliative cytology for the detection of oral cancer has received considerable interest, but specialized cytochemicals have yet to be used in this area (Fig. 272).[13,76,89,108,113,136]

An interesting discussion of the various types of normal and abnormal cells to be found in the sputum is given in the text by Philps.[97] Of particular interest is the identification of metastatic lung carcinoma in the sputum.

Fig. 271. Submaxillary gland secreting mucus in which the A antigen is demonstrated by immunofluorescence using rabbit anti-A serum and goat antirabbit serum: fluorescein. Human fetus, 8 cm. crown-rump length. This secretion and the mucus-borne antigen persist throughout life. (Courtesy Dr. A. E. Szulman.)

Fig. 272. Nonspecific esterase activity of a smear of normal oral epithelium showing localization of azo-dye to cytoplasm of cells. (×310.)

A new concept related to selectively induced calcification called "calciphylaxis" has been presented by Selye.[114] According to this view, the mammalian body contains a defensive or phylactic system that enables the body to produce calcified deposits at localized sites.

By this means the effects of a pathogen can be reduced and local inflammatory responses initiated. As with some other tissues of the body, those of the oral cavity contain both connective tissue and epithelial components. Significant chemical constituents of these tissues are mucopolysaccharides, mucoproteins (glycoproteins), mucins (mucoids), and enzymes.

Structure and chemical composition of connective tissue. Connective tissue, which is derived from the mesenchyme, consists of specialized cells, fibers, and an amorphous ground substance.[47,57] The last two may form distinct structures such as in bone and cartilage. Although the specialized connective tissues exhibit morphologic diversity, they have many chemical similarities in common.

Specific cell types appear to be implicated in the production of intercellular fibers and ground substance components. Fibroblasts and osteoblasts, for example, are associated with the formation of collagenous fibers and mucopolysaccharides of the ground substance.[39,46,57] The latter are hexosamine-containing polysaccharides. Ground substance also has proteins which contain carbohydrates, and these are referred to as glycoproteins. Mucopolysaccharides, the acid type of which is widely distributed in nature, are of primary significance in connective tissue and presumably act as binding and protective agents. The acid mucopolysaccharides of the ground substance are polymers containing acetylated amino sugars and hexuronic acids. Among the best-known mucopolysaccharides are hyaluronic acid and chondroitin sulfuric acid. Hyaluronic acid forms viscous gels that are hydrolyzed by the enzyme hyaluronidase.

As previously indicated, glycoproteins are protein complexes containing protein, mucopolysaccharide, and, in specific instances, hexuronic acid. Histochemically, glycoproteins stain with basic stains such as hematoxylin. They also stain metachromatically with dyes such as toluidine blue. This dye, which ordinarily stains tissue components blue, will stain certain tissue components a red-violet shade (metachromatic reaction). Among the tissue components that stain metachromatically are mast cell granules and the intercellular substance of cartilage. The metachromatic reaction is believed to be related to the formation of aggregates of dye molecules upon glycoprotein complexes. Fibroblasts are known to be involved in the production of a series of acid mucopolysaccharides.

Relatively little mucopolysaccharide is found in bone and dentin upon chemical analysis.[87,99] The amount is usually less than 1 per cent. The remaining organic fraction of bone consists of approximately 93 per cent collagen, 5 per cent "resistant" protein, and 1.7 per cent citrate.[48] Dentin is stated to contain 0.5 per cent of chondroitin sulfate. A chrondroitin sulfuric acid-protein complex is known to occur in cartilage.

Although fibroblasts are known to synthesize collagen, the mechanism by which fibers are produced is still under study.[79] The connective tissue fibers are embedded in the ground substance in varying proportion and thus give tissues certain gross characteristics. The vitreous humor of the eye contains few fibers, whereas the dermis of the skin and the lamina propria of the gingiva have large numbers of collagenous fibers. Many fine fibers (reticulin) associated with a ground substance form the basement membranes of epithelial surfaces and parenchymatous organs. These fibers, which characteristically stain with silver, are also found in developing connective tissue.[102] Biophysical and chemical studies have shown that reticulin of the basement membrane is a collagen in close association with carbohydrate and lipid components.[141] Two types of reticulin have been distinguished to date.

Elastin is a relatively ill-defined protein characterized by its extreme insolubility.[78] It is not considered to be an important constituent of the final product of tissue repair. From the histochemical standpoint, caution should be exercised in interpretations of the staining reactions of fibrous elements based upon the use of nonspecific staining procedures.

As previously indicated, another group of conjugated proteins is exemplified by the glycoproteins, which play an important role in the structure and function of connective tissue (Fig. 273). Coiled chains of mucopolysaccharide are attached to a central protein core. Each repeating disaccharide unit has two negative charges representing sulfate and carboxyl groups.

The so-called nucleoproteins also form an important class of conjugated proteins. The latter are combinations of protein and a prosthetic or addition group. Nucleoproteins, for example, are composed of basic proteins in combina-

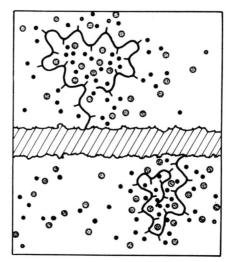

Fig. 273. Diagram of protein-mucopolysaccharide complex in connective tissue. Center core represents protein. Wavy line represents polysaccharide chain. Solid dots are sodium ions, and stippled dots are chloride ions. Background is water of the milieu. (From Dorfman, A.: J. Chron. Dis. **10**:403, 1959.)

tion with nucleic acids. The latter are complexes of purine and pyrimidine bases, sugar and phosphoric acid. Nucleoproteins constitute a major portion of nuclear chromatin. Deoxyribonucleic acid (DNA) may be visualized by the so-called Feulgen method.[63]

In addition to the basic views that cell function can be explained and controlled by enzyme activities, there are many other specific, nonenzyme proteins produced by cells. The limits of cellular capabilities appear to be determined to a large extent by the range of specific proteins that cells can synthesize. It is now believed that these limits are genetic and are restricted by the extent of genetic information coded in the DNA (deoxyribonucleic acid) of the cell nucleus. This genetic code is actuated through an intermediary RNA (ribonucleic acid) which translates genetic information into specific proteins by serving as a model for the protein. Thus, the interrelation of nucleic acids (DNA and RNA) and protein synthesis appears to play a fundamental role in the basic organization of the living cell. Young[142] has reviewed these factors with reference to protein synthesis and bone development by the application of autoradiography and other histochemical techniques. Other cytologic aspects of the cell relate the development of dentofacial structures, including defects in chromosomal changes or deletions.[65,141]

Epithelial tissues and derivatives. Details of the histochemical characteristics of the oral epithelium, the epithelial components of the tooth germ, and the salivary glands will be considered in another section of this chapter. Salivary glands contain the so-called "mucins" or "mucoids." The definition of this group is a chemical one from the biochemical standpoint and a morphologic-tinctorial one in some respects from the histochemical viewpoint. Histochemical detection of mucins generally is based upon their acid mucopolysaccharide content, which affects certain staining reactions. The acidic nature is due to the presence of glucuronic acid, sulfate, or sialic acid. Histochemical work has shown that a number of acid mucins lack sulfate esters.[121,122] The biochemical and histochemical aspects of oxidative metabolism of human oral tissues have also been reported.[5,53,93]

Ground substance in normal and abnormal conditions. Alterations in ground substance in various physiologic and pathologic states have been stressed by Gersh and Catchpole.[57] One concept suggests that depolymerization of mucopolysaccharides is reflected in a number of physiologic and pathologic changes. It is also possible that enzymatic hydrolysis of the protein component of the polysaccharide complex may be responsible for tissue alterations. The proteolytic enzyme plasmin has been found to hydrolyze the protein that binds acid mucopolysaccharide in cartilage.[83]

Enzymes. Enzymes may be considered as "living" molecular catalysts. They are proteins that catalyze a series of vital complex chemical reactions at body temperature.[124,130] Among these are synthetic, hydrolytic, and molecular transfer processes. Although over fifty enzymes have been obtained in the crystalline state, the biochemical knowledge as to their mechanism of action is incomplete.

It has been pointed out that no chemist has yet devised a catalyst that can carry out a reaction under mild conditions with the speed and selectivity of an enzyme catalyst. In the body, for example, there are enzymes which catalyze the reactions involved in blood clotting, enzymes which catalyze the reactions associated with digestion of food, and enzymes which catalyze the reactions associated with the synthesis of proteins from amino acids. In these complicated processes, which often involve a series of coupled reactions, each enzyme catalyzes its specific reaction with enormous speed and selectivity.[12] Through the evolutionary process, enzymes have arisen which exhibit these characteristics to a high degree. A particularly efficient enzyme, for example, is catalase, which has a turnover number of 10^6 per second.[12] The functional pharmacologic activity of drugs as they relate to metabolic structures has been linked to specific enzyme metabolism pathways, such as the glucose-6-phosphate phosphorylation system.[82]

Histochemistry has enabled the histologist to detect the actual sites of cellular and even intracellular enzyme activity. The topographic distribution of enzymes may be ascertained by the quantitative microchemical techniques developed by the Linderstøm-Lang group[59] or by techniques that result in the formation of visible dyes in tissue sections prepared for microscopic examination. The latter approach has been referred to as microscopic histochemistry, and it is the approach that will be considered in this chapter. During the last twenty years great advances have been made in the development of histochemical techniques for the demonstration of enzymes. The first histochemical enzyme technique was developed by Gomori in 1939 and demonstrated alkaline phosphatase.[63] During the last ten years new methods for the demonstration of aminopeptidase, succinic dehydrogenase, and cytochrome oxidase have been developed. The application of these techniques offers broad implications in the study of oral tissues in normal and pathologic conditions.[10,34]

HISTOCHEMICAL TECHNIQUES
Fixation procedures

Routine fixation procedures employing formalin or Zenker-formol solutions (see Appendix) are generally of little or no use in histochemistry. The same is true of decalcification with strong acids. These procedures not only inactivate enzymes but also denature proteins and thus alter the availability of their reactive groups. Therefore special methods of fixation had to be devised for use with histochemical techniques.

One of the simplest histochemical fixation procedures employs cold acetone or neutral formalin at 0° C. The low temperature obviates some of the deleterious effects of the fixative and at the same time facilitates mild protein denaturation.[25,63] In the case of some enzyme systems (e.g., cytochrome oxidase), unfixed tissues must be employed because of the labile nature of the enzyme. Although unfixed frozen sections retain high enzymatic activity, they are not generally recommended for histochemical procedures because the lability and solubility of the tissue constituents may give rise to serious diffusion artifacts.

One of the best types of fixation is the freeze-dry process originally devised by Altmann and subsequently developed by Gersh.[34,58] Tissues are frozen rapidly at low temperature, usually in liquid nitrogen. The frozen tissues are then placed in a refrigerated vacuum chamber where the ice in the tissues is removed by sublimation, i.e., by direct transformation into vapor without going through a liquid phase. This is the same process by which powdered human blood plasma is prepared. Following dehydration in vacuo, the specimens are embedded in paraffin and sectioned employing a standard microtome. Under optimal conditions, frozen-dried tissues exhibit excellent histologic characteristics and do not show shrinkage artifacts so commonly seen with aqueous fixatives. More important is the high degree of preservation of enzyme systems.[22,23,25]

Of greatest interest to the oral histologist and the pathologist are histochemical studies of teeth and bone in health and disease. As previously indicated, routine fixation plus decalcification of hard tissues may make any final chemical interpretation of a staining reaction difficult. Frequently, histochemical stains may be used on routinely fixed and decalcified hard tissues, with questionable results. In specific cases, however, carefully controlled decalcification in cold buffered solutions may be of value.[5,68]

A simultaneous formalin fixation and ethylene diaminated EDTA decalcification, with Carbowax embedding for the demonstration of acid phosphatase by an azo-dye method, has been described by Manning and Butler.[85] Techniques have been developed that make it possible to section certain types of frozen-dried undecalcified tissues.[29] In other cases ground sections may be prepared of undecalcified material.[21] Gray and Opdyke have described a saw for the preparation of undecalcified bone 10 to 50 microns in thickness.[66] Such sections have been employed in histochemical studies of dental decay.[94]

Specific histochemical methods

The histochemical techniques that have been primarily employed in the study of oral tissues may be classified as (1) protein and lipid methods, (2) polysaccharide and mucin methods, and (3) enzyme methods. They are all characterized by a direct staining reaction or by the formation of an insoluble dye or precipitate at the reactive site.

The mucopolysaccharide, mucoprotein, and mucin methods depend upon the use of nonspecific stains (e.g., Alcian blue) or semispecific stains (e.g., periodic acid-Schiff) that, under defined conditions, react to identify the chemical complex being studied.

Protein group methods are more specific and usually are based upon known classical reactions of protein chemistry. They employ reagents such as dinitrofluorobenzene or ninhydrin in reactions that give rise to insoluble colored products.[26]

Lipid methods employ nonspecific stains that have empirically been found to possess a strong affinity for fats.

The enzyme techniques utilize several different principles.[34] The Gomori method for alkaline or acid phosphatase uses phosphoric esters of glycerol, glucose, or adenosine. The enzymatically liberated phosphate ion is converted into an insoluble salt, and this is subsequently visualized by transformation into a cobalt compound.[63] Another procedure, originally developed by Menten, Jung, and Green, is referred to as the azo-dye technique.[88] It employs a naphthol phosphate or other type of ester. The enzymatically released naphthol is coupled in situ with a diazonium salt to form an insoluble dye. With regard to the original glycerophosphate technique, it has been shown that calcium phosphate, one of the reaction products, may diffuse and give false localizations on developing bone.[61] The tendency for this to occur is most likely in the pH range between 7.2 and 8.4. Because of this and other considerations, the azo-dye phosphatase techniques are probably the best for the study of teeth and bones.[28,29] Sophisticated new substrates for use with the azo-dye technique have been developed in recent years. They facilitate precise microscopic localization of alkaline and acid phosphatases as well as esterases.[24,31] Aminopeptidase can also be detected by an azo-dye method.[23] Recently the demonstration of phosphatase activity by ultraviolet fluorescence has been reported.[31]

There is little question that the future of histochemical research is primarily dependent upon the development and synthesis of new organic reagents for the visualization of intracellular chemical substituents. One of the important areas of research is the application of histochemical techniques to electron microscopy.

Protein and lipid histochemistry of oral hard tissues

The ground substance of the oral tissues, including bone, stains with a number of histochemical procedures. Among these are techniques for the demonstration of carbohydrate groupings, the best known of which is the periodic acid–Schiff (pa-S) technique.[62] The chemical basis of this method lies in the fact that periodic acid oxidizes glycols with vicinal hydroxyl groups to aldehydes, which in turn are revealed as a colored dye by leukofuchsin. This colorless reagent thus results in formation of a red dye when reacted with aldehydes formed in tissues.

The periodic acid–Schiff method is believed to demonstrate under specific conditions the carbohydrate moiety of a glycoprotein complex.[57] This technique probably has been employed more than any other in studying the ground sub-

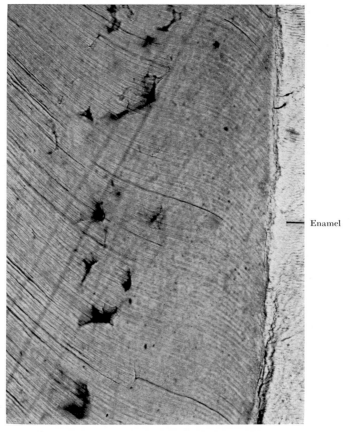

Enamel

Fig. 274. Ground section of human tooth showing periodic acid–Schiff reactivity of interglobular dentin. (×143.)

Plate 4. Photographs of several histochemical reactions. **A,** Ground section of human dentin. Dinitrofluorobenzene (DNFB) technique reveals reactive protein groups of interglobular areas. (×143.) **B,** Ground section of human odontoma, showing periodic acid–Schiff reaction of poorly calcified dentin. (×85.) **C,** Alcian blue staining of isolated group of mucous cells in a dog parotid gland. Mucicarmine counterstain. (×143.) **D,** Alkaline phosphatase activity of basement membranes of a rat sublingual gland. (×143.)

stance of teeth and bones.[26,46,50] The ground substance of normal mature bone and dentin exhibits little or no reactivity with the pa-S technique (Fig. 274).[21,50] However, resorbing bone or dentin is intensely stained.[21] Newly formed bone and dentin are also quite reactive.[21,84] This staining reaction has been interpreted to indicate changes in the submicroscopic state of organization of the ground substance.[56]

Interglobular less calcified dentin exhibits a distinct pa-S reaction (Fig. 274), as does the abnormal poorly calcified dentin matrix in dentinogenesis imperfecta and in odontomas (Plate 4, A).

Enamel matrix is essentially nonreactive with the pa-S method. However, enamel lamellae are intensely stained in ground sections (Fig. 275). In some areas the rod interprismatic substance exhibits some reactivity.

Specific protein methods identify certain amino acids or their groupings (e.g., amino, carboxyl).[26] Only a few of these techniques have been applied in the study of teeth and bone. Of interest are the dinitrofluorobenzene (DNFB) and

Fig. 275. Ground section of human enamel. Lamella stains with periodic acid–Schiff method. (×143.)

ninhydrin-Schiff methods. The DNFB reagent combines with alpha-amino groups of proteins in tissue sections to form a pale yellow complex. An intense reddish color is subsequently revealed by a reduction and diazotization technique which results in the formation of an azo-dye (Plate 4, A). The pattern of staining is essentially the same as seen with the pa-S method in both normal and abnormal dentin. The ninhydrin-Schiff method is specific for amino acids and is based on the classical ninhydrin reaction of protein chemistry.

Some of the previously discussed techniques have found application in the study of dental caries and bone and dentin resorption.[21,24,50,90]

Biochemical studies indicate a rather low lipid content of the organic matrix of dentin.[74,98,119] Histochemical studies have demonstrated the presence of lipids by the sudanophilic reaction in the odontoblastic processes and enamel rod sheaths.[117] More recent work has shown a fairly widespread lipid distribution throughout the developing tooth, with a distinct sudanophilia in the basal zone of the ameloblasts.[126] This reactive ameloblastic zone is also believed to delineate phospholipid associated with enamel matrix formation.

Polysaccharide, protein, and mucin histochemistry of oral soft tissues

Polysaccharides. The previously discussed pa-S reaction, when used in conjunction with specific tests, is a highly accurate method for the demonstration of glycogen. Carmine, a dye, has also been used to demonstrate glycogen, but it is not so specific as the pa-S method. Epithelial glycogen is known to increase during inflammation and repair.[18,45,105,131] Human attached gingiva, which is variable in keratinization, exhibits a variable glycogen content. On the other hand, the nonkeratinized alveolar mucosa virtually always contains glycogen.[138] Of interest are animal experiments that also demonstrate an increase in glycogen in benign and malignant epithelial proliferations.

The so-called "mast cells" were first reported by Ehrlich in 1879. They are readily found in various connective tissues throughout the body. Mast cells appear most prominently in acute, less so in chronic, inflammation. Mast cells are also known to contain histamine, thus further implicating them in the inflammatory processes.[100] Their staining with metachromatic dyes and certain biochemical features indicate the presence of a sulfated mucopolysaccharide.[54] Mast cells in the human gingiva have been studied in normal and pathologic states.[38] It was found that the number of mast cells decreases adjacent to the gingival sulcus. In acute necrotizing gingivitis there is a lack of mast cells.

Proteins and protein groups. Glycoproteins in human gingiva have been studied by means of the periodic acid–Schiff method.[51] The reticular fibers comprising the basement membrane are discretely stained. The lamina propria exhibits reactive elements that include collagenous, reticular, and elastic fibers. The amorphous ground substance also exhibits a variable degree of staining in suitably fixed material (e.g., frozen-dried). Study of gingiva with newer definitive protein group and amino acid methods should be undertaken.[26]

Keratinization is one of the important characteristics of the epidermis and some areas of the oral epithelium in normal and abnormal conditions. The mechanism by which cells of the malpighian layer are altered to form keratin has been only partly elucidated. The disulfide bridges in keratin are believed to result from the oxidation of sulfhydryl groups of cysteine.[135] Histochemical study of sulfhydryls and disulfides of gingiva has been reported.[132] However, further work is required to determine the precise changes of these groups in normal and pathologic states.

Mucins. Mucins found in saliva function to form a protective coating on the oral mucous membranes and also act as a lubricant. Mucins (mucosubstances) contain high molecular weight protein-carbohydrate compounds known as glycoproteins, which are capable of forming viscous fluids and water-soluble gels. Of interest is the fact that few enzymatic properties can be attributed to them. Two types of glycoproteins occur in the mucus of salivary glands. One contains L-fucose as its primary carbohydrate component and has been called fucomucin.[8] The other predominating type of mucin glycoprotein contains sialic acid in conjunction with an N-acetylhexosamine, and it is referred to as sialomucin.[15] Both fucomucins and sialomucins are found together in secretions, with one usually predominating over the other. Submandibular glands contain high sialomucin content.[86] Sialic acid is believed to confer acidity upon certain mucins.

Fig. 276. Frozen-dried mouse submandibular gland, *A,* and sublingual gland, *B,* showing periodic acid–Schiff reactivity of mucins. (×140.)

For purposes of definition, sialic acid refers to the acetylated derivatives of neuraminic acid.[16]

The use of histochemical techniques has greatly added to our knowledge of the histologic and cytologic localization of salivary gland mucins and their specific chemical constituents.[19,121] From a histochemical standpoint mucins may be identified on the basis of either nonspecific stains or by the use of reactions that have a known chemical basis. A nonspecific but highly useful reaction may be obtained with the dyes mucicarmine or mucihematin. Salivary gland mucins can also be stained by the use of the pa-S reaction (Fig. 276), aldehyde fuchsin, colloidal iron, and Alcian blue (Plate 4, *C*).[64] However, the staining reaction is variable, and species differences can be observed. Only recently have careful studies been undertaken to elucidate the chemical basis of such staining differences.

Enzyme histochemistry of oral tissues

As previously mentioned, enzymes are considered to be the biologic catalysts that control the rate of chemical reactions in bone as well as in other tissues. Definitive study of enzymes in hard tissues by means of routine *biochemical* procedures presents certain technical problems, since calcifying tissues are non-homogenous systems containing different types of cells and intercellular substance. On the other hand, *histochemical* techniques offer excellent possibilities for visualizing specific enzymes of the cellular elements in bone and dentin.

Until recently, alkaline phosphatase was given foremost consideration in histochemical studies. This is due primarily to the impetus given to modern microscopic histochemistry by the original phosphatase technique of Gomori. Application of this technique in the study of calcifying tissues has been reviewed in the text edited by Bourne.[17] More recently, histochemical localization of a number of hydrolases associated with the development of hard tissues has been reported.[28, 29] The azo-dye methods are the most desirable for studying undecalcified hard tissues since they are not affected by the presence of inorganic bone salts.

Alkaline phosphatase. The enzyme alkaline phosphatase, which has a pH optimum of around 9, is capable of hydrolyzing a number of naturally occurring as well as synthetic phosphoric acid esters. The function of alkaline phosphatase has been implicated in the synthesis of fibrous proteins and also in the passage of metabolites across cell membranes. No studies of this enzyme in human dentinogenesis have been reported. However, in animal material a marked enzymatic reaction is observed to be associated with dentinogenesis as well as osteogenesis (Figs. 277 and 278). The cytoplasm and cytoplasmic processes of osteoblasts stain intensely. The same sharply delineated reaction is also observed at neutral pH and pH 7.5. No enzyme activity is found in bone or dentin matrices per se except at the very periphery. However, fibers entering the matrix are active. Of interest is the fact that nuclear staining is never observed with the azo-dye

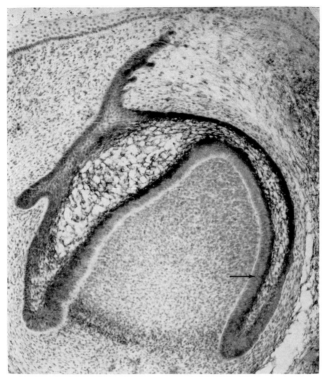

Fig. 277. Alkaline phosphatase reaction of a tooth of a monkey embryo. The ameloblastic layer (arrow) is nonreactive. (×87.)

methods.[28,29,125] Intramembranous bone formation reveals enzymatic activity of endosteum, periosteum, and osteocytes. In the case of intracartilaginous bone, high activity is associated with the matrices and cells of the hypertrophic and provisional zones of calcification. The active perichondrium is selectively and strongly stained. (See Table 6.)

In the developing molar, as well as in most of the incisor, activity is limited to the stratum intermedium, odontoblasts, and subjacent pulp (Fig. 278). Staining of Korff's fibers is also observed. No ameloblastic enzyme activity is apparent. The staining reaction in the incisors of rodents is similar with one important exception. This consists of a reaction of ameloblasts and reduced enamel organ at the incisal end of the tooth. (See Table 6.) The remaining ameloblasts, as in the molar, are unstained. The possible existence of alkaline phosphatase activity of dentin has been investigated by several workers.[11,82]

Acid phosphatase. Acid phosphatase is less widely distributed than its alkaline counterpart (Table 6). The optimal pH lies in the range of 5 to 6. Osteoclasts exhibit a striking acid phosphatase reaction.[25,28,29,99] (See Fig. 279.) It is of interest that phagocytic cells (e.g., macrophages) also show high acid phosphatase activity. This suggests that osteoclasts may be biochemically related to for-

Fig. 278. Frozen-dried undecalcified incisor of a hamster. *A,* Stratum intermedium; *B,* ameloblasts; *C,* enamel matrix; *D,* dentin matrix; *E,* odontoblasts. Note alkaline phosphatase reactivity of Korff's fibers and subjacent pulp. (×87.)

eign body giant cells. In vivo uptake of radioactive plutonium by osteoclasts has been reported.[2]

The structural and functional relationships in the osteoclast have been reviewed with reference to both histochemical and electron microscopic techniques.[71,72] This finding further suggests a possible phagocytic function. It is important to note that the high activity of two distinct enzymes, acid and alkaline phosphatase, is associated with osteoclasts and osteoblasts, respectively.[29] This tends to confirm the view that tissues endowed with intense alkaline phosphatase activity are practically devoid of acid phosphatase activity.[103] Tissue sections of bone and dentin matrices are capable of hydrolyzing phosphate esters at an acid pH. The reaction is diminished by known acid phosphate inhibitors.

Esterase. Esterases, according to histochemical definition, are enzymes which hydrolyze simpler fatty acid esters (e.g., acetates and butyrates). They also exhibit certain inhibitory preferences as contrasted with the enzymes (lipases) that hydrolyze more complex fatty acid esters.[63]

Table 6. Phosphatase activity of cellular elements associated with calcification (short incubation)*

	Alkaline phosphatase	Acid phosphatase
Bone		
Osteoblasts	+	0
Osteocytes	+	0
Osteoclasts	0	+
Cartilage		
Active perichondrocyte†	+	0
Resting chondrocyte	0	0
Hypertrophic chondrocyte	+	0
Tooth		
Stellate reticulum	+	0
Stratum intermedium	+	0
Ameloblasts‡	0	0
Odontoblasts, fibers, and subjacent pulp	+	0

0 = No reaction. + = High activity.
*From Burstone, M. S.: Hydrolytic enzymes in dentinogenesis and osteogenesis. In Sognnaes, R. F. (editor): Calcification in biological systems, Washington, D. C., 1960, American Association for the Advancement of Science, p. 217.
†From perichondrium.
‡Ameloblasts at incisal end of rodent incisor show high enzymatic activity.

Fig. 279. Acid phosphatase reaction of an osteoclast in Howship's lacuna. Frozen-dried undecalcified alveolar bone of a hamster, nuclear counterstain. (×750.)

Most histochemical techniques for the demonstration of esterases reveal no reactivity of tooth and bone structure. However, one specific type of ester substrate is rapidly hydrolyzed by developing bone and dentin matrices.[3] Of interest is the fact that certain ester substrates are also hydrolyzed by proteolytic enzymes.

Considerable esterase activity has also been found in the cells and microorganisms associated with the formation of deposits on teeth (calculus).[19]

Aminopeptidase. Aminopeptidases are proteolytic enzymes that hydrolyze certain terminal peptide bonds. In recent years an azo-dye technique has been developed for the histochemical demonstration of the enzyme, employing L-leucyl-β-naphthylamide or DL-alanyl-β-naphthylamide as synthetic substrates.[23,25] Osteoclasts in the human being exhibit an intense staining reaction, whereas those of other species (rodents) are unstained.[29] In the developing rodent dentition there is a distinct reaction of the stratum intermedium and the odontoblasts. There is some staining of the periosteum. Chondrocytes as well as the perichondrium are also reactive.

The biochemical function of aminopeptidase is not clear. It is of interest, however, that macrophages show intense activity, as do certain sites associated with breakdown of connective tissue.[25] It has been reported that osteoclasts in vivo have strong proteolytic abilities and are capable of liquefying a plasma clot.[71]

Cytochrome oxidase. The enzyme cytochrome oxidase is widely distributed in living organisms.[124] It is an iron-porphyrin-protein compound that enables cells to utilize molecular oxygen. Cytochrome oxidase is found in mitochondria. Cardiac and skeletal muscle, which are known to exhibit high oxygen consumption, likewise show high cytochrome oxidase activity (Fig. 280).

Fig. 280. Cytochrome oxidase activity of tongue muscle of a rat. (×100.)

In 1885 Ehrlich found that if α-naphthol and N,N-dimethyl-p-phenylene-diamine were injected into living tissue, a blue dye was formed in vivo. This is referred to as the "nadi" reaction from the first two letters of *naphthol* and *diamine*. Unfortunately, the "nadi" reaction is not adequate for microscopic localizations because the blue dye formed diffuses badly, is fat soluble, and fades. During the last few years, new definitive histochemical techniques for the demonstration of cytochrome oxidase have been developed.[27,30] These enable microscopic localization of the enzyme even at the mitochondrial level. Both osteoclasts and osteoblasts show activity, with the staining of the former predominating (Fig. 281).[28] This certainly suggests high metabolic activity of osteoclasts associated with physiologic bone resorption. The stratum intermedium of both molars and incisors also exhibits high oxidase activity.

Succinic dehydrogenase. Succinic dehydrogenase is an enzyme that is closely associated with cytochrome oxidase in cell mitochondria. It is one of a series of enzymes widely distributed in animal tissues which catalyzes the removal of hydrogen. In order that the reaction be continuous, the liberated hydrogen has

Stratum intermedium of adjacent tooth

Fig. 281. Cytochrome oxidase activity of osteoclasts in the jaw of a hamster. (×110.)

Table 7. Enzyme activity of cells associated with bones and teeth

	Alkaline phosphatase*	Acid phosphatase*	Amino-peptidase†	Cytochrome oxidase†	Succinic de-hydrogenase†
Bone					
Osteoblasts	++	0	+	+	+
Osteocytes	++	0	+	+	+
Osteoclasts	0	++	?	++	++
Cartilage					
Active peri-chondrocyte	++	0	++	++	++
Resting chondrocyte	0	0	+	+	+
Hypertrophic chondrocyte	++	0	+	+	+
Tooth					
Stellate reticulum	++	0	+	+	+
Stratum intermedium	++	0	+	+	+
Ameloblasts (molar)	0	0	0	0 or +	0
Odontoblasts	+ or ++	0	+	+	+

0 = No staining. + = Less active. ++ = More active.
*Frozen-dried paraffin-embedded tissues.
†Fresh-frozen tissues.

to be constantly removed by so-called "acceptors" or "carriers." Succinic de-hydrogenase dehydrogenates succinic acid to fumaric acid in the presence of a hydrogen acceptor.[124]

This enzyme usually is demonstrated by the use of colorless compounds called tetrazoles, which are changed by reducing sites (dehydrogenase) into a colored dye (formazan).[63]

In hard tissues, high dehydrogenase activity is found in osteoclasts but not in osteoblasts.[28] The stratum intermedium and the odontoblasts in developing teeth are also stained. The distribution of cytochrome oxidase and succinic dehydrogenase in oral tissues is essentially similar.

Citric acid cycle in osteoblasts and osteoclasts. A study of some of the oxidative enzymes of the Krebs citric acid cycle, including methods for the demonstration of DPNH-TPNH-diaphorases as well as alpha-ketoglutaric and isocitric dehydrognase activity, has been reported.[137] It is indicated that the osteoblasts, by maintaining a high rate of citrate and lactate production at the expense of glutamate, actively promote decalcification of the matrix of bone and calcified cartilage.

Summary. The enzymatic cellular components associated with bones and teeth are summarized in Table 7.

It is interesting to note that sites of high activity involving a number of different enzymes are to be found in the same structure (e.g., stratum intermedium). As new enzyme techniques are developed, the state of our knowledge of the cytochemistry of oral tissues in normal and pathologic conditions will be enhanced considerably.

Enzyme histochemistry of oral soft tissues

Alkaline phosphatase. In human gingiva alkaline phosphatase has been observed in the capillary endothelium of the lamina propria (Fig. 282).[134,135] Phosphatase activity ascribed to collagenous fibers may be genuine or may be a staining artifact. A staining reaction of the epithelium per se is the result of diffusion of the enzyme reaction products. On the other hand, polymorphonuclear leukocytes exhibit a genuine activity.

The oral epithelium of the rat exhibits an increased alkaline phosphatase activity during the estrous cycle, which also can be correlated with phosphatase changes in the vaginal epithelium.[101] Although alkaline phosphatase may be related to keratinization, its precise role cannot be ascertained until more is known about the function of this enzyme.

The basement membranes associated with salivary gland acini exhibit high alkaline phosphatase activity (Plate 4, *D*).[33]

Phosphatase activity of taste buds of several species has also been observed.[6,8]

Acid phosphatase. Our knowledge of the distribution of acid phosphatase in

Fig. 282. Alkaline phosphatase activity of capillaries of the lamina propria of human gingiva revealed by ultraviolet fluorescence. (×80.)

Fig. 283. Mast cells of a rat tongue incubated with substrates solution containing naphthol AS-D choloroacetate. (×250.)

human gingiva is incomplete. Studies with the glycerophosphate method indicate a primary staining reaction in the superficial layers, with the exception of the keratinized zone.[35] This pattern appears to correspond with that observed in the skin.[91] High activity is seen in macrophages in chronic inflammation (Fig. 283).[13] Further studies of this enzyme with newer histochemical techniques are obviously desirable.

Esterase. Little information is available on the esterase activity of human gingiva. A reaction is usually observed in the more superficial layers of the gingival epithelium, including the keratinizing zone.[133]

High esterase activity is found in salivary gland ducts and also in demilunes of the sublingual gland (Figs. 284 and 285).[22] A similar activity is observed in the taste buds of several species and has been related to gustatory discrimination.[6,7]

A specific type of esterases which hydrolyzes naphthyl chloroacetate acetate has been described by Gomori[63] and Burstone.[133] The use of a complex naphthol substrate, naphthol AS-D chloroacetate results in visualization of mast cells in tissues (Fig. 283).

Aminopeptidase. The activity of the enzyme aminopeptidase in human gingiva is low, with the exception of that found in polymorphonuclear leukocytes.

Aminopeptidase is also found in human salivary gland ducts.[23] With the development of newer, more sensitive methods, significant information on the

Fig. 284. Esterase activity of ducts of frozen-dried human parotid gland (nuclear counter-stain). (×110.)

Fig. 285. Esterase activity of demilune cells of frozen-dried human sublingual gland. (×210.)

distribution and role of proteolytic enzymes in the oral tissues should be obtained.

β-glucuronidases. The β-glucuronidases represent a group of enzymes that are capable of hydrolyzing the β-glycoside linkage of a number of naturally occurring and synthetic glucoronides. β-glucuronidase is found in all animal tissues, but highest activity is found in the liver, kidney, and spleen. The enzyme is believed to have three roles: the conjugation of steroid hormones, the hydrolysis of conjugated glucuronides, and a role in cellular proliferations.[55]

Activity is observed in the basal cell layers of the oral tissues of man and rat, suggesting a possible role in cellular proliferation.[36,37]

Cytochrome oxidase and succinic dehydrogenase. Studies of the enzymes cytochrome oxidase and succinic dehydrogenase in human gingiva have been made using primarily biochemical methods, and activity has been found to be relatively low.

With the application of new histochemical techniques, the precise sites of oxidase activity in normal and inflamed gingiva have been observed.[28] With these

Fig. 286. Human attached gingiva showing cytochrome oxidase activity of basal cell layer and in connective tissue of the lamina propria.

Fig. 287. Cytochrome oxidase activity of human parotid gland. (×143.)

Fig. 288. Phosphorylase activity of rat tongue muscle. (×70.)

techniques, cytochrome oxidase activity was also found to be low and was observed in the crevicular epithelium, epithelial attachment, and basal cell layer of the free and the attached gingiva (Fig. 286). In chronic gingivitis a striking increase in activity is manifested in the epithelium from the free gingival groove through the epithelial attachment. The underlying connective tissue stroma exhibits a variable increase.

Biochemical studies have shown rather high oxidase levels in the salivary glands.[96] With histochemical methods the ducts exhibit predominant staining (Fig. 287).[27,30]

Studies of succinic dehydrogenase have been made primarily with biochemical techniques. From the histochemical standpoint the basal cell zone of human gingiva exhibits the highest reducing activity.[49] Salivary gland ducts exhibit a distinct staining reaction with the tetrazole histochemical techniques.[92]

Phosphorylases. Phosphorylase or amylophosphorylase is a transferase, i.e., an enzyme that catalyzes the transfer of radicals such as phosphate or acetyl. In the case of phosphorylase, tissue glycogen undergoes an esterification reaction to form glucose-l-phosphate. When phosphorylase is demonstrated by histochemical means, skeletal muscle is intensely stained (Fig. 288).[124,129]

REFERENCES

1. Argyris, T. S.: Glycogen in the epidermis of mice painted with methylchol-anthrene, J. Nat. Cancer Inst. **12:**1159, 1952.
2. Arnold, J. S., and Jee, W. S. S.: Bone growth and osteoclastic activity as indicated by radioautographic distribution of plutonium, Am. J. Anat. **101:**367, 1957.
3. Baer, P. N., and Burstone, M. S.: Esterase activity associated with formation of deposits on teeth, Oral Surg., Oral Med. & Oral Path. **12:**1147, 1959.
4. Balogh, Károly, Jr.: Decalcification with versene for histochemical study of oxidative enzyme systems, J. Histochem. & Cytochem. **10:**232, 1962.
5. Balogh, Károly: Histochemical study of oxidative enzyme systems in teeth and peridental tissues, J. D. Res. **42:**1457, 1963.
6. Baradi, A. F., and Bourne, G. H.: Gustatory and olfactory epithelia. In Bourne, G. H., and Danielli, J. F. (editors): International review of cytology, vol. 2, New York, 1953, Academic Press, p. 289.
7. Baradi, A. F., and Bourne, G. H.: Histochemical localization of cholinesterase in gustatory epithelia, J. Histochem. & Cytochem. **7:**2, 1959.
8. Baradi, A. F., and Bourne, G. H.: New observations on alkaline glycophosphatase reaction in the papilla foliata, J. Biophys. & Biochem. Cytol. **5:**173, 1959.
9. Baratieri, A.: Biologia della polpa e della dentinogenesi: istochimica-cenni su alcune anomalie della dentinogenesi, Riv. Ital. Stomat. **14:**237, 1964.
10. Barka, Tibor, and Anderson, Paul J.: Histochemistry, theory, practice, and bibliography, New York, 1963, Harper & Row.
11. Baumgärtner, F., and Cremer, H. D.: Verschiedene Methoden zur Bestimmung der Phosphataseaktivität in Rinderzahnen, Arch. Oral. Biol. **1:**8, 1959.
12. Bender, Myron L.: Enzymes, Chem. & Engin. News **40:**64, 1962.
13. Bennett, Carroll G.: Study of exfoliative cytology of oral mucosa of children exhibiting clinical evidence of ectodermal dysplasia, J. D. Res. **42:**943, 1963.
14. Blix, G.: Neuere Forschungsergebnisse über tierische Glykoproteide und Mucopolysaccharide, Angew. Chem. **62:**171, 1950.
15. Blix, G., Svennerholm, L., and Werner, I.: The isolation of chondrosamine from gangliosides and from submaxillary mucin, Acta chem. scandinav. **6:**358, 1952.

16. Blix, G., Gattschalk, A., and Klenk, E.: Proposed nomenclature in the field of neuraminic and sialic acids, Nature **179**:1088, 1957.

17. Bourne, G. H. (editor): The biochemistry and physiology of bone, New York, 1956, Academic Press.

18. Bradfield, J. R. G.: Glycogen of the vertebrate epidermis, Nature **167**:40, 1951.

19. Burstone, M. S.: A cytologic study of salivary glands of the mouse tongue, J. D. Res. **32**:126, 1953.

20. Burstone, M. S.: Enzyme histochemistry and cytochemistry. In Bourne, G. H. (editor): Cytology and cell physiology, New York, 1964, Academic Press.

21. Burstone, M. S.: The ground substance of abnormal dentin, secondary dentin, and pulp calcification, J. D. Res. **32**:269, 1953.

22. Burstone, M. S.: Esterase of the salivary glands, J. Histochem. & Cytochem. **4**:130, 1956.

23. Burstone, M. S., and Folk, J. E.: Histochemical demonstration of aminopeptidase, J. Histochem. & Cytochem. **4**:217, 1956.

24. Burstone, M. S., and Keyes, P. H.: Studies on calcification. I. The effect of inhibition of enzyme activity on developing bone and dentin, Am. J. Path. **33**:1229, 1957.

25. Burstone, M. S.: The relationship between fixation and techniques for the histochemical localization of hydrolytic enzymes, J. Histochem. & Cytochem. **6**:322, 1958.

26. Burstone, M. S.: Histochemical methods for protein detection, Handbuch der Histochemic, vol. 3, pt. 2, Stuttgart, 1959, Gustav Fischer Verlag.

27. Burstone, M. S.: New histochemical techniques for the demonstration of tissue-oxidase (cytochrome oxidase), J. Histochem. & Cytochem. **7**:112, 1959.

28. Burstone, M. S.: Histochemical observations on enzymatic processes in bones and teeth, Ann. New York Acad. Sc. **85**:431, 1960.

29. Burstone, M. S.: Hydrolytic enzymes in dentinogenesis and osteogenesis. In Sognnaes, R. F. (editor): Calcification in biological systems, Washington, D. C., 1960, American Association for the Advancement of Science, p. 217.

30. Burstone, M. S.: Histochemical demonstration of cytochrome oxidase with new amino reagents, J. Histochem. & Cytochem. **8**:63, 1960.

31. Burstone, M. S.: Postcoupling, noncoupling, and fluorescence techniques for the demonstration of alkaline phosphatase, J. Nat. Cancer Inst. **24**:1199, 1960.

32. Burstone, M. S.: Histochemical study of cytochrome oxidase in normal and inflamed gingiva, Oral Surg., Oral Med. & Oral Path. **13**:1501, 1960.

33. Burstone, M. S.: Histochemical demonstration of phosphatases in frozen sections with naphthol AS-phosphates, J. Histochem. & Cytochem. **9**:146, 1961.

34. Burstone, M. S.: Enzyme histochemistry and its application in the study of neoplasms, New York, 1962, Academic Press, Inc.

35. Cabrini, R. L., and Carranza, F. A.: Histochemical distribution of acid phosphatase in human gingiva, J. Periodont. **29**:34, 1958.

36. Cabrini, R. L., and Carranza, F. A.: Histochemical localization of β-glucuronidase in stratified squamous epithelium, Naturwiss. **22**:553, 1958.

37. Cabrini, R. L., and Carranza, F. A.: Histochemical distribution of beta-glucuronidase in gingival tissue, Arch. Oral Biol. **2**:28, 1960.

38. Carranza, F., and Cabrini, R. L.: Mast cells in human gingiva, Oral Surg., Oral Med. & Oral Path. **8**:1093, 1955.

39. Chapman, J. A.: Fibroblasts and collagen, Brit. M. Bull. **18**:233, 1962.

40. Clark, George L.: The encyclopedia of microscopy, New York, 1961, Reinhold Publishing Corp.

41. Cobb, J. D.: Relation of glycogen, phosphorylase, and ground substance to calcification of bone, Arch. Path. **55**:469, 1953.

42. Comar, C. L., and Bronner, Felix (editors): Mineral metabolism, vol. 1, Part A, New York, 1960, Academic Press, Inc.

43. Comar, C. L., and Bronner, Felix (editors): Mineral metabolism, vol. 1, Part B, New York, 1960, Academic Press, Inc.

44. Cooke, Brian E.: Exfoliative cytology in evaluating oral lesions, J. D. Res. **42**(supp.): 343, 1963.
45. Dewar, M. R.: Observations on the compositions and metabolism of normal and inflamed gingiva, J. Periodont. **26**:29, 1955.
46. Dorfman, A.: The biochemistry of connective tissue, J. Chronic Dis. **10**:403, 1959.
47. Downes, Helen R.: The chemistry of living cells, ed. 2, New York, 1962, Harper & Row.
48. Eastoe, J. E.: The organic matrix of bone. In Bourne, G. H. (editor): The biochemistry and physiology of bone, New York, 1956, Academic Press.
49. Eichel, B.: Oxidative enzymes of gingiva, Ann. New York Acad. Sc. **85**:479, 1960.
50. Engel, M. B.: The softening and solution of dentin in caries, J.A.D.A. **40**:284, 1950.
51. Engel, M. B., Ray, H., and Orban, B.: The pathogenesis of desquamative gingivitis, a disturbance of the connective tissue ground substance, J. D. Res. **29**:410, 1950.
52. Eveland, Warren C.: Fluorescent antibody technique in medical diagnosis, Current Med. Digest **31**:351, 1964.
53. Felton, Joseph H., Person, Philip, and Stahl, S. Sigmund: Biochemical and histochemical studies of aeorbic oxidative metabolism of oral tissues. II. Enzymatic dissection of gingival and tongue epithelia from connective tissues, J. D. Res. **44**:392, 1965.
54. Fisher, E. R.: Tissue mast cells, J.A.M.A. **173**:171, 1960.
55. Fishman, W.: β-Glucuronidase. In Sumner, J. B., and Myrbäck, K. (editors): The enzymes: chemistry and mechanism of action, vol. 1, New York, 1950, Academic Press, p. 635.
56. Gersh, I.: Ground substance and the plasticity of connective tissues, Harvey Lectures, Series XLV, Springfield, Ill., 1949-1950, Charles C Thomas, Publisher.
57. Gersh, I., and Catchpole, J.: The organization of ground substance and basement membrane and its significance in tissue injury, disease, and growth, Am. J. Anat. **85**:457, 1949.
58. Gersh, I., and Stephenson, J.: Freezing and drying of tissues for morphological and histochemical studies. In Harris, R. J. C. (editor): Biological applications of freezing and drying, New York, 1954, Academic Press, p. 329.
59. Glick, D.: Techniques of histo- and cyto-chemistry, New York, 1949, Interscience Publishers, Inc.
60. Goldman, Henry M., Ruben, Morris P., and Sherman, Donald: The application of laser spectroscopy for the qualitative and quantitative analyses of the inorganic components of calcified tissues, Oral Surg., Oral Med. & Oral Path. **17**:102, 1964.
61. Gomori, G.: Sources of errors in enzymatic histochemistry, J. Lab. & Clin. Med. **35**:802, 1950.
62. Gomori, G.: The periodic acid-Schiff stain, Am. J. Clin. Path. **22**:277, 1952.
63. Gomori, G.: Microscopic histochemistry: principles and practice, Chicago, 1952, University of Chicago Press.
64. Gomori, G.: The histochemistry of mucopolysaccharides, Brit. J. Exper. Path. **35**:377, 1954.
65. Gorlin, Robert J., Redman, Robert S., and Shapiro, Burton L.: Effect of X chromosome aneuploidy on jaw growth, J. D. Res. **44**(supp.):269, 1965.
66. Gray, J. A., and Opdyke, D. L.: A device for thin sectioning of hard tissues, J. D. Res. **41**:172, 1962.
67. Gregg, John M.: Analysis of tooth eruption and alveolar bone growth utilizing tetracycline fluorescence, J. D. Res. **43**(supp.):887, 1964.
68. Greep, R. O., Fischer, C. J., and Morse, A.: Alkaline phosphatase in odontogenesis and osteogenesis and its histochemical demonstration after demineralization, J.A.D.A. **36**:427, 1948.
69. Gustafson, Gösta: The histopathology of caries of human dental enamel, Acta odont. scandinav. **15**:13, 1957.
70. Hall, Walter B., and Sreebny, Leo M.: A histochemical demonstration of the locales of tryptases in the salivary glands of rodents, J. D. Res. **43**(supp.):879, 1964. (Abst.)
71. Hancox, N.: The osteoclast. In Bourne, G. H. (editor): The biochemistry and physiology of bone, New York, 1956, Academic Press.
72. Hancox, N. M., and Boothroyd, B.: Structure-function relationship in the osteoclast.

In Sognnaes, R. F. (editor): Mechanism of hard tissue destruction, Washington, D. C., 1963, American Association for the Advancement of Science.

73. Avery, J. K.: Research in anatomy, histology and related sciences, J.A.D.A. **70**:1450, 1965.
74. Hess, W. C., Lee, C. Y., and Peckham, S. C.: The lipid content of enamel and dentin, J. D. Res. **35**:273, 1956.
75. Hoerman, Kirk C., and Mancewicz, Sandra A.: Phosphorescence of calcified tissues, J. D. Res. **43**(supp.):775, 1964.
76. Holliday, T. D.: Diagnostic exfoliative cytology, its value as an everyday hospital investigation, Lancet **1**:488, 1963.
77. Irving, J. T., and Handleman, C. S.: Bone destruction by multinucleated giant cells, mechanisms of hard tissue destruction, Washington, D. C., 1963, 75th American Association for the Advancement of Science, pp. 515-530.
78. Jackson, D. S.: Some biochemical aspects of fibrogenesis and wound healing, New England J. Med. **259**:814, 1958.
79. Jackson, D. S., and Smith, R. H.: Some aspects of the biosynthesis of collagen. In Recent advances in gelatin and glue research, New York, 1958, Pergamon Press, p. 54.
80. Kosower, Edward M.: Molecular biochemistry, New York, 1962, McGraw-Hill Book Co., Inc.
81. Kreudenstein, S.: Ueber den Phosphatasennachweis im Dentin, Deutsch. Zahn-, Mund-, u. Kieferheilk. **26**:100, 1957.
82. Laborit, Henri: Metabolic structure. Functional and pharmacological activities, Aerztl. Forsch. **17**:169, 1963.
83. Lacks, C. H., and Rogers, H. J.: Action of plasmin on cartilage, Nature **182**:948, 1958.
84. Laskin, D. M., and Engel, M. B.: Relation between the metabolism and structure of bone, Ann. New York Acad. Sc. **85**:421, 1960.
85. Manning, J. P., and Butler, M. C.: Simultaneous formalin fixation and EDTA decalcification, with Carbowax embedding for preservation of acid phosphatase, Stain Techn. **40**:7, 1965.
86. McCrea, J. F.: Studies on influenza virus receptor-substance and receptor-substance analogues. I. Preparation and properties of a homogeneous mucoid from the salivary gland of sheep, Biochem. J. **55**:132, 1953.
87. McLean, F. C., and Urist, M. R.: Bone: an introduction to the physiology of skeletal tissue, Chicago, 1955, University of Chicago Press.
88. Menten, M., Jung, J., and Green, M.: A coupling histochemical azo-dye test for alkaline phosphatase in the kidney, J. Biol. Chem. **153**:471, 1944.
89. Millard, H. D.: Oral exfoliative cytology as an aid to diagnosis, J.A.D.A. **69**:547, 1964.
90. Mjör, Ivar A.: The bone matrix adjacent to lacunae and canaliculi, Anat. Rec. **144**:327, 1962.
91. Moretti, G., Adachi, K., and Ellis, R. A.: Regional differences in acid phosphatase and between esterase activity in the epidermis of the chimpanzee and the macaque, J. Histochem. & Cytochem. **8**:237, 1960.
92. Nachlas, M. M., Tsou, K. C., DeSouza, E., Cheng, C. S., and Seligman, A. M.: Cytochemical demonstration of succinic dehydrogenase by the use of a new p-nitrophenyl substituted ditetrazole, J. Histochem. & Cytochem. **5**:420, 1957.
93. Novikoff, A. B.: Intercellular localization of chemical constituents. In Mellors, R. C. (editor): Analytical cytology, ed. 2, New York, 1959, McGraw-Hill Book Co., Inc.
94. Opdyke, D. L.: The histochemistry of dental decay, Arch. Oral Biol. **7**:207, 1962.
95. Palen, Vern W.: Electron microscopy, Biomed. Instrumentation **1**:7, 1964.
96. Person, P., and Burnett, G. W.: Dynamic equilibria of oral tissues. II. Cytochrome oxidase and succinoxidase activity of oral tissues, J. Periodont. **26**:99, 1955.
97. Philps, F. R.: A short manual of respiratory cytology—a guide to the identification of carcinoma cells in the sputum, Springfield, Ill., 1964, Charles C Thomas, Publisher.
98. Pincus, P.: Enamel protein, Proc. Royal Soc. Med. **32**:513, 1938.
99. Putschar, W. G. J.: General pathology of the musculo-skeletal system, Handb. allg. Path. **3**:363, 1960.
100. Riley, J. F.: The mast cells, London, 1959, E. & S. Livingstone, Ltd.

101. Ring, J. R., and Levy, B.: Changes in alkaline phosphatase activity of rat oral epithelium during the estrous cycle and in response to administered estrogen, J. D. Res. **29**:817, 1950.

102. Robb-Smith, A. H. T.: What is reticulin? In council for international organization of medical sciences: Symposium on connective tissue, Oxford, 1957, Blackwell Scientific Publications, p. 177.

103. Roche, J.: Phosphatases. In Sumner, J. B., and Myrbäck, K. (editors): The enzymes: chemistry and mechanism of action, vol. 1, New York, 1950, Academic Press, p. 486.

104. Rossi, F., Capurro, S., Zaccheo, D., and Crossi, C. E.: Il differenziamento dell'epitelio del canale alimentare dell'uomo e la localizzazione in esso dei mucopolisaccaridi, Soc. Ital. Anat. **23**:19, 1963.

105. Rothman, S.: Physiology and biochemistry of the skin, Chicago, 1954, University of Chicago Press, p. 468.

106. Rovelstad, Gordon H., and Calandra, Joseph C.: Enzyme studies of salivary corpuscles, Dent. Prog. **2**:21, 1961.

107. St. Whitelock, Otto v. (editor): The metabolism of oral tissues, New York, 1960, The New York Academy of Science.

108. Sandler, Henry C.: Cytological screening for early mouth cancer, Cancer **15**:1119, 1962.

109. Sandler, Henry C.: Oral exfoliative cytology for detection of early mouth cancer, Acta Cytol. **6**:355, 1962.

110. Sandritter, W., and Schreiber, M.: Histochemie von Sputumzellen. I. Qualitative histochemische Untersuchungen, Frankfurt. Ztschr. f. Path. **68**:693, 1958.

111. Schajowicz, F., and Cabrini, R. L.: Demonstration of a phosphamidasic activity in bone tissue, Acta Histochem. **17**:371, 1964.

112. Schajowicz, Fritz, and Cabrini, Romulo, L.: Histochemical studies on glycogen in normal ossification and calcification, J. Bone & Joint Surg. **40**:1081, 1958.

113. Selbach, Gustav J., and Bondar, Marilyn: Cytological filtration technics, Acta Cytol. **6**:311, 1962.

114. Selye, H.: Calciphylaxis, Chicago, 1962, University of Chicago Press.

115. Shackleford, John M., and Klapper, C. E.: Structure and carbohydrate histochemistry of mammalian salivary glands, Am. J. Anat. **111**:825, 1962.

116. Smith, Chauncey W., Metzger, Joseph F., and Hoggan, M. David: Immunofluorescence as applied to pathology, Am. J. Clin. Path. **38**:26, 1962.

117. Sognnaes, R. F.: Microstructure and histochemical characteristics of the mineralized tissues, Ann. New York Acad. Sc. **60**:545, 1955.

118. Sognnaes, Reidar F.: Mechanisms of hard tissue destruction, Washington, D. C., 1963, American Association for the Advancement of Science.

119. Soyenkoff, R., Friedman, B. K., and Newton, M.: The lipids of dental tissues: a preliminary study, J. D. Res. **30**:599, 1951.

120. Spicer, S. S.: Histochemical differentiation of mammalian mucopolysaccharides, Ann. New York Acad. Sc. **106**:379, 1963.

121. Spicer, S. S.: A correlative study of the histochemical properties of rodent acid mucopolysaccharides, J. Histochem. & Cytochem. **8**:18, 1960.

122. Spicer, S. S., and Warren, L.: The histochemistry of sialic acid containing mucoproteins, J. Histochem. & Cytochem. **8**:135, 1960.

123. Steinman, R. R., Hewes, C. G., and Woods, R. W.: Histochemical analysis of lesions in incipient dental caries, J. D. Res. **38**:592, 1959.

124. Sumner, J. B., and Somers, G. F.: Chemistry and methods of enzymes, ed. 3, New York, 1953, Academic Press.

125. Symons, N. B. B.: Alkaline phosphatase activity in the developing teeth of the rat, J. Anat. **89**:238, 1955.

126. Symons, N. B. B.: Lipid distribution in the developing teeth of the rat, Brit. D. J. **105**:27, 1958.

127. Szulman, A. E.: The histological distribution of the blood group substance in man as disclosed by immunofluorescence. II. The H antigen and its relation to A and B antigens, J. Exper. Med. **115**:97, 1962.

128. Szulman, A. E.: Histological distribution of the blood group substance in a man as disclosed by immunofluorescence. III. The A, B and H antigens in embryos and fetuses from 18 mm. in length, J. Exper. Med. **119**:503, 1964.
129. Takeuchi, T.: Histochemical demonstration of branching enzyme (amylo-1,4→1,6-transglucosidase) in animal tissues, J. Histochem. & Cytochem. **6**:208, 1958.
130. Thompson, R. H. S.: Classification and nomenclature of enzymes, Science **137**:405, 1962.
131. Turesky, S., Glickman, I., and Litwin, T.: A histochemical evaluation of normal and inflamed human gingiva, J. D. Res. **30**:792, 1951.
132. Turesky, S., Crowley, J., and Glickman, I.: A histochemical study of protein-bound sulfhydryl and disulfide groups in normal and inflamed human gingiva, J. D. Res. **36**:255, 1957.
133. Unpublished data.
134. Vallotton, C.: Étude bio-histologique de la phosphatase dans la gencive humaine normale et dans les gingivites, Schweiz Monatschr. Zahnh. **52**:512, 1942.
135. Van Scott, E. J., and Flesh, P.: Sulfhydryl groups and disulfide linkages in normal and pathological keratinization, Arch. Dermat. & Syph. **70**:141, 1954.
136. Veterans Administration Cooperative Study: Oral exfoliative cytology, Washington, D. C., 1962, U. S. Government Printing Office.
137. Walker, D. G.: Citric acid cycle in osteoblasts and osteoclasts, Bull. Johns Hopkins Hosp. **108**:80, 1961.
138. Weinmann, J. P., Meyer, J., and Mardfin, D.: Occurrence and role of glycogen in the epithelium of the alveolar mucosa and of the attached gingiva, Am. J. Anat. **104**:381, 1959.
139. Windrum, G. M., Kent, P. W., and Easto'e, J. E.: Constitution of human renal reticulin, Brit. J. Exper. Path. **36**:49, 1955.
140. Wisotzky, Joel: Effects of Neo-tetrazolium chloride on the phosphorescence of teeth, J. D. Res. **43**:659, 1964.
141. Witkop, C. J., Jr. (editor): Genetics and dental health, New York, 1962, McGraw-Hill Book Co., Inc.
142. Young, Richard W.: Nucleic acids, protein synthesis and bone, Clin. Orthop. **26**:147, 1963.
143. Zander, H. A.: Distribution of phosphatase in gingival tissue, J. D. Res. **20**:347, 1941.

Appendix

Preparation of specimens for histologic study*

INTRODUCTION

PREPARATION OF SECTIONS OF PARAFFIN-
  EMBEDDED SPECIMENS

PREPARATION OF SECTIONS OF PARLODION-
  EMBEDDED SPECIMENS

PREPARATION OF GROUND SECTIONS OF TEETH
  OR BONE

PREPARATION OF FROZEN SECTIONS

INTRODUCTION

Before any tissue specimen can be studied with a microscope, it must be treated in some way to make the structures to be examined clearly visible. A knowledge of some of the basic procedures of tissue preparation will increase considerably the student's understanding of the histologic structures seen on the microscope slides he examines during his study of histology.

The preparation of tissues for study under a microscope is a science and an art and is known as *histologic technique,* or *microtechnique.* Special methods of histologic technique seem to be almost infinite in variety, but routine methods of tissue preparation involve cutting the specimen into thin sections and then mounting the sections on microscope slides, staining them with histologic stains, and affixing a cover glass over them to preserve them. There are a number of excellent books on microtechnique, and some of these should be consulted by anyone planning to undertake the preparation of tissue specimens for histologic study.[3,6] Solely for the purpose of giving a general idea of tissue preparation to those who have had no experience with histologic techniques, a few of the more commonly used methods of preparing oral tissues for microscopic study are discussed below. Details of procedure necessarily vary with the nature of the specimen and the character of the structures of particular interest.

Four different methods of preparation of oral tissues for microscopic examination are commonly used:

1. *Specimens may be embedded in paraffin and sectioned.* The most commonly used method of preparing soft tissues for study with an ordinary light microscope is that of embedding the specimen in paraffin and then cutting sections 4 to 10 microns thick. The sections are mounted on micro-

---

*By Dorothy Permar.

382

scope slides, passed through a selected series of stains, and covered with a cover glass.

2. *Specimens may be embedded in parlodion and sectioned.* Specimens containing bone or teeth require different preparation. Such specimens must be decalcified (the mineral substance removed) before they can be sectioned on a microtome, and for sectioning they usually are embedded in parlodion rather than in paraffin.

3. *Specimens of calcified tissue may be ground into thin sections.* Sections of undecalcified tooth or bone may be obtained by preparing a *ground section.* This is done by applying the undecalcified specimen to a revolving abrasive stone until it is ground down to a section of about 30 microns or less in thickness.

4. *Specimens of soft tissue may be frozen and sectioned.* When it is important that pathologic tissue specimens be examined immediately, or if the reagents used for paraffin or parlodion embedding would destroy the tissue characteristics that are to be studied, the fresh, unfixed soft tissue may be frozen and sectioned without being embedded in any supporting substance. Such tissue sections are usually referred to as *frozen sections.*

These four methods of specimen preparation will now be described in more detail.

PREPARATION OF SECTIONS OF PARAFFIN-EMBEDDED SPECIMENS

The method of preparing a specimen for sectioning by embedding it in paraffin is suitable for oral specimens that contain no calcified tissue, such as specimens of gingiva, cheek, and tongue. The usual steps in this kind of preparation are described briefly in the following paragraphs.

Obtaining the specimen. Specimens taken from an experimental animal must be removed carefully, without crushing, either while the animal is alive or immediately after it has been killed. Specimens taken from human beings for biopsy must be removed carefully to avoid crushing.

Fixation of the specimen. Immediately after the specimen is cut out of the body, it must be placed in a *fixing solution.* Specimens that have not been placed in such a solution are seldom any good. There are many good fixing solutions available.[3] Sometimes the kinds of stains subsequently to be used determine the kind of solution to be chosen. One of the most commonly used fixing solutions for dental tissues is 10 per cent neutral formalin.

The purposes of fixation are to coagulate the protein, thus reducing alteration by subsequent treatment, and to make the tissues more readily permeable to the subsequent applications of reagents. Fixation requires from several hours to several days, depending on the size and density of the specimens and on the type of fixing solution used.

Following fixation in formalin, the specimen is washed overnight in running water.

Dehydration of the specimen. Since it is necessary that the specimen be completely infiltrated with the paraffin in which it is to be embedded, it must first be infiltrated with some substance that is miscible with paraffin. Paraffin and water do not mix. Therefore, following washing in running water to remove the formalin, the specimen is gradually dehydrated by being passed through a series of dishes which contain increasing percentages of alcohol, 40, 60, 80, and 95 per cent, and absolute alcohol, remaining in each dish for several hours. (The time in each step of the process depends upon the size and density of the specimen.) To ensure that the water is as nearly as possible completely replaced by alcohol, two or three changes of absolute alcohol are used. Then, since paraffin and alcohol are not miscible, the specimen is passed from alcohol through two changes of xylene, which is miscible with both alcohol and paraffin.

Infiltration of the specimen with paraffin. When xylene has completely replaced the alcohol in the tissue, the specimen is ready to be infiltrated with paraffin. It is removed from the xylene and placed in a dish of melted embedding paraffin, and the dish is put into a constant temperature oven regulated to about 60° C. (The exact temperature depends upon the melting point of the paraffin used.) During the course of several hours, the specimen is changed to two or three successive dishes of paraffin so that all of the xylene in the tissue is replaced by paraffin. The time in the oven depends on the size and density of the specimen: a specimen the size of a 2 or 3 mm. cube may need to remain in the oven only a couple of hours, while a larger, firmer specimen may require twelve to twenty-four hours to ensure complete paraffin infiltration.

Embedding the specimen. When the specimen is completely infiltrated with paraffin, it is embedded in the center of a block of paraffin. A small paper box, perhaps a ¾-inch cube for a small specimen, is filled with melted paraffin, and with warm pliers the specimen is removed from the dish of melted paraffin in which it has stood and is placed in the center of the box of paraffin. Attention must here be given to the orientation of the specimen so that it will be cut in the plane desired for examination. A good plan is to place the surface to be cut first toward the bottom of the box. The paper box containing the paraffin and the specimen is then immersed in cool water to harden the paraffin. The hardened paraffin block is removed from the paper box and is attached to a paraffin-coated wooden cube (about ¾-inch cube). Attachment is accomplished by laying the paraffin block, with the side which is to be cut first turned upward, on top of the wooden cube and then passing a warm spatula between the paraffin block and the wooden cube. The mounted paraffin block is trimmed with a razor blade so that there is about ⅛ inch of paraffin surrounding the specimen on all four sides and so that the edges are parallel. The specimen is now ready to be sectioned on a microtome.

Cutting the sections of the specimen. The wooden cube to which the paraffin block is attached is clamped on a precision rotary microtome, the microtome is adjusted to cut sections of the desired thickness (usually 4 to 10 microns), and the perfectly sharpened microtome knife is clamped into place. The wheel of the microtome is turned, and the paraffin block moves down across the knife edge and one section is cut. As the turn of the wheel is completed and the block is raised to its original position, it automatically advances toward the knife the number of microns determined by the adjustment previously made. Thus, with the next rotation of the wheel, another section of the same thickness is cut. As the uniformly thin sections are being cut one at a time, the edge of each section as it is cut sticks to the edge of the immediately preceding section, forming a long ribbon of sections which, with a little practice, can be easily handled.

Mounting the cut sections on slides. Suitable lengths of the paraffin ribbon are then mounted on prepared microscope slides. The preparation of the slides is done by coating clean slides with a thin film of Meyer's albumin adhesive[3] (egg albumin and glycerin). A short length of paraffin ribbon is floated in a pan of warm water (about 45° C.). A prepared slide is slipped under the ribbon and then is lifted from the water with the ribbon, which of course contains the tissue sections, arranged on its upper surface. The slide is placed on a constant

Table 8. Staining of sections

1. Xylene	2 min.	To remove paraffin from sections
2. Xylene	2 min.	To remove paraffin from sections
3. Absolute alcohol	2 min.	To remove xylene
4. 95% alcohol	1 min.	Approach to water
5. 80% alcohol	1 min.	Approach to water
6. 60% alcohol	1 min.	Approach to water
7. Distilled water	1 min.	Water precedes stains dissolved in water
8. Hematoxylin (Harris's)	3-10 min.	To stain nuclei
9. Distilled water	Rinse	To rinse off excess stain
10. Ammonium alum (saturated solution)	2-10 min.	To differentiate; nuclei will retain stain
11. Sodium bicarbonate (saturated solution)	1-2 min.	Makes stain blue
12. Distilled water	1 min.	Removes $NaHCO_3$
13. 80% alcohol	1 min.	Partially dehydrates
14. 95% alcohol	1 min.	Alcohol precedes stains dissolved in alcohol
15. Eosin (alcohol soluble)	1-2 min.	To stain cytoplasm and intercellular substance
16. 95% alcohol	Rinse, or longer	Alcohol destains eosin, and should be used as long as needed
17. 95% alcohol	Rinse, or longer	To remove excess eosin
18. Absolute alcohol	1 min.	To dehydrate
19. Absolute alcohol	2 min.	To dehydrate
20. Xylene	2 min.	To remove alcohol and clear
21. Xylene	2 min.	To clear

temperature drying table, which is regulated to about 42° C., so that the sections will adhere to the slide. The slide is then allowed to dry on this table.

Staining the sections. There are innumerable tissue stains, methods of using stains, and methods of preparing tissues to receive stains. Some of the many factors that influence the choice of stains are the kind or kinds of tissue to be studied and the particular characteristics of immediate interest.

One combination of stains often used for routine staining is hematoxylin and eosin, commonly known as *H & E.* A usual procedure for staining sections with *H & E* is as follows.

The dried slides are placed vertically in glass staining trays, and the trays are passed through a series of staining dishes that contain the various reagents (Table 8).

The slides are removed one at a time from the xylene, the sections are covered with a mounting medium, and a cover glass is affixed. When the mounting medium has hardened, the slides are ready for examination.

PREPARATION OF SECTIONS OF PARLODION-EMBEDDED SPECIMENS

Specimens which contain bone and teeth cannot be cut with a microtome knife unless the calcified tissues are first made soft by decalcification. Furthermore, if a specimen contains any appreciable amount of bone or teeth, the decalcified specimen is better embedded in parlodion (celloidin, pyroxylin) than in paraffin. It is extremely difficult, if not impossible, to get good sections of, for example, a large mandible containing teeth in situ if the specimen is embedded in paraffin.

Let us suppose that we are to section a specimen of dog mandible bearing two premolar teeth. One method of procedure is as follows.

Obtaining the specimen. The portion of the mandible containing the two premolar teeth is separated as carefully as possible from the rest of the mandible by means of a sharp scalpel and a bone saw. Unwanted soft tissue is removed. If the area of the specimen next to the line of sawing will be seriously damaged by the saw, the specimen should be cut a little larger than needed and then trimmed to the desired size after partial decalcification. It is better to have the mandible cut into several pieces before placing it in the fixing solution because a smaller specimen allows quicker penetration of the fixing solution to its center. If the tooth pulp is of interest, a bur should be used to open the crowns of the teeth to permit entrance of the fixing solution into the pulp chamber. This operation must be done with care so that too much heat does not burn the pulp tissue.

Fixation of the specimen. The specimen so cut and prepared is quickly rinsed in running water and for fixation is placed immediately in about 400 ml. of 10 per cent neutral formalin. It should remain in the formalin not less than a week, preferably longer. It may be stored in formalin for a long period.

Decalcification of the specimen. When fixation is complete, the specimen is then decalcified. Decalcification may be accomplished in several ways.[3,10] One way is to suspend the specimen in about 400 ml. of 5 per cent nitric acid. The acid is changed daily for eight to ten days, and then the specimen is tested for complete decalcification.

One way to test for complete decalcification is to pierce the hard tissue with a needle. When the needle enters the bone and tooth easily, the tissue is probably ready for further treatment.

Another way to test for complete decalcification is to determine by a precipitation test whether there is calcium present in the nitric acid in which the specimen is immersed.[8] This is done by placing in a test tube 5 or 6 ml. of the acid in which the specimen has been standing and then adding 1 ml. of concentrated ammonium hydroxide and several drops of a saturated aqueous solution of ammonium oxalate. A precipitate will form if any appreciable amount of calcium is present. If a precipitate forms, the acid covering the specimen should be changed and a couple of days later the test for complete decalcification should be repeated. If no precipitate is detected after the test tube has stood for an hour, and after several additions of ammonium oxalate, it may be assumed that the specimen is nearly completely decalcified. The specimen should be allowed to remain in the *same* acid for forty-eight hours longer and the test repeated.

The end point of decalcification is sometimes difficult to determine, but it is important. Specimens left in the acid too short a time are not completely decalcified and cannot be cut successfully and specimens left in the acid too long a time do not stain well. Because of the adverse effect of prolonged exposure to acid on the staining quality of tissues, specimens should be reduced to their minimum size before decalcification is begun in order to keep the time necessary for acid treatment as short as possible.

Washing the specimen. When decalcification is complete, the specimen must be washed in running water for at least twenty-four hours to remove all of the acid.

Dehydration of the specimen. Following washing, dehydration is accomplished by placing the specimen successively in increasing percentages of alcohol, 40, 60, 80, and 95 per cent, and absolute alcohol. The specimen should remain in each of the alcohols up to and including 95 per cent for twenty-four to forty-eight hours, and it should then be placed in several changes of absolute alcohol over a period of forty-eight to seventy-two hours. It is necessary to remove, as much as possible, all of the water from the tissues in order to have good infiltration of parlodion.

From absolute alcohol the specimen is transferred to ether-alcohol (1 part anhydrous ether, 1 part absolute alcohol), because parlodion is dissolved in ether-alcohol. There should be several changes of ether-alcohol over a period of forty-eight to seventy-two hours.

Infiltration of the specimen with parlodion. Parlodion is purified nitrocellulose dissolved in ether-alcohol. From the ether-alcohol in which the specimen has been standing, it is transferred to 2 per cent parlodion, covered tightly to prevent evaporation, and allowed to stand for a period of from two weeks to a month.

From 2 per cent parlodion the specimen is transferred to increasing percentages of parlodion: 4, 6, 10, and 12 per cent. The estimation of the time required for the infiltration of a specimen is a matter of experience, the determining factors being the size of the specimen and the amount of bone and tooth material present. For the specimen of mandible being described here, the time required for complete parlodion infiltration might vary from several weeks to several months. It is improbable that satisfactory infiltration could be accomplished by allowing *less* than two or three weeks in each percentage of parlodion, and it might be necessary to allow much longer.

Embedding the specimen in parlodion. When infiltration with parlodion is complete, the specimen is embedded in the center of a block of parlodion. A glass dish with straight sidewalls and a lid is a good container to use for embedding. Some 12 per cent parlodion is poured into the dish, and the specimen is placed in the parlodion. Then more parlodion is added so that there is about ½ inch of parlodion above the specimen, the additional amount being necessary to allow for shrinkage during hardening.

Orientation of the specimen at this point to ensure the proper plane of cutting is important. If this piece of dog mandible is to be sectioned in such a way that the premolar teeth are cut in a mesiodistal plane and the first sections are cut from the buccal surface, then the buccal surface of the mandible should be placed toward the bottom of the dish when the specimen is embedded.

The dish is now covered with a lid which fits loosely enough to permit very slow evaporation of the ether-alcohol in which the parlodion is dissolved. As the ether-alcohol evaporates, the parlodion will become solidified and will eventually acquire a consistency *somewhat* like that of hard rubber.

This process of hardening the parlodion may require two or three weeks. When the block is very firm, it is removed from the dish and placed in chloroform until it sinks. It is then transferred to several changes of 70 per cent alcohol to remove the chloroform.

Blocks of parlodion-embedded material must never be allowed to dry out. The blocks should be stored in 70 per cent alcohol to allow the parlodion to harden further. Blocks which are to be stored for many months or years should eventually be transferred to a mixture of 70 per cent alcohol and glycerin for storage.

Cutting the sections of the specimen. The hardened block of the parlodion-embedded specimen is fastened with liquid parlodion to a fiber block or to a metal object holder so that it can be clamped onto the precision sliding microtome. (This is a different instrument from the rotary microtome used for cutting paraffin.) Sections are cut with a very sharp microtome knife. For the specimen of dog mandible being described here, the sections may have to be cut at a thickness of as much as 15 microns. Unlike paraffin sections, these parlodion sections must be handled one at a time. As each section is cut, it is straightened out with a camel's hair brush on the top surface of the horizontally placed microtome knife and is then removed from the knife and placed flat in a dish of 70 per cent alcohol. It must not be allowed to become dry. If it is important that the sections be kept in serial order, a square of paper should be inserted after every fourth or fifth section as they are stored in the dish of alcohol.

Staining sections of the parlodion-embedded specimens. Ordinarily the parlodion is not removed from the sections, and the sections are not mounted on slides until after staining, dehydrating, and clearing are completed. The sections are passed through the series of reagents separately or in groups of three or four, using a perforated section lifter to make the transfer.

From the 70 per cent alcohol in which they are stored when cut, the sections may be stained with hematoxylin and eosin as follows.

Referring to Table 8, omit steps 1 to 3 and start with step 4; i.e., transfer the parlodion sections from 70 per cent alcohol to 95 per cent alcohol. Follow each step down through step 17, which is 95 per cent alcohol. At this point, for the absolute alcohol specified in steps 18 and 19, substitute carbolxylene (75 ml. xylene plus 25 ml. melted carbolic acid crystals). This substitution is made because the parlodion is slightly soluble in absolute alcohol. From carbolxylene the sections are transferred to xylene (steps 20 and 21).

The sections should not be allowed to become folded or rolled up during the staining process. When they are put into the carbolxylene, they must be flattened out carefully, because the xylene which follows will slightly harden the parlodion sections so that they cannot easily be flattened.

To mount the stained section on a slide, the clean slide (no adhesive is used) is slipped into the dish of xylene beneath the section, and the section is lifted onto the slide from the liquid, straightened carefully, and quickly and firmly pressed with a small piece of filter paper. The slide bearing the section is then quickly dipped back into the xylene and drained, and mounting medium is flowed over the section and a cover glass is dropped into place.

A modification of this embedding method, using acid celloidin instead of parlodion, will preserve much of the organic matrix of tooth enamel during the process of decalcification.[1]

For variations in the hematoxylin and eosin stain and for information on the many other kinds of stains useful for both paraffin-embedded and parlodion-embedded specimens, the student of histology must refer to books on microtechnique.[3,5,6,9,12]

PREPARATION OF GROUND SECTIONS OF TEETH OR BONE

Decalcification of bone and teeth often obscures the structures. Teeth in particular are damaged because tooth enamel, being about 96 per cent mineral substance, is usually completely destroyed by ordinary methods of decalcification.

Undecalcified teeth and undecalcified bone may be studied by making thin ground sections of the specimens.

The equipment used for making ground sections includes a laboratory lathe, a coarse and a fine abrasive lathe wheel, a stream of water directed onto the rotating wheel and a pan beneath to catch the water, a wooden block about 1-inch cube, some ½-inch adhesive tape, a camel's hair brush, ether, mounting medium, microscope slides, and cover glasses.

Let us suppose that a thin ground section is to be prepared of a human mandibular molar tooth cut longitudinally in a mesiodistal plane. The coarse abrasive lathe wheel is attached to the lathe, water is directed onto the wheel, the tooth is held securely in the fingers, and its buccal surface is applied firmly to the flat surface of the rapidly rotating wheel. The tooth is ground down nearly to the level of the desired section.

The coarse wheel is now exchanged for a fine abrasive lathe wheel, and the cut surface of the tooth is ground again until the level of the desired section is reached.

At this point a piece of adhesive tape is wrapped around the wooden block in such a way that the sticky side of the tape is directed *outward*. The ground surface of the tooth is wiped dry and then is pressed onto the adhesive tape on one side of the wooden block. It will stick fast. Holding the block securely in the fingers, the lingual surface of the tooth is applied to the coarse abrasive lathe wheel and the tooth is ground down to a thickness of about 0.5 mm. Then the coarse wheel is again exchanged for the fine abrasive lathe wheel, and the grinding is continued until the section is as thin as is wanted. A little practice will permit the operator to grind thin, even sections.

The finished ground section is soaked off of the adhesive tape with ether and then dried for several minutes. Too long drying will result in cracking. It is then mounted on a microscope slide. To do this, a drop of mounting medium is placed on the slide, the section is lifted with a camel's hair brush and placed on the drop, another drop of mounting medium is put on top of the section, and a cover glass is affixed. A little practice will enable the technician to avoid entrapping air bubbles.

The teeth used for ground sections should not be allowed to dry out after extraction, because drying makes the hard tissues brittle and the enamel may chip off in the process of grinding. Extracted teeth should be preserved in 10 per cent formalin until used.

Precision equipment for making ground sections with much greater accuracy is available. The method described here is one which equipment at hand in almost any laboratory is used. The technical literature contains a number of articles on the preparation of sections of undecalcified tissues.[2,4,11,13,14]

PREPARATION OF FROZEN SECTIONS

Fixed soft tissues or fresh unfixed soft tissues may be cut into sections 10 to 15 microns thick by freezing the block of tissue with either liquid or solid carbon dioxide and cutting it on a freezing microtome. Frozen sections can be quickly prepared and are useful if the immediate examination of a specimen is required. Frozen sections are also useful when the tissue characteristics to be studied would be destroyed by the reagents used in paraffin embedding.

Details of the preparation of frozen sections can be obtained from books on microtechnique.[3,7]

REFERENCES

1. Bodecker, C. F.: The Cape-Kitchin modification of the celloidin decalcifying method for dental enamel, J. D. Res. **16**:143, 1937.
2. Brewer, H. E., and Shellhamer, R. H.: Strained ground sections of teeth and bone, Stain Techn. **31**:111, 1956.
3. Davenport, Harold A.: Histological and histochemical technics, Philadelphia, 1960, W. B. Saunders Co.
4. Fremlin, J. H., Mathieson, J., and Hardwick, J. L.: The grinding of thin sections of dental enamel, J. D. Res. **39**:1103, 1960.
5. Gatenby, J. B., and Beams, H. W. (editors): The microtomist's vade-mecum (Bolles Lee), ed. 11, Philadelphia, 1950, The Blakiston Co.
6. Guyer, Michael F.: Animal micrology, Chicago, 1953, University of Chicago Press.
7. Krajian, Aram A., and Gradwohl, R. B. H.: Histopathological technic, ed. 2, St. Louis, 1952, The C. V. Mosby Co.
8. Morse, Anna: Formic acid-sodium citrate decalcification and butyl alcohol dehydration of teeth and bones for sectioning in paraffin, J. D. Res. **24**:143, 1945.
9. Mallory, F. B.: Pathological technique, Philadelphia, 1938, W. B. Saunders Co.
10. Nikiforuk, G., and Sreebny, L.: Demineralization of hard tissues by organic chelating agents at neutral pH, J. D. Res. **32**:859, 1953.
11. Sognnaes, R. F.: Preparation of thin serial ground sections of whole teeth and jaws and other highly calcified and brittle structures, Anat. Rec. **99**:134, 1947.
12. Sognnaes, R. F.: The organic elements of the enamel: I-IV, J. D. Res. **27**:609, 1948; **28**:549, 1949; **28**:558, 1949; **29**:260, 1950.
13. Weber, D. F.: A simplified technique for the preparation of ground sections, J. D. Res. **43**:462, 1964.
14. Yaeger, J. A.: Methacrylate embedding and sectioning of calcified bone, Stain Techn. **33**:229, 1958.

Index

A

Abrasion, 262
Accessory canal(s), 134, 135, 152
  filled, lower molar with, roentgenogram, 135
Acellular cementum, 160, 161, 162, 163, 164, 168
Acetone for fixation, 358
Acid phosphatase
  activity, 363, 367, 371
  demonstration, 358, 359
Acini
  mucous, 276
  of salivary glands, 268, 275, 282
Acinous cells, 283, 284, 285, 286, 289
Active eruption, 236, 303
Addison's disease, gingival pigmentation in, 221
Adventitial cells, 139
Age changes
  in cementum, 168
  in dentin, 110
  in enamel, 64
  in pulp, 137
  in pulp chamber, 129
  in teeth and supporting tissues, 192
Age, loss of tooth surface structure with, 55
Albumin in saliva, 291
Albuminous alveoli of submandibular gland, 274
Albuminous glands, 267, 272
Alkaline phosphatase
  activity, 364, 365, 367, 371
  demonstration, 359
Alveolar
  arteries, interdental, 224
  bone, 201, 203, 204, 205, 208, 209, 210, 211
    blood supply to periodontal ligament through, 186, 187
    changes with age, 192

Alveolar—cont'd
  bone—cont'd
    periosteum of, attachment of gingiva to, 222
    resorption and repair, 184
    resorption due to trauma, 193
    structure, alterations in, importance, 208
    tooth submerged in, 334
  crest
    fibers, 181
    growth of mandible at, 201
    shape of, 202, 203
    tooth remnant at, 332
  fundus, 305, 307
  mucosa, 218, 254
    compared to free and attached gingiva, 227
    and gingiva, differences, 222, 223, 224
  nerves, superior, 350
  process, 197-212
    bone in, 208
    development, 200
    gross relations of, 202
    mucosa of, 217
    osteoporosis of, 211
    physiologic changes, 206
    structure, 200
    two parts, 201
  ridge
    growth in prefunctional phase of eruption, 305
    mandibular, 11
  spongiosa, 204, 205
Alveoli, mucous, of sublingual gland, 270
Alveolodental ligament, 182, 183
  fibers of, 181, 182
Alveolodental membrane, 176
Alveologingival fibers, 223
Ameboid wandering cell, 144
Ameloblastic layer, 69
Ameloblasts, 72, 229, 233, 243
  chemical intoxication of, 88

Ameloblasts—cont'd
  desmolytic stage, 77
  differentiation, 34, 35, 36
  disturbance of, enamel hyperplasia, 89
  effect of vitamin A deficiency, 36
  under electron microscope, 74
  enamel cuticle from, 57
  and enamel rods, linear arrangement, 82
  formative stage, 75
  function, 36, 37
  life cycle, 72-77
  maturative stage, 76
  morphogenic stage, 72
  in mouse molar, 58
  nourishment, 75
  organizing stage, 75
  protective stage, 77
  rod formation from, 81, 83
  secretory activity, 78
  staining, 362, 365
  terminal bars of, 78, 79, 80, 81
  terminology, 72
Amelogenesis, 77
  clinical considerations, 88
Amino acids
  in enamel matrix, 41
  staining, 361, 362
Aminopeptidase, 368, 372
Amylase
  in saliva, 291, 293
  secretion, 287, 288
Amylophosphorylase, 376
Anatomic crown of tooth, 241, 243
Anatomy
  of maxillary sinus, 344
  of pulp, 128
  of temporomandibular joint, 335
Ankylosis, 314
  of deciduous tooth, 326, 328, 329, 331,
    332
Anodontia, 35, 36
Anomalies, lingual, 15
Antraoral fistula, 351
Antrum of Highmore, 344
Apatite, 39, 41
  crystals, 45, 85, 86, 88, 104, 157
Apical fibers of periodontal ligament, 182,
    184
Apical foramen, 128, 130, 131, 144, 146
  development, 130
  shape, 151
  variations, 135
Apposition
  bone, 208, 209, 210, 310, 313, 314
  of cementum, 310
  in tooth development, 37
Arches
  branchial, 12, 197
  palatoglossal, 216
Argyrophil fibers, 131, 136, 157, 158, 303,
    304

Arteries
  alveolar, interdental, 224
  of pulp, 143, 144, 145
  of salivary glands, 275
Articular
  capsule, 336, 342
  disc, 335, 336, 340, 341
  fibrous covering, 338
  fossa, 335, 337, 340, 342
  tubercle, 335, 336, 337, 338, 339, 340
Atrophy
  of gingiva, 239
  of mucous membrane, 263
Attached epithelial cuff, 229, 230, 233
Attached gingiva, 226, 227, 228
Attrition, occlusal, 309, 310
Auditory ossicles, development, 198
Auditory tube, formation, 13
Axial movement of teeth, 301, 308, 312
Azo-dye techniques, 358, 359, 364, 368

B

Bacterial plaque, 295
Bands, Hunter-Schreger, 51
Bars, terminal
  of ameloblasts, 78, 79, 80, 81
  separating odontoblasts, 138
Bartholin's duct, 279
Basal cells, 274
Basement membrane, 68, 75
  of dental papilla, 76
  in dentin development, 116, 117, 118
  of oral mucous membrane, 214
Basket cells, 274
Basophil substance of serous cells, 269, 270,
    271, 284
Bell stage of tooth development, 27, 28
  advanced, 29, 30
β-glucuronidases, 374
Birefringence of dentin, 96
Blandin-Nuhn, gland of, 282
Blood dyscrasias, 263
Blood supply
  of gingiva, 224
  of salivary glands, 275
Blood vessels
  of oral mucous membrane, 215
  of periodontal ligament, 186
  of pulp, 143, 144
  pulpstones close to, 151
Bodily movement of tooth germ, 302
Bone
  alveolar; *see* Alveolar bone
  adaptation to function, 211
  adaptation to stress, 206
  apposition, 173, 194, 208, 209, 210, 310,
    313, 314
  bundle, 204, 206, 208, 209, 210, 308, 309,
    310
  cells, enzyme activity, 370

Bone—cont'd
  cells, phosphatase activity, 367
  and cementum, 172, 178
  characteristics, 210
  chemical content, 355
  chondroid, 200, 201
  compact, 209
  deciduous tooth remnant ankylosed to, 331
  and dentin, morphologic difference, 96
  embryonic, 211
  of floor of maxillary sinus, 347, 350
  formation, enzymatic activity, 365
  ground sections of, preparation, 389
  growth, 310, 312, 313
  immature, radiolucence, 211
  internal reconstruction of, 208
  lamella of, separating permanent tooth
    germ from predecessor, 322
  lamellated, 204, 208, 209, 210
  of mandibular condyle, 336
  mineralization, 41
  new, production of, 208
  resorption, 171, 172, 192, 193, 194, 208,
    209, 210, 313, 314, 349
  of skull, development, 197
  spongy, 201, 204, 209, 211
  staining, 360, 361
  and teeth, histochemical studies, 358, 359,
    361
  trabeculae, formation, 305, 307
Bony structures of temporomandibular joint,
  336
Branchial arch, first, 1, 2
Branchial arches, 12, 14, 197
Branchial cleft cysts, 16
Branching artery in pulp, 144
Buccal glands, 267, 281
Buccal mucosa, 252
Buccinator muscle, 252, 253, 254
Buccopharyngeal membrane, 2, 19
Bud stage, dental lamina and, 22
Buds
  of salivary glands, 282
  taste, 257, 258, 260, 261
  tooth, 23
Bundle bone, 204, 206, 208, 209, 210, 308,
  309, 310
Bundles, fiber
  of alveolodental ligament, 181-182
  of periodontal ligament, 178, 181, 182

C

Calcification
  cells associated with, phosphatase activity
    (table), 367
  deficiency due to high fluoride content in
    water, 89
  of dental plaque, 296
  of dentin, linear and globular, 121
  diffuse, in pulp, 148, 149
  incomplete, causing neonatal line, 107

Calcified bodies in periodontal ligament, 191
Calcified tissues, histochemistry, 352
Calcifying tissues, 364
Calciphylaxis, 354
Calcium
  deposits in older teeth, 151
  metabolism, salivary glands and, 290, 296
Calculus
  dental, 295
  formation, esterase activity, 368
Canals
  accessory, 134, 135, 152
  perforating, of Zuckerkandl and Hirsch-
    feld, 204
  root, 128, 132, 133, 151, 152
Canine, deciduous
  erupting, 307
  resorption of root, 321
Canine, embedded, 316
Canine, permanent
  development, 303, 307, 308
  erupting, resorption of deciduous tooth
    under, 332, 333
Cap stage of tooth development, 24, 25, 26
Capillaries
  in contact with outer dental epithelium, 68
  in pulp, pericytes of, 145
  of salivary glands, 275
Capillary network, subepithelial, 215
Carbohydrate in saliva, 291
Carbohydrate-protein complexes in saliva,
  296
Carbohydrates, staining, 360
Carbolxylene, 389
Carbon dioxide tension in saliva, 296
Caries
  effect on dentin, 112, 114, 116, 123
  predisposition and control, 65
  saliva and, 294, 295
Cartilage
  cells, 341
    enzyme activity, 370
    phosphatase activity, 367
  hyalin, of mandibular condyle, 335, 336,
    338, 340, 341, 342
  Meckel's, 198, 200
Cartilaginous parts of skull, 197
Caruncula sublingualis, 279
Catalase, 357
Catalysts, enzymes as, 357
Cavity
  oral
    floor of, mucous membrane, 254
    functions, 213
    two parts, 216
  preparation
    course of enamel rods in, 65, 66
    shape of pulp chamber and, 151
  tooth, gingival margin of, 262
Cavum oris proprium, 216

Cell
  membrane, folding of, 288, 289
  nucleus, genetic information in, 356
  renewal in gingiva, 219
Cell-free subodontoblastic zone of Weil, 141
Celloidin, embedding sections in, 386, 389
Cells
  adventitial, 139
  ameboid wandering, 144
  of articular capsule, 342
  of articular fibrous covering, 338, 340
  associated with bones and teeth, enzyme
      activity (table), 370
  associated with calcification, phosphatase
      activity (table), 367
  basal, of gingiva, 221
  in cementum, 160, 162
  clear, 221
  connective tissue, 137, 141, 354
  defense, of pulp, 139, 142
  of dental papilla, 116
  of dentin, 96
  of epithelial attachment, 233, 235, 236
  epithelial, of dental organ, 68
  epithelial, in periodontal ligament, 190,
      191
  in gingival sulcus, 247
  of inner dental epithelium, 72
  of intercalated ducts, 273, 274
  lymphoid wandering, 144
  mast, 355, 362, 372
  Maximow's nomenclature, 144
  mesenchymal, undifferentiated, 141, 145
  in mixed salivary glands, 272
  mucous, 269, 271, 272, 288
  myoepithelial, 274, 290
  neuroepithelial, 261
  of oral epithelium, 221
  of periodontal connective tissue, 156
  of periodontal ligament, 184, 185, 186
  prickle, 214, 215, 217, 220
  of pulp, 131
  "resting wandering," 141
  Rouget's, 145
  of saliva, 292
  secretory, of salivary glands, 267, 268
  serous, 269, 270, 271, 272, 283
  in sputum, 353
  of stellate reticulum, 70
  of stratified squamous epithelium, 214
  of stratum intermedium, 71
  of striated ducts, 274, 289
  supporting, of taste buds, 260, 261
  taste, 260, 261
Cellular cementum, 162, 163, 164, 168
Cellular elements in pulp, 134, 318
Cemental cuticle, 244
Cementicles in periodontal ligament, 190,
      191
Cementoblasts, 34, 36, 156, 159, 160, 186
Cementocytes, 160, 162, 186

Cementodentinal junction, 166
Cementoenamel junction, 164, 165, 166, 202,
      203, 204
  different relations of tissues at, 234
  gingival sulcus and, 246
  perikymata in region of, 54
Cementogenesis, 155
Cementoid tissue, 157, 159
Cementum, 155-174
  abnormal thickening, 169
  acellular, 160, 161, 162, 163, 164, 168
  age changes, 192
  aging in, 168
  apical foramen surrounded by, 130
  appositional growth, 310, 313
  attachment of gingiva to, 181
  cellular, 162, 163, 164, 168
    root remnants in, 328
  characteristics and composition, 155
  clinical considerations, 171
  continued deposition of, 167, 168
  definition, 155
  dental cuticle and, 244, 245
  and enamel, relation at cervical region, 164
  exposure with age, 174
  fibers attached to, 177, 178
  formation, 156, 157
  fragments severed from dentin by blow,
      173
  functions, 167
  hyperplasia, 169, 170, 171
  hypertrophy, 169
  incremental lines, 161, 162, 163
  intermediate layer, 167
  lacunae, 160, 162, 163, 164, 168
  lamellae, 60
  layers, 162, 164, 168
  loss of, 262
  origin, 19
  pronglike extension, 168, 169
  relation to epithelial attachment, 234, 235,
      237, 238, 239, 240, 241, 242, 243
  resistance to pressure, 172
  resorption, 171, 172, 173
  in root canal, 128
  structure, 160
Centrioles, 72, 75
Cervical enamel, care of, 67
Cervical loop, 68, 69, 72
Cervical sinus, 13
Cheeks
  glands, 252
  lining mucosa, 252, 253
Cheilognathoschisis, 15
Cheiloschisis, 14
Chemical
  composition
    of cementum, 155
    of connective tissue, 354
    of dentin, 96

Chemical—cont'd
constituents of oral tissues, 354
correlations, salivary glands, 283
intoxication of ameloblasts, 88
properties of enamel, 41
Choanae, primary, 5, 6
Chondroclasts, 200
Chondrocranium, 197
Chondrocytes, 338, 340, 341
Chondroid bone, 200, 201
Chondroid cells, 340, 341
Chondroitin sulfuric acid, 355
Chromophil substance of serous cells, 270
Chronologic hypoplasia, 88
Chronology of human dentition (table), 317
Ciliary movement, 349
Circular fibers, gingival, 223
Circumpulpal dentin, 104
Cisternae, 284
Citric acid cycle in osteoblasts and osteoclasts, 370
Classifications of salivary glands, 267, 268
Clear cells, 221
Cleft
jaw, 15
lip, 15
median, 10
palate, 15
Clefts, facial malformation, 14-15
Clinical considerations
alveolar process, 210
cementum, 171-174
enamel development, 88
enamel histology, 65
eruption of teeth, 314
face and oral cavity, development, 14-16
maxillary sinus, 350
oral mucous membrane, 261
periodontal ligament, 192
pulp, 151
salivary glands, 294
shedding of deciduous teeth, 327
teeth, development and growth, 35
temporomandibular joint, 342
Clinical crown of tooth, 241, 243
Collagen, 355
Collagenous fibers; see Fibers, collagenous
Collagenous fibrils; see Fibrils, collagenous
Color of teeth, 40, 41
Condyle, mandibular, 335, 336, 338, 339,
340, 341
Connective tissue
cells, 137, 141, 186
fibers, 177, 354, 355
of gingiva, texture, 227
of gingival sulcus, 247
injections into, 262
of labial and buccal mucosa, 252, 253
lamina propria, 215, 222
periodontal, 156, 157, 158, 172, 176
in prefunctional eruptive phase, 303
protein-mucopolysaccharide complex, 356

Connective tissue—cont'd
pulp, 131
of salivary glands, 268, 275, 282
structure and chemical composition, 354
submucosa, 215
of tongue, secondary papillae of, 257
Contour lines of Owen, 106, 107
Copula, 14
Coronal pulp chamber, 128
Corpuscles
Krause, 226
Meissner, 225, 226
salivary, 292
Cortical plates of alveolar process, 201, 204,
208
Cracks, enamel, 56, 58
Craniomandibular joint, 335
Cribriform plate, 204
Cross-β keratins, 43
Crowns, tooth
anatomic and clinical, 241, 243
emergence of, 303
enamel-covered, color, 41
in hereditary enamel hypoplasia, 89
size and form, 37
Crypt, dental, 313
Crystals
apatite, 45, 85, 86, 88, 104, 157
enamel, 45, 46, 85
in mineralization of dentin, 122, 123
Cuff, attached epithelial, 229, 230, 233
Cushioned hammock ligament, 304, 307
Cuticle, dental, 230, 244, 245
Cuticle, enamel
primary, 57, 229, 243
secondary, 229, 230, 243, 244, 245
Cutting sections of specimen, 384, 388
Cysts
"anterior palatine," 16
dentigerous, 318
developmental, 15
periodontal, 195
thyroglossal duct, 14, 16
Cytochrome oxidase activity, 368, 369, 374,
375, 376
Cytologic correlations, salivary glands, 283
Cytoplasm
of odontoblasts, 111, 116
of serous cells, 284, 285, 287
Cytoplasmic extensions of odontoblasts, 98

D

Dead tracts in dentin, 114, 115, 116
Decalcification
of dentin, 97
of specimen, 386
Deciduous teeth
development, 19, 303
enamel and dentin of (diagram), 57
enamel development, 56

Deciduous teeth—cont'd
eruption, symptoms, 316
movements, 303
pulp during shedding, 326
remnants, 327, 330, 331, 332
resorption of, 331, 332, 333
retained, 328, 331, 333
shedding, 320-334
submerged, 332, 334
weakening of supporting tissues, 325
Defense cells of pulp, 139, 142
Defensive function of pulp, 127
Dehydration of specimens, 384, 387
Dehydrogenase activity, 370
Demilunes
of von Ebner or Giannuzzi, 272
of serous cells, 279, 282
of sublingual gland, esterase activity, 372, 373
Dendritic melanoblasts, 221, 222
Dental
calculus, 295
caries; *see* Caries
cuticle, 230, 244, 245
crypt, 313
epithelium; *see* Epithelium, dental
granuloma, 194, 195
lamina, 11, 19
bell stage, 29
and bud stage, 22
fate, 30
function, 29
lymph, 111
organ, 18, 19, 21, 22, 68
papilla, 18, 116
basement membrane of, 76
bell stage, 29
cap stage, 26
development, 131
periosteum, 176
plaque, 295, 296
pulp; *see* Pulp
sac, 18
bell stage, 29
cap stage, 28
two layers, 304
Denticles, 147, 148, 149, 150
Dentigerous cyst, 318
Dentin, 96-123
age and functional changes, 110
alkaline phosphatase activity, 365
atypical, formation of, 36
birefringence, 96
calcification, linear and globular, 121
caries and, 65
carious, 113, 114, 116, 123
cementum deposit on, 166
chemical analysis, 355
chemical composition, 96
circumpulpal, 104
collagenous fibrils, 96, 102
dead tracts, 114, 115, 116

Dentin—cont'd
decalcified section showing dentinal fibers and tubules, 99
of deciduous teeth and first permanent molar (diagram), 57
at dentinoenamel junction, 60
denuded, hypersensitivity of, 174
deposition of new layers, 111
development, 116
direction of rods from, 48, 49
exposed, care of, 123
formation, 33, 34, 36, 70, 71, 75, 118, 128
incremental lines, 104, 105, 106
innervation, 109
interglobular, 107, 108
intertubular, 102, 103, 104
mantle, 104
matrix, 104
mineral component, 104
mineralization, 41, 120-123
odontoblastic processes, 98, 100, 101
operations in, 123
origin, 19
peritubular, 41, 101, 102, 103
physical properties, 96
postnatal and prenatal, separation, 106, 107
production, function of pulp, 127
protection of pulp by, 127
reparative, 111, 114, 127
resorption of cementum continued into, 173
response to pathologic influences, 110
sclerotic, 41, 111, 115
secondary, 110, 112
sensitivity, 109, 110, 123, 262
staining, 360, 361
structure, 97
surface areas at outside and inside, 98
Tomes' granular layer, 108, 109
transparent, 111, 112, 113, 115
vitality of, 110
Dentinal tubules, 97, 98
branching, 99, 100
exposure of, 114, 115
filled with air, 113
in secondary dentin, 110, 111, 112
Dentinocemental junction, 36, 37
Dentinoenamel junction, 29, 36, 37, 60
branching of dentinal tubules close to, 99
hypermineralized zone at, 57
scalloped, 61, 63
Dentinoenamel membrane, 76, 77, 78
Dentinogenesis, 118, 364
Dentistry, restorative, 261
Dentition
deciduous, 320
human, chronology of (table), 317
permanent, 320
relation of maxillary sinus to, 344

Dentogingival junction, 228, 244
  shift of, 236, 239
Dentoperiosteal fibers, 223
Denture construction, mucous membrane in,
  263
Desmocranium, 197
Desmolysis, 238
Desmolytic stage of ameloblasts, 77
Desmosomes, 70, 71, 215
Desoxyribonucleic acid (DNA), 356
Development
  of alveolar process, 200
  of dentin, 116-123
  of face, 1-6
  of maxilla and mandible, 197
  of maxillary sinus, 344
  of periodontal ligament, 177
  of pulp, 131, 136
  of salivary glands, 282
  of secondary palate, 6-12
  of teeth, 18-37
  of tongue, 12-14
Developmental cysts, 15
Diaphragm, epithelial, 32, 33, 312
Differential growth, 312
Diffuse calcifications, 148, 149
Digestive function of saliva, 293
Dinitrofluorobenzene (DNFB) method, 361
Discs, rod arrangement shown by, 49, 51
Diseases, systemic, effect on oral mucosa, 263
Distal terminal bars of ameloblasts, 81
DNA, 356
DNAse, 287, 288
Dorsal lingual mucosa, 256
DPNH-TPNH-diaphorases, 370
Drifting of teeth, 209, 301, 308, 312
Ducts
  intercalated, 273, 288
  nasopalatine, 249
  of parotid gland, 276, 277
  of salivary glands, 268, 271, 273
  striated, 274, 288, 289
  of sublingual glands, 277, 279
  of submandibular gland, 277, 279
Dyes, 355, 359, 364

E

Ear, formation, 13
von Ebner
  demilunes of, 272
  glands of, 258, 282
  incremental lines of, 104, 105, 106
Ectoderm, oral, 18, 19
Elastin, 355
Electrolytes and water, secretion by salivary
  glands, 290, 291
Electron microscope
  ameloblasts under, 74
  apatite crystals under, 104
  crystals under, 45, 56

Electron microscope—cont'd
  dentin studies, 101, 102, 103, 105
  dentinoenamel membrane seen in, 77
  in future of histochemistry, 360
  glands, value of studies, 283
  intercalated ducts, studies, 288
  mineralization of dentin under, 122
  mitochondria, studies, 75
  mucous glands, studies, 288
  myoepithelial cells, studies, 290
  odontoblast, typical, under, 117
  predentin formation, studies, 119, 120
  rod contours under, 44
  rod sections under, showing crystals, 86,
    87
  rod sheath under, 46
  salivary glands under, 267
  serous cells, studies, 283, 286
  striated ducts, studies, 288
Electrophoretic components of saliva, 291
Embedded remnants of deciduous teeth, 330,
  331
Embedded teeth, 316
Embedding specimen
  in paraffin, 384
  in parlodion, 388
Embryo, human
  advanced bell stage of tooth development,
    30
  bell stage of tooth development, 27
  bud stage of tooth development, 23
  cap stage of tooth development, 24, 25, 26
  enamel organ layers, 67
  frontal section through head, 7, 8, 9
  median section through head, 2
  nasomaxillary and nasolacrimal grooves, 3
  palate reconstruction, 9
  roof of primitive oral and pharyngeal cav-
    ities, reconstruction, 7
  skull reconstruction (plate), 198
  tongue development, 12, 13
  tooth development, initiation of, 22
Embryonic bone, 211
Embryonic pulp, 131
Emergence of teeth; *see* Eruption
Enamel, 39-90
  age changes in, 64
  attachment of epithelium to, importance
    in restorative dentistry, 261
  caries spreading from dentin, 123
  and cementum, relation at cervical region,
    164
  chemical properties, 41
  cord, 26
  cuticle, 57, 83
    mechanical influences, 58
    of mouse molar, 58
    primary, 229, 243
    secondary, 229, 230, 243, 244, 245
    sections of, 59
  decalcified section, showing rods, 43

Enamel—cont'd
  of deciduous teeth
    development, 56
    and first permanent molar (diagram),
      57
  demineralized, showing rod contours, 44
  development, 68
    processes of, 77
  drop, cementum hyperplasia on, 169, 170
  epithelial attachment and, relation, 237,
      238, 239, 241, 243, 244
  epithelium, reduced, 61, 77
  in erupting teeth, 230, 233, 234, 236, 237,
      238, 239
  fissures, 65, 66
  formation, 36
    beginning, 70
    defective, 88
  function, 39
  gnarled, 51
  hardness, 39
  in hereditary hypoplasia, 89
  histology, 39
  hypocalcification, 88, 89
  hypoplasia, 88, 89
  incremental lines of Retzius, 52, 53, 57
  influence on color of teeth, 40, 41
  knot, 26
  lamellae, 56, 58
  matrix
    fibrils, orientation, 48, 49
    formation, 75, 78, 81, 82, 83, 88
    in hereditary hypocalcification, 89
    mineralization of, 83
    of mouse molar, 58
  maturation, 76, 85
  mottled, 60, 89
  neonatal line in, 56, 57
  organic elements, 41
  origin, 18
  outer, of recently completed human tooth,
      83
  pearls, 35
  permeability, 40
  physical characteristics, 39
  prenatal, 56, 57
  production of, 34
  pulp, 24
  rods
    and ameloblasts, linear arrangement, 82
    contours under electron microscope, 44
    course of, 65, 66
    direction of, 48, 49, 50
    ends, 54
    formation, 78, 79
    interprismatic substance, 46, 48, 49
    number and measurements, 43, 44
    sections showing crystals, 86, 87
    segmentation, 83
    striations, 47
  specific density, 40

Enamel—cont'd
  spindles, 62, 64
  spurs, pearls, or drops, formation, 166
  staining, 361
  structure, 43, 45
  surface
    care of, 67
    fluoride and, 295
    structures, 54, 55
  thickness, 39
  translucency, 41
  tufts, 60, 63
Endochondral bones of skull, 197
Endochondral ossification, 197, 200
Endocrine disturbances, 263
  retarded eruption due to, 314
Endocrine interrelations of salivary glands,
    294
Endoplasmic reticulum, 117, 284, 285, 288
Entodermal epithelium of pharyngeal
    pouches, 13
Enzyme(s)
  activity of cells associated with bones and
    teeth (table), 370
  as catalysts, 357
  histochemistry, 353, 357
    of hard tissues, 364
    of soft tissues, 371
  proteolytic, 368
  staining methods, 359, 364
Epithelial
  attachment, 221, 229, 234, 235, 236, 237,
      238, 239, 240, 241, 242, 243, 244,
      245, 246
    to enamel, mode of, 243
    firmness, 246
    importance in restorative dentistry, 261
    relation to tooth, 237, 238, 239
    separation from enamel, 236, 244
    separation from tooth surface, 246
    structure, 233
  buds, salivary glands from, 282
  cells
    of dental organ, layers, 68
    of saliva, 292
  cuff, attached, 229, 230, 233
  dental organ
    development, 68
    layers, 28
  diaphragm, 32, 33, 312
  laminae, 11
  masses, pathologic, 191
  pearls, 252
  pegs, 215
  rests, 10, 310
    cysts from, 15
    degenerated, 170
    of Malassez, 32, 156
    periodontal cyst from, 194
    in periodontal ligament, 187, 188, 189,
      191

Epithelial—cont'd
  root sheath of Hertwig, 29, 32, 128, 147,
      156, 166, 167, 190, 304
  structures in periodontal ligament, 190
  suture, 10
  tissues, histochemistry, 356
Epithelium
  dental, 22, 165, 166
    cap stage, 24
    cyst formation, 316
    inner, 28, 72, 73
    outer, 29, 69
    reduced, 229, 230, 231, 233, 303
  enamel, reduced, 77
  gingival, 219, 220, 254
  glandular, morphogenesis, 282
  of hard palate, 247
  keratinized, 214, 215, 216, 217, 219, 229
  of maxillary sinus, 348
  mode of attachment, 243
  of mucosa on lips and cheek, 252
  nonkeratinizing, 214, 217, 218
  oral, 229, 231, 247, 303
  in palatal formation, 10
  parakeratinized, 229
  of pharyngeal pouches, 13
  of sinus mucosa, 349
  strands in periodontal ligament, 189, 190
  stratified squamous, 214, 233, 260
  of striated ducts, 288
Ergastoplasm, 270, 284
Eruption, 229, 230, 232, 236, 301-318
  active, 236, 303
  clinical considerations, 314
  of deciduous teeth, symptoms, 316
  forces, 311, 312
  functional phase, 308
  histology, 301
  mechanism, 310-314
  passive, 236, 237, 238, 239, 240, 241, 303
    diagram of stages, 243
  phases, 301
  preeruptive phase, 301
  prefunctional phase, 303
  retarded, 314
  time of, 314, 315
  vertical, 308, 309, 310, 313
Eruptive cyst, 318
Eruptive movements of teeth, 199, 208
Esterase activity, 366, 372, 373
Ethylene diaminated EDTA decalcification,
    358
Evolution of periodontal ligament, 179
Excementoses, 168, 169, 170, 174, 191
Excentric growth of tooth germ, 302
Exposed pulp, 129, 152
Exposure, tooth; *see* Eruption
Extension of maxillary sinus, 347, 350
Extraction wounds, healing, 211
Eyes, position, 6

F

Face
  development, 1-6
  primordia, 2
  upper, bones of, development, 197
Facial malformations, 14
Fatty zone of hard palate, 247, 248, 249,
    250
Fauces, anterior pillars of, 216
Fetus, human
  sagittal section through head, 31
  tooth germ of, dentin and enamel forma-
      tion, 70
Feulgen method, 356
Fibers
  of alveolodental ligament, 181, 182
  argyrophil, 131, 136, 157, 158, 303, 304
  of articular disc, 341
  collagenous, 158, 177, 223, 224, 227, 304,
      338, 340, 349, 354, 355
  connective tissue, 177, 354, 355
  in dental papilla, 131, 136
  destruction in tooth exposure, 238
  elastic, of alveolar mucosa and submucosa,
      223, 224
  gingival, 181, 223
  Korff's, 118, 119, 120, 136, 365
  loss of regular arrangement, 192
  mechanism of production, 355
  nerve, of pulp, 109, 146
  of periodontal ligament, 162, 177, 178,
      179, 181-184
  pulp, 127, 131, 134
  in salivary glands, 275, 276
  Sharpey's, 160, 161, 162, 171, 192, 194,
      204, 208, 244
  Tomes', 98
  of transseptal ligament, 181
  "ultraterminal," 225, 226
Fibrils
  collagenous, 157, 158, 161
    of dentin, 96, 102, 104, 105, 111
    in mineralization of dentin, 121, 122
    of predentin, 119, 120
  in embryonic bone, 211
  of organic matrix, crystals and, 87
Fibroblasts, 131, 134, 184, 341, 342, 354,
    355
Fibrocartilage, 340, 341
  symphysial, 200
Fibrosis in pulp, 151
Fibrous covering of mandibular condyle, 337,
    338, 340, 341
Fibrous elements in pulp, 138
Filiform papillae, 257, 258
Filling root canals, 151, 152

Fissures, enamel, 65, 66
Fistula, antraoral, 351
Fixation procedures, 358
Fixation of specimens, 383, 386
Floor of maxillary sinus, 347, 348, 350
  accidental removal, 350, 351
Fluoride
  in caries control, 65
  hypocalcification, 89
  levels, effect on enamel formation, 88
  in saliva, 295
  in water, cause of mottled enamel, 89
Fluorosis during amelogenesis, 88
Folding of cell membrane, 288, 289
Foliate papillae, 260, 261
Foramen, apical, 128, 130, 131, 144, 146,
  151
Foramen cecum, 14, 260
Forces in eruption, 311, 312
Fordyce spot, 252, 253, 263
Forebrain, 1
Foregut, 2
Formalin, 358, 383, 386
Formation of primary palate, 3-6
Formative function
  of periodontal ligament, 176
  of pulp, 127
Formative stage of ameloblasts, 75
Fornix, vestibular, 254
Fractures
  healing, 211
  of temporomandibular joint, 342
Free gingiva, 226, 227
Free gingival groove, 226, 228
Freeze-dry process of fixation, 358
Frenula, labial, 254
Frontonasal processes, 2, 3
Frozen sections, preparation, 391
Frozen tissues, 358, 362
Fucomucin, 363
Function
  adaptation of bone to, 211
  of cementum, 167
  of maxillary sinus, 349
  of periodontal ligament, 176
  of pulp, 127
  of salivary glands, 290
Functional changes in dentin, 110
Functional eruptive phase, 308
Functional repair of cementum resorption,
  173
Fungiform papillae, 257, 258, 261
"Fusions," 3

G

Genetic code, DNA and RNA and, 356
Germ, tooth
  with beginning dentin formation, 71
  decalcified section of enamel showing rods,
    43
  developing, 200
  of embryo, layers of enamel organ, 67
  eruption, 311
  of fetus, dentin and enamel formation, 70
  growth, 311
  histodifferentiation, 36
  permanent, 320, 322
    positions, 305
    of premolars, position, 324, 325
  in preeruptive phase, 302
  zones around, 177
Giannuzzi, demilunes of, 272
Gingiva
  and alveolar mucosa, differences, 222, 223,
    224
  and alveolar mucosa, separation, 254
  atrophy, 239
  attached, 226, 227, 228
  attachment to cementum, 181
  attachment to teeth, 222
  blood supply, 224
  characteristics, 218
  connective tissue of, 227
  cytochrome oxidase activity, 374, 376
  detachment from tooth, 244
  divisions, 226
  effect of mastication on, 218
  epithelial attachment, 229, 243
  free, 226, 227
  histochemistry, 362
  injuries, 262
  interdental papillae, 224, 226, 227, 228
  lamina propria of, 221, 222
  marginal, 230
  nerve supply, 226
  and palatine mucosa, structural differ-
    ences, 248
  phosphatase activity, 371, 372
  pigmentation, 221
  recession of, 240, 262
  submucosa, 218
  surface, 219
  surface characteristics (diagram), 226
  and tooth surface, relation, 236
Gingival
  epithelium, 219, 220, 254
  fibers, 223
  groove, free, 226, 228
  ligament, 223
    fibers of, 181
  margin
    discoloration, 263
    extension of, in restorative dentistry, 262
  pockets, 261

Gingival—cont'd
  region of hard palate, 247
  sulcus, 230, 233, 236, 237, 238, 240, 241,
    244, 246
    formation and depth, 246, 247
    importance in restorative dentistry, 261,
    262
Gingivitis, 67
Glands
  buccal, 252, 281
  von Ebner's, 258
  glossopalatine, 281
  labial, 252, 281
  lingual, 282
  palatine, 281
  parathyroid, 13
  parotid, 266, 267, 276, 277, 291
  salivary; *see* Salivary glands
  sublingual, 254, 266, 267, 279, 280, 291
  submandibular, 266, 267, 276, 277, 278,
    279, 291, 294
  of tongue, 282
Glandular epithelium, morphogenesis, 282
Glandular zone of hard palate, 247, 248,
  249, 250
Globular calcification of dentin, 121
Globular processes, 3
Globulins in saliva, 291
Glossitis, median rhomboid, 15
Glossopalatine glands, 281
Glossopharyngeal nerve, 261
Glucose-6-phosphate phosphorylation system,
  357
Glycerophosphate method, 359, 372
Glycogen complex, carbohydrate moiety of,
  360
Glycogen, staining, 362
Glycoproteins, 288
  in connective tissue, 354, 355
  in saliva, 291
  in salivary gland mucus, 363
  staining, 355, 362
Gnathoschisis, 14
Goblet cells, 349
Golgi
  apparatus, 72, 75, 270, 271, 285, 286
  bodies, 285, 286, 287
  lamellae, 286, 287
  vacuoles, 288
  vesicles, 285, 287
Gomori method, 358, 359, 364
Granular layer, Tomes', 108, 109
Granuloma, dental, 194, 195
Groove, free gingival, 226, 228
Ground sections of teeth or bone, preparation, 389
Ground substance
  of connective tissue, 354, 355
    in normal and abnormal conditions, altera-
    tions, 357

Ground substance—cont'd
  of oral tissues, histochemical procedures,
    360
Growth
  development and, of salivary glands, 282
  differential, 312
  of teeth, 18

H

Hammock ligament, 304, 307, 313
Hard palate; *see* Palate, hard
Hard tissues, 244
  oral, enzyme histochemistry, 364
  oral, protein and lipid histochemistry, 360
  relation to soft tissues, 242
Hardness, scale of, 40
Harelip, 14
Haversian lamellae, 208
Haversian systems, 203, 204, 206, 208
Head, frontal sections, 345
Heidenhain's classification of salivary glands,
  267
Hematoxylin and eosin, staining sections
  with, 386, 389
Hereditary enamel hypoplasia and hypocal-
  cification, 89
Hertwig's epithelial root sheath, 29, 32, 72,
  128, 147, 156, 166, 167, 190, 304
Highmore, antrum of, 344
Hirschfeld, canals of, 204
Histiocytes, 139
Histochemical reactions (plate), 360
Histochemical techniques, 352, 353, 358-376
  classification, 359
Histochemistry
  of enzymes, 357
  lipid, 360
  microscopic, 357
    advantage, 353
  mucin, 363
  of oral tissues, 352-376
  polysaccharide, 362
  protein, 360, 362
Histodifferentiation, fundamental law of, 76
Histodifferentiation of tooth germs, 36
Histologic specimens, preparation, 382-391
Histologic technique, definition, 382
Histology
  of enamel, 39
  of eruption, 301
  of maxillary sinus, 349
  of temporomandibular joint, 336
Histophysiology, development and growth of
  teeth, 35
Horizontal fibers, 181
Howship's lacunae, 185, 207, 208, 209
Hunter-Schreger bands, 51

Hutchinson's incisor, 37
Hyalin cartilage of mandibular condyle, 335, 336, 338, 340, 341, 342
Hyaluronic acid, 355
Hyaluronidase, 303
Hydrogen removal by enzyme activity, 369
Hydroxyapatite, 45, 97, 122, 296
Hyoid bone, 13, 198
Hypercementosis, 169, 351
Hypermineralized zones, 57
Hyperplasia of cementum, 169, 170, 171
Hypertrophy, cementum, 169
Hypocalcification
    enamel, 88, 89
    hereditary, appearance of teeth in, 90
Hypoparathyroidism as cause of enamel hypoplasia, 89
Hypophysis and salivary glands, 294
Hypoplasia, enamel, 88, 89

I

Imbrication lines of von Ebner, 104, 105
Impacted third molar, 316
Incineration of dentin, 97
Incisive fissure, 200
Incisive foramen, 200
Incisive papilla, 249
Incisor
    course of dentinal tubules in, 97
    deciduous, root resorption, 323
    developing, alkaline phosphatase activity, 366
    incremental appositional patterns (diagram), 105
    lower central, deciduous and permanent, stages in development, 304, 305
    mineralization pattern of (diagram), 84
    permanent, development, 303, 308
Incremental lines
    in cementum, 161, 162, 163
    of von Ebner, 104, 105, 106
    of Retzius, 52, 53, 57
Incus, 13, 198
Infections
    in oral cavity, 262
    sinus, due to periapical infection, 350
Infiltration of specimen
    with paraffin, 384
    with parlodion, 387
Inflammation, periodontal, 194
Initiation of tooth development, 35
Injections into oral cavity, 262
Injuries
    to gingiva, 262
    to temporomandibular joint, 342
Innervation of dentin, 109
Intercalated ducts, 273
    electron microscope studies, 288

Intercellular bridges, 70, 138, 214, 217
Intercellular substance
    of acellular cementum, 161
    of bone, 208
    in dentin, 96
    of pulp, 131
Interdental
    alveolar arteries, 224
    ligament, 181
    papillae, 224, 226, 227, 228, 244
        pigmentation in, 221
    septum, 177, 204, 210, 309, 330
    trabeculae, 204
Interglobular dentin, 107, 108
Intermediate cementum layer, 167
Intermediate plexus of periodontal ligament, 178, 179, 180, 194, 304
Intermediofacial nerve, 261
Internal reconstruction of bone, 208
Interprismatic substance, 43, 46, 48, 49
Interradicular fibers, 182
Interradicular septum, 204
Interradicular trabeculae, 204
Interstitial connective tissue of salivary glands, 275
Interstitial spaces of periodontal ligament, 185, 192, 193
Interstitial tissue of periodontal ligament, 186
Intertubular dentin, 102, 103, 104
Intramembranous bone, development of mandible as, 198
Intramembranous ossification, 197
Iodide concentration of saliva, 293
Iodine metabolism, role of salivary glands in, 290, 293

J

Jacobson's organ, 249
Jaw
    cleft, 15
    growing, tooth development in, 302, 305, 309
    remnants of teeth in, 328
    structural changes, 206
Joint, temporomandibular, 335-342

K

Keratin, enamel and, 41, 43
Keratin formation
    in gingiva, 218
    histochemistry, 363
Keratinization of gingiva, 219
Keratinized epithelium, 214, 215, 216, 217, 219, 229
Keratohyalin granules, 215
Koplik's spots, 263

Korff's fibers, 118, 119, 120, 136
  staining, 365
Krause corpuscles, 226
Krebs citric acid cycle, 370

L

Labial
  frenula, 254
  frenum, upper, 11
  glands, 267, 281
  mucosa, 252
  pits, 15
  sulcus, 11
Lacunae
  of cementum, 160, 162, 163, 164, 168
  Howship's, 185, 207, 208, 209
  resorption, 185
Lamellae, bone
  circumferential, 203, 204, 208
  interstitial, 203, 208
  longitudinal, 204
  separating permanent tooth from prede-
    cessor, 322
Lamellae, enamel, 56, 58
  caries and, 65
  staining, 361
  types, 58, 59
Lamellated bone, 204, 208, 209, 210
Lamina, dental, 11, 19
  bell stage, 29
  and bud stage, 22
  fate, 30
  function, 29
  of mandible, 21
Lamina propria
  of gingiva, 221, 222, 229
    alkaline phosphatase activity, 371
  of hard palate, 247, 249
  of labial and buccal mucosa, 252, 253
  of oral mucous membrane, 213, 214, 215,
    217, 218
  of sinus mucosa, 349
  staining, 362
Lamina, successional, 29
Lamina, vestibular, 11, 31
Larynx, formation, 198
Laser spectroscopy of calcified tissues, 352
Leukocytes, polymorphonuclear, enzyme ac-
    tivity, 371, 372
Life cycle
  of ameloblasts, 72-77
  of odontoblasts, 116
Ligament(s)
  alveolodental, 181, 182, 183
  gingival, 223
    fibers of, 181
  hammock, 304, 307, 313
  interdental, 181
  periodontal; *see* Periodontal ligament
  subdivisions, 181

Ligament(s)—cont'd
  suspensory, 178
  temporomandibular, 336, 342
  transseptal, 181, 182
Linear calcification of dentin, 121
Lines, contour, of Owen, 106, 107
Lines, incremental
  in cementum, 161, 162, 163
  in dentin, 104, 105, 106
  in enamel, 52, 53, 57
Lingual
  anomalies, 15
  crypt, 260
  follicles, 259, 260
  glands, 282
  mucosa, dorsal, 256
  papillae, atrophy of, 263
  tonsil, 260
Lining of maxillary sinus, 348, 349
Lining mucosa, 217, 252
Lip
  cleft, 15
  drying of, 217
  glands, 252
  lining mucosa, 252
  section of, 216
  skin of, 216
  upper, development, 11
  vermilion border, 216
Lipid histochemistry of oral hard tissues, 360
Lipid staining methods, 359, 360
Lipids in teeth, studies, 362
Loss of function, structural changes with,
    192
Lymph
  dental, 111
  supply of salivary glands, 275
  vessels in pulp, 146
Lymphatic portion of dorsal lingual mucosa,
    257
Lymphatic vessels of periodontal ligament,
    187
Lymphocytes, 260
  in gingival sulcus, 247
Lymphoid wandering cells, 144

M

Macrophages
  acid phosphatase activity, 365, 372
  in gingiva, 222
Malassez, epithelial rests of, 32, 156, 190
Malformations
  facial, 15
  tooth, 37
Malleus, 13, 198
Mandible
  appositional growth, 203
  cortical plates, 201
  dental lamina and dental organs, 21
  deposition of bone, 208

Mandible—cont'd
  development, 198, 200
  growth, 6
  and maxilla, 197-212
  reptilian, 179, 180
Mandibular
  alveolar ridge, 11
  arch, 1
  articulation, 335, 342
  condyle, 335, 336, 338, 339, 340, 341
  fossa, 337
  processes, 2, 3
  symphysis, development, 199
Mantle dentin, 104
Mantle predentin, 119
Marginal gingiva, 230
Marrow of mandibular condyle, 336
Mast cells, 355, 362, 372
Mastication, effect on
  enamel, 58, 64
  gingiva, 218
  oral mucosa, 217
Masticatory forces
  resistance of gingiva to, 229
  role in shedding of deciduous teeth, 325
  trauma due to, 327
Masticatory movements
  during eruption, 309
  limiting by periodontal ligament, 182
Masticatory mucosa, 217, 218
Matrix
  of dentin, 104
  enamel, mineralization of, 83
  of hard dental structures, deposition, 37
Maturation of enamel matrix, 85
Maturative stage of ameloblasts, 76
Maxilla
  body of, 344
  cortical plates, 201
  deposition of bone, 208
  development, 198
  and mandible, 197-212
Maxillary processes, 2, 3
Maxillary sinus
  anatomy, 344
  clinical considerations, 350
  compartments, 349
  development, 344
  disease, 350
  enlargement, 347, 348
  floor of, 347, 348, 350
  function, 349
  histology, 349
  involvement during extraction, 350, 351
  lining, 348, 349
  and oral cavity, accidental communication
    between, 350, 351
  relations, 346
  size, 345
Maxillary sinuses, supplemental, 349

Maximow's nomenclature, cells, 141
Measles, 263
Measurements of periodontal ligament, 191
Mechanism of eruption, 310-314
Meckel's cartilage, 13, 198, 200
Median cleft, 10
Meissner corpuscles, 225, 226
Melanin, 221
Melanoblasts, dendritic, 221, 222
Membrana preformativa, 29
Membrane
  basement, in dentin development, 116,
    117, 118
  dentinoenamel, 76, 77
  mucous; *see* Mucous membrane
  Nasmyth's, 57
  peridental, 176
  periodontal, 192, 194
Mental ossicles, 200
Merocrine glands, 266
Mesenchymal cells
  reserve, 207, 208
  undifferentiated, 141, 145
Mesenchymal tissues, salivary glands and,
  294
Mesenchyme, 18, 19
Mesial drift, 192, 208, 209, 308
  physiologic, 310
Mesoderm, 5, 10
Metabolic activity of salivary glands, 290
Metachromatic reaction, 355, 362
Metal poisoning, 263
Meyer's albumin adhesive, 385
Microscope
  electron; *see* Electron microscope
  salivary glands under, 266, 267
  study of tissues under, preparation, 382
Microscopic histochemistry, 352, 353, 357
Microtechnique, definition, 382
Microvilli at distal extremities of ameloblasts,
  76
Mineral component of dentin, 104
Mineral content of enamel, defect due to, 88
Mineralization
  of dentin, 120-123
    interglobular dentin and, 107
  of enamel matrix, 83
  of enamel, primary and secondary, 41
  full, of enamel, 76
  pattern of incisor (diagram), 84
Mineralized tissues, formation, mineraliza-
    tion, and maturation, 41, 42
Mitochondria, 72, 117, 269, 270, 271, 274,
    286, 287, 288, 289, 368, 369
  electron microscope studies, 75
Mitotic index of cell renewal, 219
Mixed glands, salivary, 267, 272
Mohs scale of hardness, 40
Molar
  with accessory canal filled, roentgenogram,
    135

Molar—cont'd
  deciduous
    of human fetus, cross section, 302
    lower, stages of development, 306
    maturation, 84
  excementoses in bifurcation, 170
  glands, 281
  mandibular
    second, root resorption, 316, 317
    third, eruption, 316, 317
    third, exposed pulp, 129
  maxillary
    hypercementoses on roots, 351
    loss of, 350
    third, impaction, 316
  permanent, first
    age changes in pulp chamber, 129
    enamel and dentin of, 57
  rat, periodontal ligament, 179
Molars
  deciduous
    relation to erupting premolars, 324, 325
    root remnants, 328, 330
    root resorption, 324, 325, 327
  permanent, developing, position, 305
Morphodifferentiation in tooth development, 36
Morphogenesis of glandular epithelium, 282
Morphogenic stage of ameloblasts, 72
Motor fibers of pulp, 127
Mottled enamel, 60, 89
Mounting cut sections on slides, 385
Mouth, floor of
  glands, 268
  mucous membrane, 255
Movements, tooth, factors responsible, 313, 314
Mucigen granules of mucous cells, 269, 270, 271
Mucins
  histochemistry, 356, 357, 363
  of mucous cells, 288
  staining, 364
Mucogingival junction, 218, 254
Mucoids; see Mucins
Mucopolysaccharides
  acid, disappearance, 303
  in connective tissue, 354, 355
  of dentin, 97
  depolymerization of, 357
  in enamel, 43
  epithelial cuff attached by, 229, 243, 245
  in ground substance of matrix, 121
  in intermediate plexus, 178
  of periodontal connective tissue, 157, 158
  staining, 359
Mucoproteins
  in saliva, 267
  staining, 359
Mucosa; see also Mucous membrane
  alveolar, 218, 254
  dorsal lingual, 256

Mucosa—cont'd
  lining, 217, 252
  masticatory, 217, 218
  oral, effect of systemic diseases, 263
  oral, subdivisions, 217
  specialized, 217, 256
  sublingual, 254
  and submucosa of oral cavity, glands in, 266
Mucous acini, 276
  alveoli of sublingual gland, 270
  cells, 269, 271, 272
    electron microscope studies, 288
  glands, 267
Mucous membrane; see also Mucosa
  of cheeks and lips, attachments, 254
  of denture construction, 263
  of floor of oral cavity, 260, 261
  of hard palate, 247
  of inferior surface of tongue, 254, 255
  of maxillary sinus, 348, 349
  of mouth in old age, 263
  oral, 213-263
    diagram, 214
    morphologic structure, 213
  and skin, transition between, 216
  of soft palate, oral surface of, 254, 256
  of tongue, body and base, differences, 257, 258
Multirooted teeth, erupting, histology, 308
Muscles
  lining mucosa covering, 252
  of tongue, 14
Myelinated nerve fibers in pulp, 147
Mylohyoid muscle, 277
Myoepithelial cells, 274
  electron microscope studies, 290

N

"Nadi" reaction, 369
Naphthol As-D chloroacetate, 372
Nasal
  cavity
    floor of, relation to floor of sinus, 348
    relation of maxillary sinus to, 345, 346
  meatus, middle, 344, 345
  pits, 4
  processes, 2, 3
  sacs, 4
  septum, 6, 8
  sinuses, reason for development, 349
Nasmyth's membrane, 57
Nasobuccal membrane, 5
Nasolabial cysts, 16
Nasolacrimal grooves, 3
Nasomaxillary grooves, 3
Nasopalatine ducts, 249
Necrosis, pulp, 152
Neonatal line, 56, 57, 106, 107

Nerve fibers
of oral mucous membrane, 215, 216
of pulp, 109, 127, 146
Nerve growth factor, 293
Nerves
of gingiva, 224
palatine, 249, 251
of periodontal ligament, 187
of pulp, 146
pulpstones close to, 150
of salivary glands, 275
below taste buds, 261
Nervous system in regulation of growth of
salivary glands, 283
Neumann, sheath of, 103
Neuraminic acid, 364
Neuroepithelial cells, 261
NGF, 293
Ninhydrin-Schiff method, 361
Nose, formation, 4-6
Nostrils, 6
primary, 4
Nuclei
of osteoclasts, 206
of serous cells, 270, 271
Nucleic acids and protein synthesis, 356
Nucleoproteins, 355, 356
Nucleus, cell, genetic code and, 356
Nutritional deficiencies, retarded eruption
due to, 314
Nutritive function of pulp, 127

O

Oblique fibers, 182
Obtaining specimens for histologic study,
383, 386
Occlusal
movement of teeth during growth, 309
plane, 309
stress, cementum hyperplasia due to, 174
trauma, 193
loss of retained deciduous teeth due to,
332
Occlusion, tooth in, 237
Occlusomesial movements, 309, 310, 314
Odontoblastic processes
degenerating, 114, 115, 116
in dentin, 98, 100, 101
in enamel, 62, 64
Odontoblasts, 75, 326, 330
degeneration of, 115, 116
in dentin, 96, 97, 110, 111
differentiation, 33, 36, 116, 117, 119
form and arrangement in pulp, 138, 139
function, 36, 37
life cycle, 116-118
nourishment of dentin through, 127
of pulp, 131, 136-139
typical, electron photomicrograph, 117
variations in different regions of tooth, 140

Olfactory pits, 4, 5
Oncocytes, 275
Operations in dentin, 123
Oral cavity
development, 1
floor of, 12
membrane, 254
functions, 213
and maxillary sinus, accidental communication between, 350, 351
proper, glands of, 268
roof, 6, 7
two parts, 216
Oral ectoderm, 18, 19
Oral epithelium, 229, 231, 247, 303
Oral fossa, 1, 2
Oral mucous membrane, 213-263
effect of systemic diseases on, 263
subdivisions, 217
Oral orifice, size, 6
Oral roof, 11
Oral tissues; *see* Tissues
Oral vestibule, 12
Orbicularis oris muscle, 254
Organ, dental, 18
development, 68
Organelles in salivary secretion, 287
Organic
elements of enamel, 41
matter in ribbons forming sheaths for
crystals, 87
reagents, new, in future of histochemistry,
359
Organizing stage of ameloblasts, 75
Organogenesis, fundamental law of, 76
Orthodontic tooth movement, 209
stimuli, 193
Orthodontic treatment
adjustment period, 193
cementum resorption and, 171, 172
Orthokeratosis, 218, 220
Ossicles
auditory, development, 198
mental, 200
Ossification
centers of premaxilla and maxilla, 198
endochondral, 197, 200
intramembranous, 197
Osteoblasts, 184, 354
alkaline phosphatase activity, 366, 367
citric acid cycle in, 370
staining, 364
Osteoclastic resorption, 325
Osteoclasts, 184, 206, 207, 208, 326, 365,
366, 367, 368, 369, 370
citric acid cycle in, 370
enzyme activity, 369, 370
root resorption by, 320
staining, 368, 369, 370
Osteocytes, 207, 208, 365
in embryonic bone, 211

Osteodentin, 36
Osteogenesis, 364
Osteoid tissue, 208
Osteoporosis of alveolar process, 211
Ostium maxillare, 345
Owen, contour lines of, 106, 107

P

Pain
   dental, due to maxillary sinus disease, 350
   receptors in periodontal ligament, 188
   sensation in pulp, 147
Palate
   cleft, 15
   hard, 198, 247, 248, 250, 251
      development, 8, 10
      glands of, 282
      mucous membrane of, 247
      relation to maxillary sinus, 349
      submucosa, 218
      zones, 244, 248, 250
   of human embryo, reconstruction of, 9
   mucosa of, 217, 219
   primary, formation of, 3-6
   primary, six stages in development, 4-5
   secondary, development of, 6-12
   soft, 8, 248, 250
      glands of, 282
      mucosa of, 252
      oral surface, mucous membrane, 254,
         256
Palatine
   glands, characteristics, 281
   mucosa, 248
   papilla, 11, 249, 251
   processes
      development, 6-12
      transposition, 8
   raphe, 218, 247, 249
   rugae, 11, 249
   tonsil, 13
   torus, 247
   vessels and nerves, 249, 251
Palatoglossal arches, 216
Papilla
   dental, 18, 116
      basement membrane of, 76
      bell stage, 29
      cap stage, 26
      development, 131
   incisive, 249
   palatine, 11
Papillae
   of connective tissue, 222
   filiform, 257, 258
   foliate, 260, 261
   fungiform, 257, 258, 261
   interdental, 224, 226, 227, 244
      pigmentation in, 221

Papillae—cont'd
   of lamina propria, 215
   lingual, 14
      atrophy of, 263
   vallate, 14, 257, 258, 259, 260
      glands of, 267, 282
Papillary portion of dorsal lingual mucosa,
     257
Paraffin, infiltration of specimen with, 384
Paraffin-embedded specimens, preparation of
     sections, 383-386
Parakeratinized epithelium, 229
Parakeratosis, 218, 219, 220
Parathyroid glands, 13
Parietal plexus, 147
Parlodion, infiltration of specimen with, 387
Parlodion-embedded specimens, preparation
     of sections, 386-389
Parotid acinous cell of mouse, 283, 284, 285,
     286
Parotid glands, 266, 267, 276, 277
   ducts, enzyme activity, 373
   ducts and terminal secretory portions, 273
   secretions, 291
Parotid saliva, secretions, 267
Parotin, 294
Pars glabra, 11
Pars villosa, 11
pa-S technique; *see* Periodic acid–Schiff
     technique
Passive eruption, 236, 237, 238, 239, 240,
     241, 303
   diagram of stages, 243
Pathologic changes in periodontal ligament
     due to trauma, 193
Pathologic conditions related to salivary
     glands, 294
Pearls
   enamel, 35
   epithelial, 252
Periapical infection, 350
Periapical inflammation, hyperplasia of ce-
     mentum with, 170, 174
Pericementum, 176
Pericytes of capillaries in pulp, 145
Peridental membrane, 176
Perikaryon of odontoblasts, 98, 110
Perikymata, 54, 55, 57
   disappearance of, 64
Periodic acid–Schiff technique, 359, 360,
     361, 362, 363, 364
Periodontal connective tissue, 156, 157, 158
   stress on, 172
Periodontal cyst, 195
Periodontal disease
   pathogenesis, 261
   pulp necrosis in, 152
   salivary factors, 295

Periodontal ligament
blood supply, 186
cells, 184, 185, 186
cementicles, 190, 191
clinical considerations, 192
comparison in different locations around
same tooth, 192
of deciduous teeth, traumatic changes,
325, 326, 328
development, 177
effect of mesial drift on, 192
epithelial rests in, 187, 188, 189, 191
epithelial structures, 190
evolution, 179
fibers, 162, 177, 178, 179, 181-184
gingival, 181, 223
function, 176
of functioning tooth and periodontal membrane of nonfunctioning tooth, comparison, 194
intermediate plexus, 178, 179, 180, 194
interstitial tissue, 185, 186
lymphatics, 187
measurements 191
of monkey premolars, 178
narrowing of, 192
nerves, 187
origin, 19
in orthodontic tooth movement, 193
pathologic changes due to trauma, 193
physiologic changes, 191, 192
primitive, layers, 304
protective function, 182
of rat molar, 179
structural elements, 177
terminology, 176
thickness, 191
three zones, 177
trauma to, 327
Periodontal membrane, 192, 194
Periosteum
of alveolar bone, attachment of gingiva to,
222
attachment to alveolar mucosa, 254
dental, 176
of hard palate, 247, 249
Peritubular dentin, 41, 101, 102, 103
Permanent teeth, development, 303
Permanent tooth, retardation of eruption, 314
Phagocytic cells, 365
Pharyngeal pouches, 13
Pharynx, anterior wall, 12
Phleboliths, 147
Phosphatase
acid, 365, 367, 371
activity, 359, 367
alkaline, 364, 365, 367, 371
Phosphate in saliva, 295
Phosphorescence of oral tissues, 352, 353
Phosphorylase activity, 375, 376

Physical characteristics
of cementum, 155
of enamel, 39
Physical properties of dentin, 96
Physiologic
changes
in alveolar process, 206
in periodontal ligament, 191, 192
correlations, salivary glands, 283
growth processes in tooth development, 35
mesial drift, 310
movement of teeth, 192, 208
Pigmentation of gingiva, 221
Pinocytotic vesicles, 290
Piriform aperture, 198
Pits, labial, 15
Plaque, dental, 295, 296
Plasma cells in gingival sulcus, 247
Plasmin, 357
Plexus
intermediate, 304
of periodontal ligament, 178, 179, 180,
194
parietal, 147
subodontoblastic, 139
Pneumatization of body of maxilla, 347, 348
Polymorphonuclear leukocytes, enzyme activ-
ity, 371, 372
Polysaccharide histochemistry of oral soft
tissues, 362
Polysaccharide-protein complex in enamel,
43
Polysaccharides, 283, 287
in connective tissue, 354, 356
staining, 362
Pore, taste, 260, 261
Potassium, secretion by salivary glands, 289
Predentin, 118, 119, 120
Preeruptive phase, 301
Prefunctional eruptive phase, 303
Premaxilla, 198, 200
Premolar, first
permanent, stages in development, 306
upper, buccolingual section, 347
Premolars, eruption of, 324, 325
of monkey, periodontal ligament of, 178
permanent, development, 303
permanent, remnants of roots near, 328
Preparation of specimens for histologic study,
382-391
Pressure
in dental crypt, 313
effect on bone, 210
Prickle cells, 214, 215, 217, 220
Primary enamel cuticle, 229, 243
Primordia
of face, 2
of salivary glands, 282
of teeth, 23
Primordial cysts, 16
Prisms, enamel, 43
Process, alveolar; *see* Alveolar process

Processes
  nasal, 2, 3
  odontoblastic, 62, 64
    in dentin, 98, 100, 101
  palatine, development, 6-12
  Tomes', 78, 79, 80, 81, 83
Proliferation stage of tooth development, 36
Pronglike excementoses, 168, 169
Proprioceptive reflexes, 188
Prosencephalon, 1
Protective function of periodontal ligament, 182
Protective stage of ameloblasts, 77
Protein
  complexes in connective tissue, 355
  histochemistry of oral tissues, 360, 362
  staining methods, 359, 360
  synthesis
    nucleic acids and, 356
    in salivary glands, 283, 285, 287
Protein-carbohydrate complexes in saliva, 296
Protein-mucopolysaccharide complex in connective tissue, 356
Proteins
  in connective tissue, 354, 355, 356
  of saliva, 267, 291, 296
Proteolytic enzymes, 268
Pseudoalveolar ridge, 11
Pseudoglandular structure of epithelial rest in periodontal ligament, 189
Pulp
  age changes, 137
  anatomy, 128
  arteries, 143, 144, 145
  capping, 153
  chamber, 128
    age changes, 129
    shape, 151
  clinical considerations, 151
  of deciduous teeth during shedding, 326
  defects in, 35
  defense cells of, 139, 142
  defensive reactions, 127
  dental, longitudinal growth, 312
  denticles, 147, 148, 149, 150
  destruction, causes, 128
  development, 131, 136
  diffuse calcifications, 148, 149
  embryonic, 131
  enamel, 24
  exposed, 129, 152
  fibrosis, 151
  function, 127
  intercellular substance, 131
  longitudinal growth, 312
  lymph vessels, 146
  necrosis, 152
  nerve fibers, 109, 127, 131, 134
  nerve supply, 146
  odontoblasts, 131, 136-139
  origin, 18

Pulp—cont'd
  pain sensation, 147
  pericytes, 145
  pulpstones, 147-151
  regressive changes, 147
  structural elements, 131
  veins, 143, 144
Pulpal horns, 128, 151, 152
Pulpal tissue, growth, 312
Pulpstones, 128, 147-151
Pyroxylin, embedding sections in, 386

R

Radioisotope studies of protein synthesis, 285, 287
Radiolucence of immature bone, 211
Raphe, palatine, 218, 247, 249
Rathke's pouch, 2
Receptors, pain, in periodontal ligament, 188
Recession of gingiva, 240
Reconstruction of bone, internal, 208
Red color of lips, 216, 217
Reduced dental epithelium, 229, 230, 231, 233, 303
Regressive changes in pulp, 147
Remnants of deciduous teeth, 327, 330, 331, 332
Repair of resorbed cementum, 172, 173
Reparative dentin, 111, 114, 127
Reptiles, mandible of, 179, 180
Resorption
  bone, 208, 209, 210, 313, 314, 349
  of cementum, 171, 172, 173
  of deciduous teeth, 331, 332, 333
  lacunae, 185
  osteoclastic, 325
  root, 314, 316, 317
    of deciduous teeth, 320, 321, 323, 324, 327
Rest periods in shedding of deciduous teeth, 326
Resting cells, enzyme activity, 370
Resting lines, 208
Restorative dentistry, 261
  importance of structural changes to, 192
Retained deciduous teeth, 328, 331, 333
Retarded eruption, 314
Reticulin, 355
Reticulum
  endoplasmic, 117, 284, 285, 288
  stellate, 24, 25, 28, 68, 69, 70
Retromandibular fossa, 276
Retzius, incremental lines of, 52, 53, 57
Reversal lines, 206, 208, 210
Ribbons of organic matter forming sheaths for enamel crystals, 87
Ribonuclease, 284, 287
Ribonucleic acid (RNA), 284, 285, 356
Rickets as cause of enamel hypoplasia, 89

RNA, 356
  particles, 285
RNAse, 287
RNP particles, 284, 287
Rod ends, 54
  loss of, 64
Rod sheaths, 43, 47
  fibrillar character, 46
Rods, enamel; *see* Enamel rods
Root
  apices in sinus cavity, 347, 348
  canals, 128
    drawings, 132, 133
    filling, 151, 152
  of deciduous teeth
    remnants, 327, 328, 330, 331
    resorption, 320, 321, 323, 324, 327
  development, 34, 304
  end, undeveloped, 130
  formation, 32
  growth, 312, 313
  resorption, 314, 316, 317
  sheath of Hertwig, 29, 32, 128, 147, 156,
    166, 167, 190, 304
  transparency in tooth, 112, 115
Rotating of teeth, 301, 308, 312
Rouget's cells, 145
Rugae, palatine, 11, 249

S

Sac, dental, 18
  bell stage, 29
  cap stage, 28
Saliva, 213, 275, 291
  constituents of, 291, 292
  and dental plaque, 296
  digestive function, 293
  influence on oral health and disease, 294
  modifications in oral cavity, 291
  mucins in, 363
  production of, 266, 290
  protein secretion, 267
  relation to dental caries, 294, 295
  relation to periodontal disease, 295
  separation of proteins from, 291
Salivary corpuscles, 292
Salivary factors
  in dental caries, 294, 295
  in periodontal disease, 295
Salivary glands, 266-300
  atrophy of, 263
  blood supply, 275
  classifications, 267, 268
  clinical considerations, 294
  collection of secretions for study, 292
  connective tissue, 275, 282
  cytologic, chemical, and physiologic cor-
    relations, 283
  development and growth, 282
  ducts, 268, 271, 273
    enzyme activity, 372, 373

Salivary glands—cont'd
  endocrine interrelations, 294
  fibers in, 275, 276
  functions, 290
  histochemistry, 353
  in iodine metabolism, 293
  major, 266
    comparison, 277
  minor, 266, 281
  mucins, histochemistry, 363, 364
  nervous system in growth of, 283
  pathologic conditions, 294
  primordia, 282
  protein synthesis, 283, 285, 287
  structural elements, 268
  terminal portions, 268, 271, 273, 274
Scarlet fever, 263
Sclerotic dentin, 41, 111, 115
Sebaceous gland in cheek, 252, 253, 263
Secondary dentin, 110, 112
Secondary enamel cuticle, 229, 230, 243,
    244, 245
Secretion granules of serous cells, 270, 271
Secretion, salivary, process of, 283, 285, 286,
    287, 288
Secretory cells of salivary glands, 267, 268
Secretory cycle, salivary, changes in mito-
    chondria, 287, 288
Sections
  cut, mounting on slides, 385
  embedded, cutting, 384, 388
  frozen, preparation, 391
  paraffin-embedded, preparation, 383-386
  parlodion-embedded, preparation, 386-389
  staining, 386, 389
  of undecalcified tissues, 359
Semilunar hiatus, 345
Sensitivity of dentin, 109, 110, 123
Sensory fibers of pulp, 127
Sensory nerves of oral mucous membrane,
    215
Septum
  interdental, 177, 210, 309
  in maxillary sinus, 349
Serous cells, 269, 270, 271, 272
  electron microscope study, 283, 286
Serous glands, 267
Serum proteins in saliva, 291
Sex organs and salivary glands, 294
Sharpey's fibers, 160, 161, 162, 171, 192,
    194, 204, 208, 244
Sheath
  of Neumann, 103
  root, of Hertwig, 128, 147, 156, 166, 167,
    190, 304
Sheaths, rod, 47
Shedding deciduous teeth, 320-334
Shedding process, periods of activity and
    rest, 326
Shortened tooth, 314

Sialic acid, 288, 363, 364
  in formation of dental plaque, 295
  mucoproteins in saliva, 267
Sialomucin, 363
Sinus
  cervical, 13
  extension, enlargement of maxillary sinus
    due to, 347
  infection, 350
  maxillary, 344-351
  mucosa, 349, 350
Sinuses, nasal, reason for development, 349
Skin
  of lip, 216
  and mucous membrane, transition be-
    tween, 216
Skull
  bones of, 197
  fetal, three parts, 197
  of human embryo, reconstruction (plate),
    198
Slides, mounting cut sections on, 385
Sockets, tooth, 204
  radiograms, 212
  support, 200
Sodium fluoride, 65
Sodium, secretion by salivary glands, 289
Soft palate; *see* Palate, soft
Soft tissues, 244
  oral, enzyme histochemistry, 371
  oral, polysaccharide, protein, and mucin
    histochemistry, 362
  relation to hard tissues, 242
Specialized mucosa, 217, 256
Specimens
  for histologic study, preparation, 382-391
  for microscopic examination, preparation,
    382, 383
  paraffin-embedded, 383-386
  parlodion-embedded, 386-389
Spindles, enamel, 62, 64
Sponge and stone comparable to organic and
    mineral elements of enamel, 42
Spongiosa, alveolar, 204, 205
Spongy bone, 201, 204, 209, 211
Sputum, cells in, 353
Staining
  gingiva, 219
  glycoproteins, 355, 362
  methods, classification, 359
  oral tissues, 355
  secretion granules, 270, 271
  sections, 386, 389
Stains, 355, 359, 364
Stannous fluoride, 65
Stapes, 13, 198
Staphyloschisis, 14
Stellate reticulum, 68, 69
  bell stage, 28
  cap stage, 24
  development and purpose, 70, 71

Stensen's duct, 276
Stippled attached gingiva, 226, 227, 228
Stomodeum, 1, 2, 18
Stone and sponge comparable to organic and
    mineral elements of enamel, 42
Stratified squamous epithelium, 214, 233,
    260
Stratum corneum, 218
Stratum intermedium, 28, 68, 69
  development and function, 71
  enzyme activity, 371
Stratum lucidum, 215
Strawberry tongue, 263
Stress, adaptation of bone to, 206
Striated ducts, 274
  electron microscope studies, 288
Striations
  in cytoplasm of osteoclasts, 207
  in enamel rods, 47
Structural changes
  importance to restorative dentistry, 192
  in jaws, 206
  in teeth and supporting tissues, 192
Structural elements
  of periodontal ligament, 177
  of pulp, 131
  of salivary glands, 268
Structure
  of alveolar process, 200
  of cementum, 160
  of connective tissue, 354
  of dentin, 97
  of enamel, 43
Stylohyoid ligament, 198
Styloid process, 13, 198
Sublingual fold, 279
Sublingual glands, 266, 267, 279, 280
  ducts and terminal secretory portions, 273
  esterase activity, 372, 373
  secretions, 291
Sublingual mucosa, 254
Submandibular glands, 266, 267, 276, 277,
    278, 279
  ducts and terminal secretory portions, 273
  effect of thyroidectomy on, 294
  rat, growth experiments, 283
  secretions, 291
Submaxillary gland
  rat, growth experiments, 283
  secreting mucus with A antigen, 353
Submerged teeth, 314
  deciduous, 332, 334
Submicroscopic structure of enamel, 45
Submucosa, 213, 214, 215, 217, 218
  of gingiva, 218
  of hard palate, 218, 247
  of lining mucosa, zones, 252
  of oral cavity
    glands in, 266
    structure, clinical importance, 262
Subodontoblastic plexus, 139

Subodontoblastic zone of Weil, 139, 141
Successional lamina, 29
Succinic dehydrogenase, 369, 374, 376
Sulcus, gingival; *see* Gingival sulcus
Sulfhydryl groups in enamel matrix, 41
Supernumerary teeth, 36
Supporting tissues, changes with age, 192
Supportive function of periodontal ligament, 176
Surface areas of dentin, 98
Surface layer of cementum, 162, 163, 164
Surface structures of teeth, 54, 55
Suspensory ligament, 178
Sympathetic nerve cells, growth and maintenance of, 293
Sympathetic nervous system, salivary glands and, 290
Symphysial fibrocartilage, 200
Symphysis, mandibular, development, 199
Synovial
  fluid, 342
  membrane, 336, 342
  villi, 341, 342

T

Taste
  buds, 257, 258, 260, 261
    characteristics and location, 260
    esterase activity, 372
  pore, 260, 261
  sensations, regions of tongue for, 261
  stimuli, receptors, 261
Tears in epithelial attachment, 235, 236, 244, 246
Techniques, histochemical, 352, 353, 358-376
Tectal ridge, 11
Tectolabial frenum, 11
Teeth; *see* Tooth
Tegmen oris, 10
Temporal bone, 335
Temporomandibular joint, 335-342
  anatomic remarks, 335
  clinical considerations, 342
  histology, 336
  injuries, 342
  sagittal section, 336, 337
  synovial villi on, 341
Temporomandibular ligament, 336, 342
Tension, effect on bone, 210, 211
Terminal bars, 72, 138
  of ameloblasts, 78, 79, 80, 81
Terminal portions of salivary glands, 268, 271, 273, 274
Tetrazoles, 370, 376
Thickness of periodontal ligament, 191
Thymus, 13
Thyroglossal duct, 14
  cysts, 14, 16
Thyroid cartilage, 13

Thyroid gland, 14
  salivary glands and, 293, 294
Thyroxin, salivary glands and, 293
Tilting of teeth, 301, 305, 308, 312
Tipping of teeth, 301, 308
Tissues
  calcified, histochemistry, 352
  cementoid, 157, 159
  chemical constituents, 354
  epithelial, histochemistry, 356
  fluorescence, 353
  frozen, 358, 362
  hard
    enzyme histochemistry, 364
    protein and lipid histochemistry, 360
    and soft, 228, 242, 244
  histochemistry, 352-376
  mineralized, formation, mineralization, and maturation, 41, 42
  preparation for histologic study, 382, 383
  pulpal, growth, 312
  soft, enzyme histochemistry, 371
  soft, polysaccharide, protein, and mucin histochemistry, 362
  undecalcified, sectioning, 359
Tomes'
  fibers, 98
  granular layer, 108, 109
  processes, 78, 79, 80, 81, 83
Tongue
  anomalies, 15
  body and base, difference in mucous membrane, 256, 257, 258
  changes, diagnostically significant, 263
  derivation from branchial arches, 14
  development, 6, 7, 8, 12-14
  glands of, 268, 282
  inferior surface of, mucous membrane, 254, 255
  lining mucosa, 252
  mucosa, 217
  muscles, 14
  redness, 263
  regions for different taste sensations, 261
  superior surface, 256
  surface view, 257
Tonofibrils, 71, 214, 215, 217
Tonsil
  lingual, 260
  palatine, 13
Tooth (teeth)
  in abnormal locations, 35
  absence of, 35, 36
  with accessory canals, sections, 134
  age changes, 64
  attachment, 179
  buds, 18, 19, 23
  calculus on, 368
  cells, enzyme activity, 370
  cells, phosphatase activity, 367
  and cleft jaw, relation, 15
  color, 40, 41

Tooth (teeth)—cont'd
  crowns, anatomic and clinical, 241, 243
  crowns, size and form, 37
  deciduous; *see* Deciduous teeth
  development
    apposition, 37
    bell stage, 27, 28
    bud stage, 23
    cap stage, 24, 25, 26
    first sign, 22
    and growth, 18-37
    initiation, 35
    morphodifferentiation, 36
    proliferation, 36
    stages, 19, 33, 34
  drifting, 209
  embedded, 316
  emergence, time of, 314, 315
  enamel hypoplasia, 89
  eruption; *see* Eruption
  eruptive movements, 312
  formation and eruption, chronology (table), 317
  germ; *see* Germ, tooth
  gingival attachment, 222
  ground sections
    preparation, 389
    reactivity with pa-S technique, 360
  growth, stages (table), 35
  in hereditary hypocalcification, 90
  histochemical studies, 358, 359, 361
  life cycle, 20
  movements, 301, 308
    factors responsible, 313, 314
  multirooted, erupting, histology, 308
  in occlusion, 237
  permanent, developing, position, 305
  physiologic movement, 192
  primordia of, 23
  recently completed, outer enamel layer of, 83
  relation to soft and hard tissues, 242
  rodent, predentin and dentin layers in, 120
  root canals, drawings, 132, 133
  root transparency, 112, 115
  shortened, 314
  sockets, 204
    radiograms, 212
    support, 200
  structure, submicroscopic, 45
  submerged, 314
  supernumerary, 36
  and supporting tissues, structural changes, 192
  surface
    attachment of epithelium to, 229
    and gingiva, relation, 236
    structure, loss with advancing age, 55
  vital, dead tracts in, 114, 115, 116
Torus, palatine, 247

Trabeculae
  at alveolar fundus, 305, 307
  between alveoli, 204, 205
  of mandibular condyle, 336
  of mucous cells, 269
Trajectorial pattern of spongy bone, 204
Transitional zone between skin and mucous membrane, 216
Translucency of enamel, 41
Transparent dentin, 111, 112, 113, 115
Transseptal ligament, 181, 182
Transverse palatine ridges, 249
Trauma
  occlusal, loss of retained deciduous teeth due to, 332
  to periodontal ligament, 193, 327
  to temporomandibular joint, 342
Traumatic changes of periodontal tissues, 325, 326, 328
Traumatic lesions, ankylosis of deciduous tooth due to, 332
Tropochrome cells, 269
Tubercle, articular, 335, 336, 337, 338, 339, 340
Tuberculum impar, 14, 15
Tubules
  dentinal; *see* Dentinal tubules
  epithelial rests as, 191
  of salivary glands, 268
Tubuloacinous glands, 276, 279
Tufts, enamel, 60, 63
Turgidity of substance in loose connective tissue, 134

U

"Ultraterminal" fibers, 225, 226
Unmyelinated nerve fibers in pulp, 147
Upper lip, development, 12
Uranoschisis, 14
Uvula, 8
  glands of, 282

V

Vallate papillae, 14, 257, 258, 259, 260
  glands of, 267, 282
Veins of pulp, 143, 144
Ventral lingual mucosa, 254
Vertical eruption, 308, 309, 310, 313
Vessels, blood; *see* Blood vessels
  palatine, 249, 251
Vestibular fornix, 254
Vestibular lamina, 11, 31
Vestibule, oral, 216
  formation, 12
  glands of, 267
Vestibulum oris, 216
Visceral nerve fibers of oral mucous membrane, 216
Vitality of dentin, 110

Vitamin deficiencies, tongue changes due to, 263
von Ebner; *see under* Ebner

W

Washing specimens, 383, 387
Water
  and electrolytes, secretion by salivary glands, 290, 291
  fluoridation in caries control, 65
  fluoride levels, effect on enamel development, 88
  fluoride levels, high, cause of mottled enamel, 89

Weil, zone of, 139, 141
Wharton's duct, 277

X

Xerostomia, 263
Xylene, 385, 386, 389

Z

Zone of Weil, 139, 141
Zones around tooth germ, 177
Zuckerkandl, canals of, 204
Zymogen granules, 270, 285, 286, 287, 288